THE BEST OF JAPAN

Kodansha Ltd., Tokyo

Distributed in the United States by Kodansha
International/USA Ltd., through Harper & Row, Publishers, Inc.,
10 East 53rd Street, New York, New York 10022, U.S.A.

Published by Kodansha Ltd., 12-21, Otowa 2-chome, Bunkyo-ku,
Tokyo 112, in cooperation with Kodansha International Ltd., 2-2,
Otowa 1-chome, Bunkyo-ku, Tokyo 112, Japan, and Kodansha
International/USA Ltd., 10 East 53rd Street, New York, New York
10022, U.S.A.

First edition, 1987.

Library of Congress Cataloging-in-Publication Data

The Best of Japan.

  Includes index.
  1. New products—Japan—Awards.   2. Design—
Japan—Awards.
HF5415.153.B47 1987   338.4'7'000952   86-40432
ISBN 0-87011-801-3 (U.S.)
ISBN4-06-193401-5 (0) (Japan)

Contents

The 1986 Nikkei Awards

The 1982–85 Nikkei Awards

Publisher	Katsuhisa Katō
Project Director	Minoru Fujita

Editorial Staff
  Editor in Chief — Moritaka Matsumura
  Managing Editor — Yoshimi Sugiyama
  Senior Editor — Stephen Comee
  Editors — Peter Aterman
    Sandra Earley
    Kikuko Itasaka
    Setsuko Suzuki

Artistic Staff
  Cover Design — Shin Matsunaga
  Editorial Design and Layout — Pheidias Design Ltd.
    Hideko Tauchi
  Photo Director — Taku Ogawa
  Photo Editor — Yukio Ichikawa
  Photographs — Bon Color Photo Agency
    Toshihide Higuchi
    Mitsuaki Iwagō
    Kazushige Kuroda
    Mamoru Kusuda
    Tadao Matsuo
    Osamu Murai

Contributing Staff
  Original Manuscripts — Nihon Keizai Shimbun, Inc.
    Kazuyo Yano

Production Staff
  Typist — Tomoko Karasawa
  Preparation of Charts — Ejima Kikaku
  Preparation of Advertisements — IR Japan, Inc.
  Typesetting and Proofreading — Corporate Images, Inc.
  Printing — Toppan Printing Co., Ltd.
  Binding — Kamishima Binderies, Inc.

Editor's Note

The Best of Japan introduces 263 products and services that have received the prestigious Nikkei Award for creative excellence over the past five years. The purpose of this award, presented by Japan's leading economic newspaper, the *Nihon Keizai Shimbun* (shortened to *Nikkei*), is to contribute to the growth and diversification of the Japanese economy by acknowledging new products from a variety of industries.

Every year a screening committee of Nikkei journalists selects approximately 150 products from over 20,000 introduced annually in the *Nikkei* newspaper group. A panel of distinguished scholars and specialists makes the final selection of around fifty products, based on the following six criteria: originality, planning and design, effective use of high technology, commercial success, cost performance, and impact on society.

The Best of Japan is not merely a catalogue, but rather an introduction to the stories behind the creation of the award-winning products. It documents successful product development and marketing techniques, as well as social customs and business practices that are unique to Japan.

Moritaka Matsumura
Editor in Chief

The Selection Panel

Takashi Mukaibō
(Chairman)
Professor Emeritus,
The University of Tokyo

Ichirō Katō
Dean,
School of Science
and Engineering,
Waseda University

Jun'ichi Nishizawa
Professor,
Research Institute
of Electrical Communication,
Tōhoku University

Saburō Fukui
Professor Emeritus,
Faculty of Engineering,
Kyoto University

Noboru Makino
Chairman,
Mitsubishi
Research Institute, Inc.

Kōichi Tanouchi
Professor,
Faculty of Commerce,
Hitotsubashi University

Takemochi Ishii
Professor,
Faculty of Engineering,
The University of Tokyo

Shōji Murata
Professor,
Faculty of Business
and Commerce,
Keiō University

Hisao Yoshimura
Former Editor in Chief
Nikkei Sangyo Shimbun

The Freedom to Foster Originality

by Takashi Mukaibō *(Takashi Mukaibō is Professor Emeritus of the University of Tokyo.)*

It has been said so often that it has become a cliché: "The Japanese excel at imitating and improving the inventions of others but lack creativity." Ever since the Meiji era (1868–1912), when Japan entered the race for modernization as a late starter, the country has taken the shortest route possible in order to catch up with the leaders, the U.S. and Europe, by purchasing superior information and technology from them. In doing so, Japan has not been pinching pennies. When Toyo Rayon (now Toray Industries) bought the technology for producing nylon, it invested so much capital that it was accused of staking the company fortunes; eventually, however, it came to dominate the field worldwide.

So if the Japanese have progressed in recent decades by imitating and improving, it has been because they simply did not have the extra time and resources necessary for original creation. In some ways, it was a reality that could not be helped.

Does this mean that historically the Japanese have been lacking in creativity? Certainly not. In the seventeenth century, at a time when Japan was still completely cut off from the mathematics of the West, a scholar named Takakazu Seki (1642–1708) discovered matrix formulae and did other important work in mathematics that was in no way inferior to the work of his contemporaries in Europe.

Similarly, the inventions of Gennai Hiraga (1728–1780), such as the induction coil and a variety of fire-prevention devices, demonstrated a level of creativity comparable to that anywhere in the world.

In a lecture entitled "A Single or a Home Run?" Dr. Frank Press, president of the American Academy of Arts and Sciences, pointed out that in the U.S., when someone makes a new technological discovery, development, or material, the first thought is of application to a military or space project. Then, if it succeeds, it is like a home run with the bases loaded, bringing in all the players at once. In Japan, however, rather than turning over a new discovery to some large, state-sponsored project, the developers are more likely to look for applications to daily life and to develop it into a viable consumer product. This approach is more like a straight drive through the infield that puts one player firmly on first.

A good example of this kind of development is that of carbon fibers. When first produced in the U.S., everyone immediately began to search for possible military and space applications; but Japanese engineers went to work and developed them for use in such objects as golf clubs and tennis rackets, bringing their quality, as a by-product of extensive research, up to the highest standard in the world.

As long as a nation is struggling to get enough to eat, laboring to rebuild itself from the rubble of war, it is not likely to have enough extra strength to nourish creativity. After busily rebuilding itself over the last four decades, Japan has at last achieved such leeway.

With a population of 110 million people crowded onto its small land area, Japan has accepted competition as its fate. Indeed, this has served to propel the Japanese forward, enabling them to come as far as they have. At the same time, creative technology should make it possible to overcome the problem of their limited land area.

One should take the optimistic view that however limited the area of their country, the fields in which their creativity can be exercised are unlimited in size. Moreover, the fruits of Japanese creative efforts have the potential to contribute to the welfare of all the people of the world. Indeed, this will be the future goal of the science and technology of Japan.

Japanese Creativity

by Koya Azumi

(Koya Azumi is Professor of Sociology at Rutgers University.)

Some people are more creative than others. The differences in individual creativity arise from the interaction between hereditary and environmental factors, but no one knows the prescription for bringing up individuals so as to make them unusually creative. Even if hereditary and biological factors might partly explain individual variations in creativity, there is no evidence that such biological factors are distributed unevenly among different peoples. If there is one genius in a million among people in Europe and North America, for example, then there should also be one genius in a million in Africa and Asia and Latin America as well.

If there are variations in creativity among peoples, how can they be explained? One can only look for explanations in environmental factors. Important explanatory factors can be ascertained within the culture, social structure, and external factors surrounding that society. First, an important factor lies in the importance accorded to creativity itself within the culture. Furthermore, culture tends to channel creativity into certain institutional areas and not into others. Some cultures may channel creativity to the arts, religion, or literature, but not to politics, the economy, or science and technology.

That there *are* variations among peoples in creativity in science and technology can be explained mainly through the uneven distribution of modernization among the societies of the world.

Japan realized its backwardness when it was forced out of isolation in the middle of the nineteenth century by the encroaching Western powers. Japan, in order to safeguard its national sovereignty, saw that catching up with the West was an absolute necessity that would be no easy task. To be equal to the West and to become independently creative in science and technology required cultivating a whole array of social institutions that support such action. The most expedient and least expensive method of catching up was to acquire or copy the more advanced knowledge and technologies of other countries. It is really no secret that Japan acquired an international reputation as a copycat. And the belief that the Japanese excel in copying but not in being creative themselves is still widely held. Do the Japanese, in fact, lack creativity?

One objective and systematic source of data to help provide clues concerning Japanese creativity is U.S. patent data. Examining this informational perspective for the 13-year period from 1969 through 1981 reveals the following. First, in terms of sheer volume, Japanese companies collectively ranked fifth in the world in the late 1960s in the number of U.S. patents granted. By 1975, Japan had surpassed France, Britain, and West Germany and ranked second, just behind the U.S. By 1981, the volume of U.S. patents granted to Japanese companies in one year approached 13% of the total volume of U.S. patents granted. Secondly, when the standardized rates of U.S. patent generation per employee by company are computed, and then when Japanese company rates are compared with those of U.S. companies, one can see that there were a number of Japanese firms that had maintained rates of innovation comparable to those of highly innovative U.S. firms. In fact, there are even four Japanese firms that had rates higher than those of the most innovative U.S. firms during the 13-year period.

In Japan today, major companies share the feeling that one cannot expect to survive without being innovative. The research-and-development budget for fiscal 1985 for the entire nation relative to GNP reached 2.77%, surpassing the rate for the U.S. The proportion of company employees working in R&D has also been on the rise, having grown, on the average, by 41.6% during the preceding five years.

Most firms in Japan are searching for ways in which

their R&D operations and the people who work in them may be made more innovative. The Japanese appear to be less tolerant of those who stand out from the crowd in any way. Their educational system tends to place everyone into the same mold, and the all-important and highly competitive entrance examination system tends to nip any flower of creativity in the bud. No Newtons and Einsteins could be expected to emerge out of the present Japanese social environment.

In Japanese companies, the lines that demarcate individual tasks are less clearly drawn and less firmly adhered to. By and large, organizations are more flexibly structured and employees are more multiskilled. In R&D operations, as Takeuchi and Nonaka have pointed out (in the Jan/Feb 1986 *Harvard Business Review)*, the American method of developing a new product is like a relay race in which one team of specialists relays the project to the next team, and so on until the project is complete. This stands in stark contrast to the Japanese method, which they liken to a game of rugby in which the whole team works as a unit to carry the project through its various stages—from conception to completion.

According to a study of factories in the U.S. and in Japan, conducted by Frank Hull and myself between 1982 and 1984, the average length of a research project in American R&D is longer than that in Japanese R&D. U.S. firms tend to spend less time in the early stages of product development and more time in the final stage of commercialization. In contrast, Japanese firms tend to spend relatively more time in the early stages, but are then able to go through the stage of commercialization of a new product far more quickly. How can they do so?

Another study done in collaboration with Frank Hull provides a clue by pointing out that all related sections of a firm, including marketing and sales, become involved relatively early on in the stage of product development, and by the time the project reaches the commercialization stage the necessary consensus among the various sections has already been reached, smoothing out the commercialization process. That is, Japanese firms tend to perform better than American firms in accomplishing intraunit, cooperative tasks.

Japan is now being forced to reconsider many of the practices that are part and parcel of Japanese management due to rapid changes in society and in the world context. Personnel management, including the institutionalized lifetime employment system, is under close scrutiny.

If Japanese companies should succeed in transforming themselves so that they can favor heterogeneity over homogeneity in personnel, to recruit employees from colleges and universities hitherto ignored, to provide more opportunities for those with less formal education, to open more doors to women, and to cultivate the hitherto untapped human resources of the population, then Japanese creativity should prove itself to be a formidable force in shaping the world of the future.

THE 1986 NIKKEI AWARDS

CARS, WATCHES, HOME APPLIANCES, AND CAMERAS

TRENDS IN THE 1980s

As befits its size, Japan's car industry is experiencing mounting problems at the same time that it is enjoying huge success in the marketplace. —— *Cars*

Long a giant, the Japanese timepiece business is being buffeted by the winds of change. It is fighting hard to adapt. —— *Watches*

The challenge is coming from next door, and the stakes are high. Japan is struggling to keep its lead in a race it once appeared to have won. —— *Home Appliances*

Now more than ever, Japan relies on technology to dominate the camera market. With the NICs at its heels, the industry has turned to a new concept. —— *Cameras*

Cars

The Japanese automobile industry became the largest in the world in 1980, when it passed the U.S. rate of production with 11 million cars. Despite such success, the business climate for Japanese automakers is growing steadily harsher. The U.S. trade deficit with Japan is blamed to a great extent on the popularity of Japanese cars with American consumers. Since the fall of 1985, the yen has strengthened against the dollar, severely shaking the business base of Japanese automakers. Furthermore, Japan faces new competition near its own shores—from South Korea and Taiwan. It is clear that the Japanese auto industry is now facing a major turning point.

In recent years, competition between Japanese automakers and America's Big Three—General Motors, Ford, and Chrysler—has grown fiercer than ever. Self-imposed restraints limited the import of Japanese passenger cars in 1986 to 2.3 million and, as a result, prices rose. Nevertheless, Japan continues to account for 20% of the new car market in the United States. As a result, top executives of General Motors, Ford, and Chrysler have joined a chorus of warnings against Japanese automobiles.

In reality, the difficulties should not be painted as a simple standoff between the two countries, since Japanese and American automakers are now so interrelated that they compete and cooperate at the same time. Mutual reliance began in 1984 with Toyota Motors and its joint venture with General Motors to make the Nova and the Corolla FX in the U.S. Numerous Japanese automakers have since set up similar arrangements in North America. Mazda is allied with Ford, for example, and Mitsubishi with Chrysler. Other manufacturers, such as Honda and

Nissan, already have plants producing their cars in North America, and are being followed by their competitors.

After 1988, Japanese automakers may well be producing more than 2 million cars annually in North America. This production, combined with Japanese exports to the United States, may mean the American car market will be flooded with Japanese brands. Some observers predict that 1988 will bring a showdown, forcing major reorganization by automakers in both countries and a new storm of joint ventures.

Developments elsewhere in Asia are also forcing reconsideration of the existing market. Auto manufacturers in South Korea and Taiwan are growing rapidly on a diet of cheap labor and solid research and development, and are beginning to export to the U.S. in direct competition with Japanese cars. The strength of South Korean manufacturers is illustrated by the story of the Pony. When that small passenger vehicle, made by Hyundai Motors of South Korea, arrived in the U.S. in January 1986, it exceeded its sales goal of 100,000 cars by an astounding 160,000 vehicles.

Any discussion of the South Korean and Taiwanese auto industries must keep in mind the power of Japanese automakers behind them. The growing interrelation among not only the U.S., Japan, South Korea, and Taiwan but also their major automotive manufacturers has added other dimensions to the competition on the world market. Hyundai, for example, receives technical assistance from Mitsubishi. Kia Motors, a South Korean manufacturer of 1,300-cc-class cars, gets comprehensive technical assistance from Mazda, and began to export to the U.S. in May 1987.

In Taiwan, the situation is similar. Nissan has provided a quarter of the capital for Yue Loong Motors, Taiwan's largest automaker. Mitsubishi has helped finance the China Motor Corporation, and Toyota, Kuozui Motors. Each of Taiwan's eight manufacturers of four-wheel vehicles receives some financial or technical assistance from Japanese automakers.

In the midst of forging international alliances, Japanese automakers are also devoting increasing energy to sales inside their own country. Until recently, they had used profits from exports to support a policy of underselling domestic competition. Now the rise of the yen and the resulting loss of dollars is forcing them to operate at a profit at home, too.

Toyota, for example, has adopted a policy of securing its citadel before doing battle abroad, and has set itself a goal of capturing 50% of the domestic market in 1987, starting from a 42.5% share at the beginning of the year. In January 1987, Nissan announced that it was changing its policy of having five different sales networks competing separately. Nissan dealers in many areas were engaged in wasteful price wars with each other, fighting over the same customers, and the majority of the company's sales outlets operated in the red. Nissan is now attempting to promote efficient management by allowing its dealers to sell every line it produces instead of limiting them to a single make of car.

Facing a host of troubles at home and abroad, the Japanese automobile industry is finding itself thrust into a new era. It appears clear that manufacturers in Japan, the United States, South Korea, and Taiwan will soon be forced to combine in various ways to respond to the changing demands of the world market. And all the while, Japanese automakers will have to work hard to please their customers at home.

Watches

In 1980, Japan established itself as the world's top producer of wristwatches. The quartz watch—a far more accurate timekeeper than the mechanical, windup watch—was the invention that catapulted Japan into the No. 1 position. Then, just six years later, the value of the yen shot up and plunged Japan's watchmakers into a painful recession.

In response, Japanese watchmakers, like those in so many other industries, have begun shifting their factories to the newly industrializing nations of Asia, such as Taiwan and South Korea, where production costs are low. The shifts make it certain that, in time, these nations will become the main source of the world's wristwatch supply.

In 1985, 440 million wristwatches were produced worldwide, according to industry figures. Japan produced almost 40% of them, with a volume of 170 million. Hong Kong came in second with 22% and Switzerland was third with 13%.

The effect of the strong yen—rising steadily since September 1985—can be seen clearly in a comparison between production volume and value. In 1986, Japan's volume, comprising domestic and overseas sales, was 190 million units, an increase of more than 10% over the previous year, according to the Japan Clock and Watch Association. But the monetary value of the watches was only ¥302 billion, a 17% drop from 1985. Most of this drop was accounted for by export figures that, while registering an 8% increase in volume, showed a decrease in monetary value of more than 20%.

The causes of this phenomenon are threefold. The first is the sudden rise in the value of the yen, resulting in a loss of yen-based net receipts. The second is the trend toward lower-priced wristwatches. Today, 80% of all Japanese-made watches sell for less than ¥10,000. The third cause is the increase in the export of cheap, unfinished movements and chablons (complete sets of units). No more than 40% of Japan's 1986 export volume comprised finished products, according to the industry's trade association. The majority of these unfinished products go to manufacturers in Asia, particularly Hong Kong.

Hong Kong makers depend on Japanese imports for their watches because they lack the technology to produce their own quartz movements. The Hong Kong companies then export their finished watches to the rest of the world. Since the value of their exports, like their currency, is linked to U.S. dollars, the rise of the yen has strengthened their competitive position and made their watches cheaper than Japanese ones. The result is that Japanese makers are finding themselves pushed under by Hong Kong makers, particularly in the area of medium- and low-priced products. Thus, what once was a sales-increase strategy—the export of unfinished products—has given birth to the opposite effect—a loss of market share for Japan's finished products. The answer of Japanese manufacturers to the drop in both exports and net profits is a policy of hurriedly shifting production bases to other Asian countries where production costs are 20% lower. The strategy is to continue manufacturing the movements that require sophisticated technology in Japanese factories but then to send these watchworks to plants in cheap-labor countries to be fitted into cases and wristbands. Japan's Citizen Watch, for example, increased the 1986 assembly of finished products at its South Korean and Hong Kong subsidiaries by almost 10% over the 1985 figure. The Seiko group and Casio Computer are following similar strategies of relying on foreign labor to reduce costs. When manufacturing finished products in Japan, they often import the cases and wristbands from other Asian countries.

Japanese manufacturers are also beginning to turn to high-tech modifications of familiar products as a way to weather the storm of the strong yen. They are working on, for example, data-bank wristwatches for information storage, and card watches. Citizen's World-Time Card Alarm Clock (see pp. 22–23) is just such an instance of innovation in answer to foreign competition. However, the rise of the yen has been so fast that the countermeasures have had little effect.

Clocks fare no better than wristwatches in the current economic climate. Figures from the Clock and Watch Association tell the same story: while the volume of clocks manufactured in Japan increased 1% in 1986 over the previous year for a total of 82 million units, the value was down 8%, for a total of ¥100 billion. Again, the threat comes from the strong yen and overseas competition, and it looks as if the struggle will go on for some time.

Home Appliances

The year 1986 highlighted the precarious position of Japanese electrical-appliance makers in international markets. Faced with stiff competition from South Korean manufacturers, Japanese makers have worked hard to bring down costs. Their success, however, has only incurred the wrath of American and European manufacturers. In December 1986, a string of dumping charges, first for color television picture tubes in the U.S. and then for microwave ovens in Europe, was brought against Japanese home-electrical-appliance makers, forcing them to greet the new year in a scramble to collect materials for the inquiries. Caught in this vicious circle, and squeezed by the rising value of the yen, these companies have been plunged into a fight for survival.

The charges of dumping television tubes, brought by American labor unions, bore an element of irony for the Japanese manufacturers. The manufacturers had deliberately chosen television sets as the first item whose American-based production scale they would increase in response to the rise in the value of the yen and in shipping costs.

In addition to strengthening local production in their own factories, the companies had also adopted a policy of procuring color picture tubes from such powerful U.S. manufacturers as RCA and Zenith. Thus, the five big Japanese makers (Matsushita, Hitachi, Mitsubishi, Toshiba, and NEC) were puzzled when, despite these efforts, they became the object of dumping charges. "Even though the number of picture tubes exported has increased," pointed out one company representative, "the net effect has been to strengthen production in the U.S. Since the exports were intended for our own factories there, we were actually slow in raising the procurement price in dollars, despite the rapid rise in the yen." Indeed, Japanese makers considered it a source of pride that the strengthening of local production of finished sets had bolstered employment in the U.S.

The fierce competition for a U.S. market share between Japan and the newly industrializing countries, as well as the retreat of U.S. manufacturers, has produced a somewhat hostile climate. Such an atmosphere prevails in Europe as well, where Japan, South Korea, and Singapore have been charged with the dumping of microwave ovens. European manufacturers complain that Japan and South Korea export goods at prices 10–32% lower than those of European-made goods and thus are unfairly stealing the market from local makers. Fearing the European market would be overrun by the leading South Korean manufacturers, Japanese makers began to strengthen local production, while holding down exports of finished products.

In fact, Japanese exports of microwave ovens to Europe in 1986 are estimated to have stayed at the same level as in the previous year: just over 1.6 million units. South Korean manufacturers, meanwhile, are catching up even faster than expected. Armed with low prices, South Korean makers increased their exports to Europe in 1986 to 400,000 units—some eight times the level of 1985. With the sum of Japanese and South Korean exports at 2 million units—double the total production of local European makers—friction is, understandably, growing.

In response, Japanese manufacturers have begun to cooperate with the South Koreans. While Toshiba is purchasing compact refrigerators for the Japanese market from South Korea's Samsung Electronics, NEC has begun OEM procurement of microwave ovens as well as black-and-white and color televisions from Gold Star for sale in the U.S. and Europe under the NEC label. While this is one of many steps taken to reduce costs in the face of the strong yen, Japanese manufacturers also hope that such strengthening of the international division of labor will serve to reduce the trade friction with the U.S. and Europe.

These shifts overseas, however, are bringing cries at home against the "hollowing" of domestic industries. Indeed, cases like Sanyo Electric's are beginning to emerge: as it strengthens production of color televisions in the U.S. and Europe, Sanyo is being forced to reconsider production of them in Japan.

Japanese companies are all eager to develop the next generation of products, but they are having trouble expanding sales even of such industry mainstays as videodisk and CD players. Their new DATs (digital audio tape recorders), capable of reproducing several generations of copies with virtually no loss in sound quality, are under attack from U.S. and European tape and record producers as a threat to copyrights, so for the moment they cannot be developed as a major new export product. Makers are searching for a new product to succeed the industry's biggest money-maker, videocassette decks, which bring in profits of some ¥2 trillion a year. The wave of "employment adjustment" that has swept the audio-manufacturing industry may well spread to the electrical and electronic manufacturers. With 50% of their business in exports, trade friction growing, and the yen rising, home-electrical-appliance makers are now like ships forced to sail on uncharted seas.

Cameras

Japanese still cameras, accounting for 40% of total world sales, have been the world leaders since 1967. Japan now leads the way in the development of new products designed to reignite interest in the market. The country's superiority is not only in numbers, but also in advanced technology.

A typical example of the new-technology products is the autofocus, single-lens-reflex camera. The SLRs have gradually been eliminating the need for the photographer to set shutter speeds and lens openings. Now even focusing is becoming unnecessary. Beginning in 1985, with the introduction of Minolta's α-7000 (see p. 176), a number of autofocus SLRs have appeared on the market.

The growth of advanced technology in cameras can be seen most clearly in the use of semiconductors. Only one semiconductor was needed in Nippon Kogaku's Nikomat EL in 1972. But by 1985, the α-7000 was using ten semiconductors. It not only features two 8-bit central processing units at its heart, and one integrated circuit each for the light meter, display, and memory system, but also the first ROM inside the lens. With this model, still cameras entered an age in which both the body and the lens of the camera have a brain, and the two are capable of exchanging information.

The inexpensive, easy-to-operate, auto-compact camera has not been left behind as advanced technology has been applied to the SLR—it now accounts for 70% of total camera production. A typical case is the dual-focus compact camera that can be switched from wide-angle shots to telephoto. Since Fuji Photo Film introduced the TW-300 compact camera featuring a switchable lens in 1985 (see p. 177), various other companies have put out their own versions.

The next logical innovation after wide-angle/telephoto focusing was a zoom lens in a compact camera. In 1986, Asahi Optical put the Zoom 70 Date on the market. It is an autofocus compact camera with a lens that zooms between 35 and 70 mm. With such innovations, the compact camera has risen to a level almost functionally equal to that of the single-lens reflex.

But technological advances have been able to do little to hold off the effects of the soaring yen. Since the rise began in September 1985, the business climate for the industry has worsened and is now severe. Over 80% of the country's camera production is exported. The strong yen has slowed the growth of production volume, particularly for the already-expensive, high-quality single-lens reflex. While the 1986 production of compact cameras was 16 million units—nearly 20% higher than the previous year—shipments of single-lens reflexes dropped by 15% from the 1985 volume of 5.8 million units.

During the 1970s, Canon, Asahi Optical, and Ricoh began producing compact cameras in Taiwan and other newly industrializing Asian countries where labor costs are low. As the yen remains strong, there is a strong possibility that the level of foreign production will increase. The Japanese domestic market is also being invaded by other Asian countries. In 1986, a South Korean–made, low-priced compact camera was imported into the country. There are predictions that such countries may even catch up with Japanese production in the long term.

Still, the Japanese remain ahead in technology. One product of this technology is an electronic still camera that uses a tiny magnetic disk rather than ordinary film. Images can be recorded on the disk and viewed immediately on a television monitor. The electronic still camera can not only project its color photo on a television screen, it can also produce a hard copy with a special printer. Its images can be transmitted over telephone lines as well. If development of the product leads to lower costs and a higher-quality image, the electronic still camera has great potential for major growth in the future. But it may also mean more competition for Japanese still camera manufacturers. Since the technology of the electronic still camera is a cousin to that of the VCR, manufacturers such as Sony, Matsushita Electric Industrial, and Sharp are looking for opportunities to enter the market. Their presence is expected to heat up competition.

Soarer: A Prestige Specialty Car
Toyota Motors

Instrument panel, with an electronic multivision panel

The Toyota Soarer was first put on the market in 1981 as a high-class specialty car, and underwent a full model change in 1986. Available with four different types of powerful engines, the car features a number of new technologies in the structure of the chassis. The suspension uses the same four-wheel double-wishbone design as the Toyota Formula One. The top models have electronically controlled air suspension, giving them even better handling than the highest-class European cars. The Soarer is also attracting attention for its luxurious accoutrements, placing it in the top position among Japanese cars.

The Soarer model was created in 1981 as a hybrid of Toyota Motors' technology and highly advanced car styling, to serve as an image leader for the company. The second generation of the Soarer, which appeared in January 1986, embodies the same development concepts. Toyota invested its most advanced technology in the new model to create an automobile that would represent the best of Japan's car industry. The engine is a case in point. A newly developed, 230 hp, 3,000 cc DOHC turbo, it was combined with a four-wheel, double-wishbone air suspension that is electronically controlled, placing it in the highest category of engines with explosive acceleration capabilities.

The electronically controlled air suspension provides the car with the handling stability and riding comfort of a Mercedes-Benz. The instant the front wheels come into contact with faults in the road, a microcomputer adjusts the air suspension of the rear wheels to absorb even the tiniest shock. This permits the chassis to respond to even the smallest bumps or cracks in the road with much greater sensitivity than one equipped with conventional shocks. The car is also equipped with an electronic multivision panel that visually displays such information as fuel consumption. In this sense, it is truly a high-tech car.

Yet from the standpoint of new car development, the Soarer represents a new approach for Toyota. Automobile

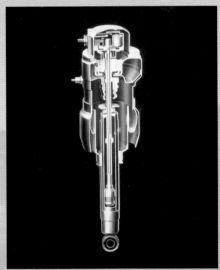

Electronic-control air suspension

makers usually proceed with development of a new car in accordance with market trends, following surveys and research that tell them what it is that consumers are looking for. The Soarer, however, was designed to suit Toyota's idea of "what a car should really be like," with the conviction that there must be a market of people who would truly appreciate its qualities. This approach was embodied in the planning team's indifference to cost barriers. In devel-

Laser α-7M twin-cam, 24-valve, turbo engine

oping any new car, even a single prototype costs several tens of millions of yen, meaning that completion of the entire process requires an investment of several billion yen. Since this directly affects the sales price, developers are often forced to give up in the face of high costs. The Soarer's developers, however, were free from such pressure, since the company considered the project so important that it allowed them to develop the model with no thought to how much was spent in the process.

With a price range that goes as high as ¥4.8 million, the Soarer is as expensive as an imported luxury car, such as a

inherited the same exquisite styling and refined it further. The development chief was most attentive to styling in planning the car. A designer himself, he gave the project designer considerable flexibility in the task, feeling that this was the best way to draw out his potential. After repeated consultations and discussions, the final design was realized, and proved to be exactly what had been hoped for at the outset.

Thus, the Soarer represents the result of Toyota's desire to produce a truly high-quality passenger car. It has enjoyed high praise from consumers, who bought 40,000 units in the first

growth has slowed to only 1 or 2%. However, consumer tastes are beginning to diversify, and cars with a design like that of the Soarer are gradually gaining popularity. Japanese consumers have become refined in their tastes, and are paying greater attention to detail and overall quality when purchasing new cars, instead of simply buying an image. The project development chief says that this is "the main reason for the popularity of the Soarer among young people.... If the Soarer becomes a long-term seller, it will serve to move Toyota toward the inclusion of the good points of the Soarer in all models." The Soarer continues to act as

BMW or a Mercedes. Company officials felt that they would do very well to sell even 1,000 cars per month, nowhere near the rate of 10,000 per month that they had achieved with the Corolla. Such a car could not sell for its driving capabilities alone, but must also offer outstanding styling and appearance. The first-generation Soarer won acclaim for its warm, clean style, never before attained in a Japanese car. The second-generation Soarer

year, a number that far exceeded all expectations. It now finds itself a market leader in terms of sophisticated style and high technology. A consumer profile reveals that it is young people in their twenties and thirties who flock to buy it, contrary to predictions that only high-salaried people in their forties would do so. This is of considerable significance for Toyota's future. The Japanese new car market has reached maturity, and its annual

a strong driving force in pushing Toyota Motors toward a prosperous future.

1986 Award for Excellence

3.0 GT-Limited (air-suspension car)
Dimensions: 4,675 (L) × 1,725 (W) × 1,335 (H) mm; wt: 1,520 kg
Capacity: 5 persons
Engine: 6-cyl, in-line, DOHC
Displacement: 2,954 cc
Maximum power: 230/5,600 ps/rpm
Maximum torque: 33.0/4,000 kg-m/rpm

Nissan Terrano: A Passenger Wagon with the Power of a Jeep
Nissan Motors

The Terrano 4WD (exported as the Pathfinder) is a recreational vehicle designed to provide the feel of a passenger car. The noise and vibrations of its engine and the suspension system were reduced to afford a degree of comfort not normally found in a four-wheel drive. American designers worked on this model, with an eye to the American market. It has become extremely popular in the United States for its command of rough terrain as well as for its suitability for city streets. Sales in Japan are expected to be 500 units per month, with sales in the U.S. expected to reach 3,500 per month.

Nissan Motors has advertised the Terrano as the symbol of a revitalized Nissan. In returning to the fundamentals of car design, the company hopes to promote a new image within Japan and broaden its appeal. Ironically, however, the Terrano has largely been designed for the American market. City-modified 4WDs such as the Chevrolet Blazer and the Ford Bronco are very popular in the U.S. Nissan Motors believes that a manufacturer can only be successful in America if it includes this kind of car in its lines.

In the middle of 1983, the key man on this project, Toshiro Ueda, chief designer of the Product Planning and Marketing Group No. 3, asserted that the project should be implemented. Nissan thus began considering such a car. Taking into account the influence of the American lifestyle on Japan, the company wanted a recreational car for the whole family, not just for young people. Ueda decided to avoid being influenced by Japanese and American differences of taste. Rather, he decided that the concept of "lifestyle" should be emphasized and that the new vehicle should have a "California feeling." Bearing this in mind, the company chose for this project three American designers—Gerald Hirshberg, design director; Thomas Semple, design chief;

A new 4WD adventure vehicle as comfortable as a conventional passenger car

and Douglas Wilson, designer—all of whom had been recruited from General Motors when Nissan Motors established its San Diego–based design firm in 1981. It was their job to provide the kind of design for the car that would evoke the feeling of America and the American lifestyle.

The key to the car's success lies in the determination of all the workers involved. The combination of Nissan's staff with the American designers bore excellent results, and Ueda felt deeply grateful for their efforts. He used to think that Americans were less devoted than Japanese. He assumed that the Americans would leave the office the minute their official working hours were over, but that was not the case. They worked hard even on holidays, and on one occasion, when they wanted to see the clay model in natural light, they took it outside at 5 AM and waited for the first rays of the sun to illuminate it. This scene was most inspirational to Ueda, who said that he was "captured by their zeal."

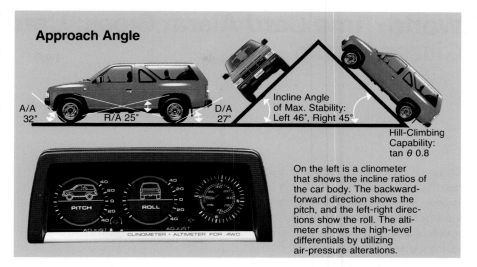

Approach Angle

A/A 32° R/A 25° D/A 27°

Incline Angle of Max. Stability: Left 46°, Right 45°

Hill-Climbing Capability: tan θ 0.8

PITCH ROLL

CLINOMETER · ALTIMETER FOR 4WD

On the left is a clinometer that shows the incline ratios of the car body. The backward-forward direction shows the pitch, and the left-right directions show the roll. The altimeter shows the high-level differentials by utilizing air-pressure alterations.

In addition, the American designers were extremely thorough. Take, for example, the window design. Regardless of the cost, they wanted to employ three-sided windows. The main characteristics of the vehicle that they finally produced are a rollbar design, the subtle angle of the central pillar, and the blister fenders. Ueda even went as far as to say, "I'd like to have all of their names printed right on the car!"

Naturally, the development of the car was not a perfectly smooth process. For example, some employees voiced concern that the blister fenders would be difficult to repair in the case of a collision and therefore should simply be a flat surface. However, Ueda, as leader of the project, refused to waver from his design policy and rejected the idea. A similar disagreement occurred over the suspension system. Members of the Production Department maintained that a conventional pickup suspension was adequate for the car, since its base was to be similar to that of a pickup truck that can carry one ton. Again, Ueda insisted on his own plan, asserting that this kind of suspension would not convey the feeling of driving a passenger vehicle. As a result, the team developed a five-link coil spring to provide suspension equal to that of an ordinary car.

Exactly one year after the project started, two different designs of the model were examined by the then Nissan president Takashi Ishihara. "Though the meeting was only a for-

mality, the three American designers believed that everything would be finally settled at the meeting. Their highly charged enthusiasm was extraordinarily impressive," said Ueda. The president did nothing but nod during the explanation.

Nissan's Terrano is the first car of its kind to adopt a sheet-copper body, expanded windows, a new kind of engine that allows controlled, swift, and quiet acceleration, and an alloyed metal rocker arm in the engine. More than anything else, the Terrano achieves an ideal balance between a Jeep and a car. It provides the power and ruggedness necessary for an outdoor recreational vehicle, while at the same time providing comfort not usually associated with a Jeep. It includes a large luggage area and cloth-covered ceiling, and even offers optional tweed upholstery. A recreational vehicle for the great outdoors, the Terrano has certainly met the company's goal of breaking into the U.S. market with a strikingly new car.

1986 Award for Excellence

R3M (Station Wagon)
Dimensions: 4,365 (L) × 1,690 (W) × 1,680 (H) mm; wt: 1,700 kg
Capacity: 5 persons
Engine: 4-cyl, in-line, OHC
Displacement: 2,663 cc
Maximum power: 85/4,300 ps/rpm
Maximum torque: 18.0/2,200 kg-m/rpm

World-Time Card Alarm Clock: Card-Type World Clock
Citizen Watch

Citizen Watch has produced a credit-card-sized alarm clock that tells time in twenty-four areas of the world and incorporates a calendar as well. One touch of a button gives the local time in any of the time zones shown on the card in liquid-crystal display. The zones are designated by numbers corresponding to their difference in hours from Greenwich mean time; for example, numbers indicate 0 for London, 1 for Paris, −5 for New York, and so on. New York time, London time, and the user's home time are displayed continuously, and the alarm can be set to sound at any programmed city's local time.

World-time clocks have existed for a long time. They are often large, wall-mounted affairs that give a digital read-out of local times in selected major cities of the world, and are commonly found in hotel lobbies or office buildings. There are also some wristwatches that show world times by means of a ring that can be rotated around the watch face. However, the drawback of such watches is that city names are hard to read, as they are etched in very small letters, and that the time-zone selection ring is bothersome to use. In addition, the ring is not particularly attractive, limiting the popularity of such watches. Yet overseas travel has now become commonplace, and New York, Tokyo, and Paris are no longer so far from each other in terms of travel time. In addition to businessmen, ordinary travelers on holiday or attending professional conferences have a need for more convenient timepieces. Citizen guessed, therefore, that there might actually be a solid clientele for a world-time clock, provided it was stylish and convenient. It occurred to Katsuo Nishimura of the Planning Section of Citizen Watch's Watch Development Department, who was in charge of developing the new product,

that a card-style clock was the obvious answer. With the spread of bank and credit cards for conducting financial transactions, almost everyone nowadays carries some kind of card. Thus, this thin, flat, world-time clock is very suitable for a wallet or breast pocket, where it can fit in with all of the user's other cards. This makes it convenient to carry and perfect for travel.

The concept was given the go-ahead, and a team of salesmen, designers, and production technicians was assembled to turn the idea into a product. Their main aim was to come up with a clock that was easy to use. Its design and shape had to be such that at first glance one could tell that the product was a world-time clock. Advice on setting out a world map on the card that was easy to read was provided by a designer who had worked on a pocket-sized liquid-crystal-display television. The continuous display of home, New York, and London times was designed to enhance its appeal as a world-time clock.

It was essential that the advantage of portability be complemented by ease of operation. For this reason the clock was designed to allow call-up of local times in twenty-four different time zones at the touch of a button. Punching in a number corresponding to one of the twenty-four time zones in the world instantly gives the local time in that zone on the liquid-crystal display. Other convenient features include the ability to set an alarm for another time zone (the clock can be set to ring, for example, at 2 PM New York time) and an adjustment feature for daylight savings time in the zones that adopt it.

Citizen was at the same time manufacturing a card-type calculator, and it used the same production technology

Convenient card size (actual size)

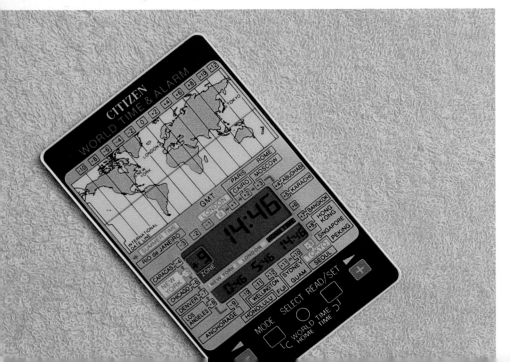

An easy-to-use design

for the clock. The company's extensive experience in linking liquid-crystal cells to integrated circuits proved useful in overcoming the most difficult technical problems. For example, the print base for operating the liquid-crystal display had to show four different times simultaneously, necessitating complicated connections between the liquid-crystal-display panel and the print base. This problem was somewhat simplified by the fact that the times in the different zones are exactly one hour apart, permitting the developers to use a common route for information commands. Similarly, the location of several cities in a single time zone eliminated the need for calling up each city by name. Instead, they adopted a system of calling up times according to zone, greatly reducing the number of integrated systems required to operate the card-type clock.

In January 1986, Citizen exhibited prototypes of the World-Time Card Alarm Clock at a consumer electronics show in the United States. Nishimura was certain after the show that the clock would sell well, since visitors eagerly went away with nearly every one of the thirty samples exhibited. Six months later the clock was launched on the market. Priced at an easily affordable ¥3,900, the watch found avid buyers among businessmen and companies. The low price makes the clock an ideal corporate souvenir or gift, and companies have ordered it in large quantities. By the end of 1986, about 120,000 clocks had been sold, and monthly production had reached 15,000 units. This is considered a great success in the clock market, where annual sales of more than 100,000 units make a model a hit product. While Citizen was confident in its World-Time Card Alarm Clock, it was

indeed surprised by the popularity it enjoyed on the market.

1986 Award for Excellence

Accuracy at normal temperatures: Average monthly rate within ±30 sec
Effective temperature range: 0–50° C
Display: FE (field effect)-type nematic LCD
World time: Local zone time of the 24 zones of the world
Battery: Disk-shaped manganese-lithium battery
Battery life: About 3 years

VHS VideoMovie GR-C7: Mini VHS Camera/Recorder/Player
Victor Company of Japan (JVC)

The compact, light, fully automatic GR-C7

The GR-C7 is a video camera, recorder, and player all in one unit. With such features as a 6:1 power zoom, autofocus, fully automatic color tracking, and automatic iris control (with backlight compensation), it is designed to appeal to all users, from beginners to experts. Weighing just 1.3 kg, the GR-C7 is the smallest and lightest one-hour VHS camera-recorder in the world among those with both recording and playback functions. Its dimensions are only 121 (W) × 165 (H) × 223 (D) mm, power consumption is 7.5 W (up to a maximum of 9 W with optional accessories), and the retail price in Japan is ¥248,000.

On January 8, 1986, a conference room in Tokyo's Imperial Hotel resounded with the excited voice of Yuzuru Inoue, general manager of the Compact Video System Division of JVC's Video Sales Department. "Weighing just 1.3 kg, this is the world's lightest video camera-recorder-player." JVC was holding a press conference to announce the VideoMovie GR-C7, the "secret weapon" it had been developing in the video wars to battle the 8-mm-format video camera-recorder-player put out by its greatest rival, Sony.

Combining the functions of video camera, videocassette recorder, and videocassette player in a single unit, JVC's GR-C7 represents the third-generation model of the VideoMovie GR-C1, which JVC released in 1984. In addition to being much smaller and lighter, the new product uses compact VHS-format cassettes, and its camera section features a 1/2-in CCD pickup in place of the standard pickup tube.

The compact videocassette used in the GR-C7 is the size of a pack of cigarettes, as opposed to the three-pack size of the standard VHS cassette. Its inclusion was crucial to making a much smaller camera-recorder. Slipped into an adapter, the recorded compact cassette can be played back on any standard home VHS player. To make the GR-C7 so compact and lightweight, the developers struggled to make each and every part smaller and lighter. The development process often involved hard-fought battles just to shave off a few milligrams.

Toward the end of 1984, a VideoMovie project team of twenty members, led by Inoue, was put together. The team began by dividing itself into four groups, with one group assigned to work on each of the following categories: electric circuitry, the camera, the mechanism of the whole, and the exterior. Competing with one another, each group worked to make its part of the GR-C7 smaller and lighter. On the walls of the conference room where the project was based, graphs and charts were hung, illustrating in detail the changes and progress being made by each group. This served to heighten the sense of competitiveness and to stimulate the groups to greater efforts.

The group in charge of the mechanism was the first to produce concrete results. Its efforts centered on the drum that performs the central function of winding tape when a video recorder plays back the images. A major factor accounting for the small size and weight of the original GR-C1 had been the reduction of the diameter of the drum to 41 mm. Because the diameter of the drum is related to the speed at

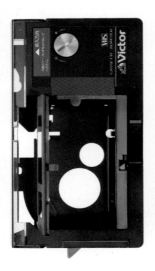

The VHS cassette adapter (left) and the VHS-C tape [92 (W) × 23 (H) × 59 (D) mm]

which the tape is wound, however, reducing it is a very difficult prospect. Rather than work on this, the team took a different approach and succeeded in reducing the thickness of the drum instead. This lowered the weight of the mechanism, and was an important contribution in making this third-generation camera-recorder-player lighter than the second-generation model.

By the summer of 1985, the team had succeeded in reducing the weight to 1.5 kg, but it suddenly found itself at an apparent dead end. As the deadline for development—the end of 1985—approached, team members grew increasingly frustrated. The idea of further reducing the camera's weight was staggering, and the specter of failure loomed. The sense of frustration was heightened by the knowledge that rival Sony was steadily making inroads in the video camera market with its 8-mm-format video equipment. JVC's vice president, Shizuo Takano, urged them on, however. It was his dream that a videocassette recorder could be made into something more than just an adjunct to the television. He wanted to see it become a tool for the family—as easy to use as a normal camera—but for this it truly had to be made lightweight.

His enthusiasm inspired the groups to keep looking for a way to bring his dream to reality.

Just two months before the end of the development period, the camera section solved its major problem. If the aperture of a camera lens is made smaller, then its ability to admit light is reduced and the image recorded made darker. Therefore, while trying to make the camera section more compact overall by shortening the focal distance of each of the many lenses in the system, the team also experimented with ways of maintaining brightness by changing the electrical circuitry. They succeeded in reducing to just 15 lux the brightness needed by the pickup to allow shooting. This marked a substantial improvement over existing equipment, which required at least 20–30 lux. In addition, the weight of the viewfinder was reduced by half compared to the previous model, and JVC's goal was at last realized—a camera-recorder-player weighing just 1.3 kg. Unveiled at the January 1986 press conference, the camera represents a significant achievement for the company. Much as it has reason to be content, however, the development team has already armed itself for the next challenge in its intense video wars with Sony with a newer model, the GR-C9.

1986 High Award for Excellence

Recording system: Luminance: FM system;
 Color: Converted subcarrier direct-recording;
 VHS format
Usable cassettes: VHS-C cassettes
Recording time: Maximum 60 min (TC-20 tape)
Pickup: 1/2-in CCD
Viewfinder: Electronic viewfinder with
 0.6-in b/w CRT
Lens: 6:1 power zoom lens, f1.6, f9—54 mm

An easy-to-operate video product

CLD-7: Compact-Disk/LaserVision™ Videodisk Player
Pioneer Electronic

The CD/LV-compatible 120-mm-high CLD-7

This new piece of home-entertainment equipment from Pioneer plays both compact disks and LaserVision videodisks, both enormously popular

in Japan. The CD/LV-compatible CLD-7 was developed in response to direct consumer and retailer demand. During the first three months of sales, 15,000 units were distributed per month, a record for Pioneer in its videodisk-related products. Until the end of 1985, Pioneer's LaserVision videodisk players competed heavily with similar machines from Victor Company of Japan (JVC). However, with the success of the

CLD-7, Pioneer pulled ahead with sales of 130,000 units in 1986.

The CLD-7, marketed in the United States as the CLD-909, was a major factor in establishing Pioneer's leading position in the field of VHD (video high density) videodisk systems, in front of its primary competitor, JVC. "The CLD-7 was born from the needs of the consumer," said Kentaro Tani, assistant general manager of Pioneer's

Small size has been accomplished by fixing the LD motor (foreground) and leaving only the CD motor (background) in a free-swinging state

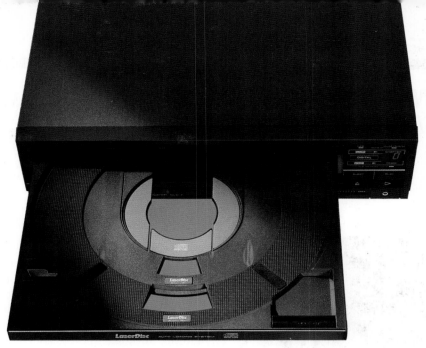
The machine automatically senses the type of disk

Systems Products Division. Many customers who had purchased separate Pioneer LaserVision and compact-disk players in the past often asked for one machine capable of playing both. Product reply cards for both products expressed similar sentiments, and retailers, too, often requested a combined machine.

Despite the many potential technical difficulties, the company decided to proceed with development plans. So early in 1983, Pioneer planners gathered at the company's factory in Tokorozawa City, Saitama prefecture, to begin development.

The result was new technologies for both the compact-disk and the videodisk players, designed to compensate for the differences between the two kinds of disks. The CD sound is recorded digitally, whereas the LV sound is recorded in both digital and analog form, and the picture is analog. The two disks also differ in size. A CD disk measures 12 cm in diameter and weighs 20 g. By contrast, a videodisk weighs 200 g and measures 30 cm in diameter. The CD's rotation speed is 200–500 rpm and the LV's is 1,800 rpm. The electrical circuits inside the CD and LV players are not very different in themselves, but the disks are so dissimilar that a special unit that could rotate the motor effectively for both types of disks in one unit had to be developed.

A year after development began, some of the new technologies were in place, and, in September 1984, the world's first compatible player—Pioneer's CLD-9000 (see p. 173)—was born. The machine's average retail price was a surprisingly low ¥249,800 at a time when videodisk players alone sold for nearly ¥200,000. Hi-tech fans received the CLD-9000 enthusiastically, and it sold at the rate of 10,000 units per month after it first debuted. Between September 1984 and the end of 1985, about 90,000 units were sold.

The CLD-9000, now obsolete and no longer manufactured, featured a "swing mechanism" system that rotates, thereby adjusting to both the CD and LV motors to accommodate each kind of disk. When the two kinds of players were combined, the height of the new machine grew to 168 mm, a size that was unpopular with owners of the older, slimmer, separate models. As a result, the general consumer never embraced the CLD-9000 as enthusiastically as the hi-tech fan did.

Pioneer's development group wanted to develop a product with more mass appeal. With this as its goal, the group began work on designing a popular machine once again. This time, the development staff adopted three goals for the new product: to decrease its size; to reduce its cost; and to improve its performance.

The first goal was reached by stabilizing a part of the LV motor and transforming only the compact-disk motor to a swing system. These two spindle motors are selected as needed by the player's 8-bit microprocessor; the CD motor swings out of the way when a LaserVision disk is to be played. The result was a machine only 120 mm in height.

To reduce the cost, the Pioneer staff reduced the number of circuit parts in the CLD-7, designed a smaller pickup that projects laser beams, and used, in addition to aluminum, a high-molecular resin to absorb vibration.

The CLD-7 was put on the market in late January 1986, at a price of ¥158,000, over ¥90,000 less than the earlier model; three months later, almost 50,000 units had been sold, making the product a hit. The industry was surprised that Pioneer succeeded in pricing a product with such high performance at such a low price. The CLD-7 owners now include female office workers and university students. This means that Pioneer's goal of making a combined CD and videodisk player with mass-consumer appeal was achieved. Quickly, videodisk-related companies such as TEAC and Marantz Japan purchased models and began marketing the compatible players under their own brand names.

Nippon Gakki (Yamaha) began selling a competing machine toward the end of 1986, but sales did not live up to projections. Pioneer was left the undisputed leader in the field not only in Japan but worldwide. The company is expected to continue to develop new models, retaining its sales strategy of concentrating on laser-disk players.

1986 Award for Excellence

System: LaserVision™ videodisk system and digital CD audio system
Horizontal resolution: 400 lines
Dynamic range: 95dB
Dimensions: 420 (W) × 120 (H) × 408 (D) mm; wt: 11 kg

World Square 37C960: A 37-Inch Color Television
Mitsubishi Electric

Realization of a 2,000-chr display

Mitsubishi Electric's World Square 37, a 37-inch color television, is the largest nonprojection television being mass-produced and marketed in the world. The area of the screen is 75% greater than that of the popular 28-inch televisions that had been the largest models available up to now. The radical expansion of the television screen in this model is timely, as consumers are increasingly demanding a system that gives movie-theater-like entertainment in their own homes. First put on sale in October 1985, the World Square 37 went into mass production in mid-1986.

The development of this ultralarge color television began in 1983 at the Kyoto Works of Mitsubishi Electric. The great popularity of the 40- and 50-inch projection televisions, which are also manufactured at the Kyoto Works, led the management to believe that a radically enlarged nonprojection TV might also sell well. Manufacturing such a large television, however, involves more than simply making an expanded version of existing sets. What is required is the solid engineering ability to design and build a larger, and quite different, picture tube. The circuit design that controls a jumbo television is also important, but the

major prerequisite is the ability to produce a tube that gives a clear picture with no distortion near the edges of its huge screen. This involves particularly tricky problems in its design, including the subtle shape of the screen surface and the thickness of the glass. For this purpose, the designers at Mitsubishi Electric used a CAD system to design the picture tube over and over again, trying to find the shape that would produce a square screen with minimal rounding at the corners.

The problem of design was compounded by the issue of safety during production. Since a picture tube is evacuated, breaking one is extremely dangerous. Consequently, it is necessary to design a tube with the requisite strength to prevent it from shattering easily, but the flatter the screen, the more difficult this is to achieve in a large-scale tube. Moreover, color television picture tubes undergo four stages of heat treatment in the manufacturing process. Tubes with thick glass are comparatively stronger at ordinary room temperatures, but those with thin glass are safer when subject to changing temperatures. Thinner glass also has the advantage of making the the delicately designed shape less likely to warp during heat treatment. The team at Mitsubishi Electric decided on a thickness of 15 mm for the glass in the center of the screen. This was the limit of technically feasible thinness, and was only 4 to 5 mm thicker than the glass of a tube for 14-inch screens. In order to protect the glass of the tube, it was decided to place a second layer of glass over the screen surface and to pour transparent resin in between the two layers. Thus, the 37-inch tube differs from ordinary television picture tubes, in which the glass of the tube itself is actually exposed. This three-

layer construction presented a further challenge to the team, necessitating considerable research in selecting the composition of the glass and type of resin best suited to preventing diffraction of light and clouding of the image.

Having designed a prototype, the Kyoto Works then turned to the question of actual production. The picture tube and TV circuit engineering teams worked hand in hand, along with cooperation from engineers at Nippon Electric Glass, the manufacturers of the tubes, to begin test production of the television in 1984. This was followed by a decision to build a special factory for the 37-inch tube, which was completed in May 1986, at a total cost of ¥7 billion. Investing in a special factory that can only produce one size of picture tube is a rather drastic decision, and costs were increased by the decision to equip the factory with state-of-the-art automation. Almost the entire production process is carried out by robots, with the construction of each picture tube controlled by computer at every step in the process. Although the screen glass was made as thin as possible, the tube weighs a hefty 60 kg, too much to be safely handled by humans. Moreover, the attachment of the shadow mask and electron-beam gun had to be performed with a much higher degree of accuracy than that necessary in the manufacture of tubes of ordinary size. Thus, the transport and positioning of the tubes at approximately 1,000 points in the production process were entrusted to robots. Extra attention was paid to safety in the factory. A conveyor system guards each picture tube, after it has been evacuated, in an individual steel cage. The attention to safety even extended to separating supervisory personnel from the production line with tough acrylic sheets.

A dynamic, 37-in, high-contrast TV screen with horizontal resolution density of 560 TV lines; the screen is the same size as 2 newspaper pages

Output at the Kyoto Works tube factory was 10,000 tubes per month in early 1987. Only about half of these tubes were used in Mitsubishi Electric's own television sets and sold under its brand name. The rest were supplied to other major manufacturers, or built by Mitsubishi Electric into television sets manufactured under original-equipment-manufacturing agreements for other firms. By supplying other firms in the industry with these tubes, Mitsubishi Electric, having concentrated its development efforts and investment on achieving the leap from a 28-inch to a 37-inch screen, is expanding the market for jumbo televisions. This strategy seems to be paying off, as interest in the tubes has now been expressed overseas.

1986 Award for Excellence

Reception system: NTSC system, Japan UV
  channel reception
Resolution: Horizontal resolution density 560 TV
  lines (video direct input)
Power consumption: AC 100 V/159 W
Dimensions: 973 (W) × 776 (H) × 604 (D) mm;
  wt: 105 kg

Yamaha DSP-1: A Digital Sound-Field Processor
Nippon Gakki

The DSP-1 is the first commercially available sound-field processor using digital technology. The system recreates actual acoustical sound fields that give a sense of live presence and spatial realism. It does so by treating the original sound signal sent to a stereo by a CD player, for example, with a layer of acoustical effect sounds gathered from places like concert halls or jazz clubs. The processor can be employed not only with a stereo but also with other devices, such as synthesizers or electronic keyboards, to create a variety of sounds.

In 1982, Hiroshi Kawakami, the president of Nippon Gakki, sat down with Yasunori Mochida, the manager of technical development, to discuss improvements in sound reproduction technology. "Can't we come up with audio equipment that puts out a sound that has the same impact as a live concert?" he asked. "As musical instrument makers, we, of all companies, should be able to do that." Putting their heads together, the two considered what kind of technology was required to recreate the "real" sound of live performances.

The "real" sound we experience in a concert hall is created by infinitesimal differences in the times it takes for

435 (W) × 72 (H) × 312 (D) mm; wt: 4.5 kg

sounds to reach the ears of the listener. The rich sound of a violin solo filling a well-designed concert hall is only due in part to the ability of the player or the quality of the violin. What really creates the full tones of a live instrument is not just the sound that comes directly from the instrument but also the multiple reflections of the original sound. There are two distinct types of sound reflections that combine to make up the sound field: "early reflections" of the sound, which bounce off surfaces or objects in the room, and "subsequent reverberations," sound reflections from more than one surface—walls, ceiling, floor—so numerous that they merge to form a continuous sonic "afterglow." The reflection of sound provides auditory cues to the listener, allowing him to gauge the shape and dimensions of the room. This is what gives depth and breadth to the sound, informing it with an emotional tone quite different from that of recorded music.

Was it possible to create these conditions artificially? In the spring of 1984, Nippon Gakki embarked on a project to find out. A development team was assembled, with members drawn from its technical lab, its electronic instruments production division, and its architectural acoustics research section. The approach that development activities should take had already been decided. Were it just a matter of adding time delays, it could be achieved quite simply with the use of resistors, but the group's head was aiming for sound reproduction which made full use of LSI technology.

The group began by gathering acoustical data from many places, such as concert halls, cathedrals, and jazz clubs, and recording it on a ROM chip. With this data as a standard, it then

went on to devise a way to check the sound signal sent to a stereo from its source (such as a CD player) and to blend the "place" sounds into the signal using an LSI, which can process information very rapidly. A device able to do this could instantly convert the user's listening room into a concert hall or a discotheque.

The first step in the development process was to simulate ideal sound fields, using a CAD (computer-aided-design) system. To test the routes, direct and reflected, by which sounds reach the human ear in different performance halls, the team conducted a lengthy series of tests on many different hypothetical cases. Its purpose was to generate and store the basic data for a VLSI that could instantaneously assess complex sounds and process them for delivery. Simultaneously, it worked on designing the VLSI itself.

A test model was ready by early 1985. The team next proceeded with a "personal inspection" operation. Was the sound produced by the machine like the sound in a concert hall? If not, how and why did it differ? Using a CAD system for careful analysis of the data collected, the team painstakingly produced blends of signals on the test machine. After an exhausting trial period, it emerged confident that it had a system that could recreate a sound faithful to the original spatial sound.

The Yamaha DSP-1 made its debut in June 1986, at a price of ¥138,000. It is the latest and most astonishing product to emerge from Nippon Gakki's expertise in the field of digital music. It introduces a new and exciting phase in music reproduction—a phase that actually redefines the listening experience. Its primary sales point was its ability to create spatially realistic sounds for a selection of sixteen differ-

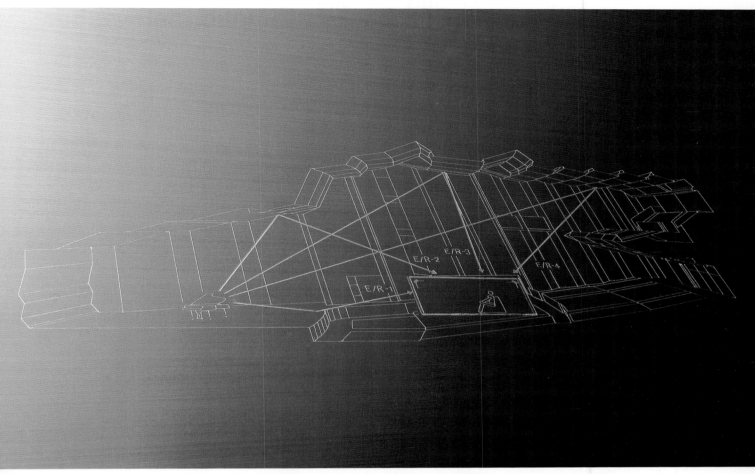

The time it takes sound to reach the listener divides the echo pattern of a hall into early reflections (E/R) and subsequent reverberations

ent places, including a concert hall, a church, a cathedral, a jazz club, a loft, a pavilion, and an outdoor stadium. The processor employed the actual data on acoustical effects that the team had acquired by traveling around Europe, particularly in the famous concert halls of Germany, including Munich's philharmonic hall and the Beethovens-halle.

More than 10,000 Yamaha DSP-1s have been shipped since the product came out, a measure of the strong appeal of the "real sound" that was the developers' original goal. Calling its processor "the third major development in sound recreation," after monaural and stereo, Nippon Gakki is now considering the possibility of adapting its functions to compact-disk and videodisk players, in the hope of further broadening its appeal.

1986 High Award for Excellence

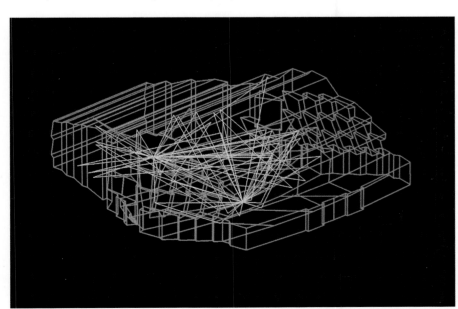

Echo pattern of multiple early reflections in a concert hall

Programs	
Acoustic/Surround:	16 programs
Hall 1/Hall 2/Hall 3/Chamber/Münster/ Church/Jazz club/Rock concert/Disco/ Pavilion/Loft/Stadium/Presence/ Surround 1/Surround 2/Dolby Surround	
Sound effects:	16 programs
User programs:	Up to 16 programs

NP-600: Household Compact Automatic Dishwasher
Matsushita Electric Industrial

The NP-600 dishwasher was developed as a compact model to fit conveniently in the kitchen of the average Japanese house. At a price of ¥77,000 it embodies a significant reduction in cost over the most compact dishwasher to date, which sells for ¥135,000. All three processes of washing, rinsing, and drying are completely automatic. The standard full cycle lasts 107 minutes. The low price was realized with a production level of 5,000 units per month.

While the annual sales of dishwashers in America are 3 million units, and the household penetration ratio is 50%, sales in Japan are considerably lower. Japanese manufacturers began putting home dishwashers on the market in the 1950s, but even after 1975, the annual sale of home dishwashers was barely 10,000 units.

The lack of popularity of dish-

Dishes for a family of 4 can all be washed at one time

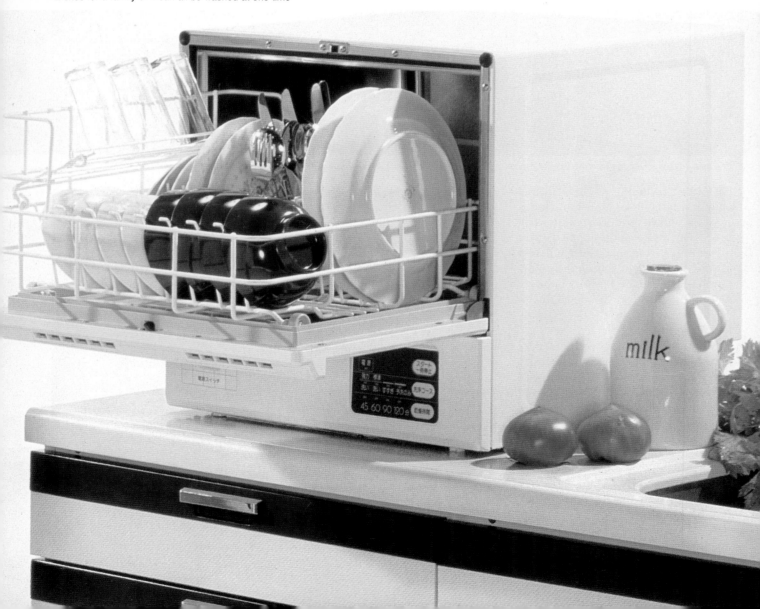

washers in Japan contrasts strongly with attitudes in other advanced economies. According to a JETRO (Japan External Trade Organization) poll, the dishwasher placed second in New York, Paris, and Stockholm among the "products recommended by working housewives." And in other major cities of the world, it ranked in the top five items. Yet Japanese housewives apparently did not view the dishwasher as a household necessity.

Matsushita Electric has recently changed this. The company had put home dishwashers on the market in both 1960 and 1968, but both were commercial failures, and only a small number were produced since then. At the end of 1983, however, a decision

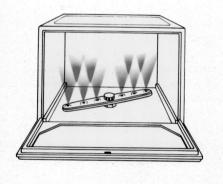

Strong spray from revolving nozzle with hot water of about 60° C

was taken to break through the existing stalemate and make the dishwasher the third pillar of the company's washing-machine business, alongside washers and dryers.

The spread of the dishwasher in America coincided precisely with the growth of the employment rate among women to around 50%. In Japan the women's employment rate has also begun to rise recently, opening up the possibility of truly solid demand for dishwashers. The Westernization of Japanese eating habits, including increased use of meats and oils, further reinforced the belief of the head of the Washing Machine Division at Matsushita Electric that the time was right for another effort.

But success required that a dishwasher be modified to suit Japanese conditions. A small size was the key, since dishwashers in the past had been large affairs that had to be placed on the floor next to the sink. Thus Matsushita came up with the NP-600, whose major sales point is that its compact size [45 (W) × 45 (H) × 50 (D) cm] allows it to sit next to the kitchen sink and fit snugly into even the small kitchens of Japanese homes. At ¥77,000, it is only half the price of even the smallest of Matsushita's earlier dishwashers, which sold for ¥135,000. In addition, it can wash at one time all the twenty-four eating utensils and cutlery normally used by a Japanese family of four at a single meal (four each of large, medium, and small plates; rice bowls; soup bowls; tea cups; and sets of knives, forks, spoons, and chopsticks). A further advantage of the NP-600 is that it requires less water than washing by hand.

In a mere five months, it sold between 17,000 and 18,000 units, nearly double the annual 10,000-unit volume of the entire industry up to that time. The machine's reputation continued to spread, until its sales reached 30,000 units within one year.

The main target customer for the NP-600 was the working housewife in her thirties with a need to rationalize housework, but demand has actually been stronger from women in their fifties and over. Interestingly enough,

the decision to purchase a dishwasher is not always made by the housewife alone, but is often influenced by the husband, the children, and other family members. This is largely due to the desire to allow the mother to spend more time with the family.

Reaction from consumers has been highly favorable. Other household electrical appliance makers such as Sharp and Sanyo have been stimulated by the success of Matsushita to take steps toward producing similar products of their own. As a result the automatic dishwasher market, which had been virtually stagnant up to this time, has suddenly begun to expand on a broad scale. In this context, it is safe to say that Matsushita's dishwasher strategy has proved highly successful.

Since the dishwasher was born out of the eating customs of the West, there will undoubtedly be a number of problems to be solved in adapting it to Japan. Consumer specialists have already pointed out areas for improvement, noting that the variety of Japanese eating utensils demands a versatile machine, and that the noise of washing and rinsing could be reduced. But as competition increases, improved machines will undoubtedly appear in the near future.

Anticipating competition, Matsushita Electric put the advanced NP-700 model on the market in December 1986. It features the basic functions of the NP-600, but includes a forced-exhaust fan as well. This new model and the NP-600 together will go into a monthly production rate of 5,000 units by the latter half of 1987.

1986 Award for Excellence

Power consumption:
  Motor: 120/130 W (50/60 H$_z$);
  Heater: 900 W;
  Maximum: 1,020/1,030 W (50/60 H$_z$)
Standard-cycle water consumption: About 17 L

Fujicolor Utsurun-desu: A Lens-Equipped Film
Fuji Photo Film

Utsurun-desu is a disposable camera made up of a roll of film equipped with a lens. Its simple structure comprises a plastic lens, a film-winding device, and a shutter mounted on the cardboard box of a twenty-four-exposure 110-cartridge color film. It is about the size of two boxes of 35-mm film laid side-by-side. Perfect for occasions when people "wish they had a camera," it can be purchased almost anywhere and has been an instant hit. Over 1.5 million were sold since it was put on the market in July 1986. With its convenience and simplicity, it has tapped consumers' spirit of playful spontaneity.

It used to be an accepted fact that one had to plan ahead in order to take pictures. Almost everyone has somewhere at some time thought, "If only I had a camera…" If on such occasions one could conveniently buy an inexpensive, throwaway camera in a local shop, who would not do so? Thus, the camera market would be greatly expanded.

The concept of such an "instant camera" is over twenty years old at Fuji Photo Film, and on three occasions in the past had been considered for development but abandoned because of a lack of information on market demand and pricing policy questions.

In 1984, Fuji Photo Film made a concerted effort to bring this long-held desire to fruition. Encouraged by company president Minoru Onishi, the manager of the Consumer Photo Products Division, Keiji Nakayama, headed a four-section-manager team that combined optical instrument technology and industrial design. Although it

Shooting outside in clear weather, minimum distance of 1 m

Actual size of Utsurun-desu; it comes in 3 colorful packages faced uncertainty at the beginning, the team was determined to succeed where others had failed before. Marketing strategies, production costs, and quality control were all coordinated to ensure success. This was evident in the planning process, which emphasized open exchanges of ideas to achieve mutual consensus.

In May 1985, the five-man team was expanded to eighteen as factory representatives joined the development team. They all decided that the target market would be teenagers and young adults, and that photographic conditions of use would have to be limited. The key concept was *utsuru,* which means to take a picture, emphasizing simplicity. Photography with a high-tech camera and today's quality film can meet any shooting conditions, but the team wanted to direct its product "back to basics." Since the retail market already offered a simple nondisposable camera that sold for less than ¥2,000, Fuji set as its goal a product that would cost less than ¥1,500. In the search for ways to lower the price, the lens system itself came under scrutiny. It was decided to limit photographic conditions to outdoors in bright daylight, and that focusing and diaphragm devices would be eliminated.

The design concept held that the camera should look as little like an actual camera as possible, to avoid competing with photography's high-tech, sophisticated image. Thus, a compact, box-shaped unit was designed in order to overcome resistance to the "use-it-only-once" idea, with emphasis on attractiveness and simplicity—no film to unwrap and put into the camera, no doors to fumble with and open, just a small, colorful, "magic" box.

The paper-box design was chosen specifically for the youth market, and produced in three different styles for regular merchandising. A fourth, which allows the purchaser to put original designs on the box, was intended for use in company sales-promotion campaigns or as incentives or awards. The film-protecting outer bag was designed to match the box inside.

In the autumn of 1985, while gearing up for actual production, Fuji

Photos taken with Utsurun-desu

Photo Film began looking for a name for the new product. Many ingenious suggestions were proposed, including combinations of Japanese-English loan words, such as *firumu* (film) and *kamera* (camera) to make "Kamerumu" or "Fimera." Lengthy considerations finally led to the selection of Utsurun-desu, which literally means "It can take a picture." The first prototype was made in February 1986, and market sales were set for launch in July.

When the product was announced, the company's stock leaped forward. This was quite a surprise, but it provided a foretaste of what was to come. Sales greatly exceeded the company's expectations, with demand far outpacing the planned annual production of one million units. Part of the success of Utsurun-desu derives from an unexpected source: user surveys have shown that the largest group of purchasers is made up of men in their thirties—businessmen who are well informed and who are curious about the latest technology. But unquestionably, the general reason for its success lies in its sheer convenience and adaptability to a wide range of uses—from

family picnics to school graduations, and from taking pictures of the family pet to snapping shots while sightseeing in Hawaii—making it a perfect gadget for a more leisure-oriented society.

The project team's enthusiasm and dogged efforts were rewarded by the brilliant success of its little "picture-taker," Utsurun-desu, with a resulting expansion of the camera market.

1986 High Award for Excellence

Shutter speed: 1/100 sec
Film speed: ISO 100
Lens: f11 fixed focus
Focal distance: 1 m to infinity
Dimensions: 98 (W) × 48 (H) × 35 (D) mm;
  wt: 75 g

SPORTS, LEISURE, AND SUNDRY ITEMS

TRENDS IN THE 1980s

The high-tech miracles of Japan are not confined to cars and stereos. They are even producing better golf balls, tennis rackets, musical instruments, and stationery goods.

In the past, the Japanese market has been flooded with sports, leisure, and sundry items imported from abroad. But as the economy matured, Japanese manufacturers began to make progress against imports. During the 1970s, they began producing goods that were competitive with imported products.

The innovation of the 1980s has been high-technology products that feature electronics and new materials. With these innovations, Japan has begun to make inroads in the world market. Only in sports such as skiing and camping do imported products retain a large part of the Japanese market.

Sports products are big business in Japan, totaling an estimated ¥1.5 trillion in sales in 1985. Golf supplies accounted for ¥300 billion of the total, with fishing, skiing, and tennis equipment totaling about ¥100 billion each. Camping equipment, motorcycle supplies, and health and fitness products are showing growth spurts currently. Interest in baseball and volleyball appears to have peaked.

"High technology" is the key phrase for Japanese manufacturers of sports equipment, just as it is in the nation's economy as a whole. This is most apparent in golf and tennis. In recent years, new golf products have included the double-layer ball and graphite-head clubs. In tennis, there is the carbon-based racket.

Sumitomo Rubber Industries and Bridgestone are in direct competition over the manufacture of golf balls, with intensive product development aimed at grabbing the largest share of the market. The two combined already share 90% of sales, almost completely shutting out American competitors such as Spalding and Links. But still they struggle—over possible new golf ball materials, over the number of dimples on the ball, over the kind of computer graphics used to design the balls and, finally, over their balls' ability to fly over long distances.

In the field of golf clubs, the market was dominated by imported brands such as Spalding, Links, and American Wilson until around 1975. These days, however, Japanese manufacturers hold almost 80% of the market and are secure in their reputation among consumers for easy-to-use, superior-quality products.

Particularly notable products are: a club with a graphite shaft known for making balls fly true and far; other shafts made of composites of such high-tech materials as whisker fibers, advanced ceramics, boron fibers, and aramid fibers; the graphite-head wood; and, in 1986, the graphite-head iron. In 1985, Bridgestone Sports marketed a set of clubs, called the All Target 11 (see p. 186), that bridges the gap between irons and woods. The product was so popular that Spalding followed with a rival.

Japanese golf club manufacturers have become so successful that they have begun assembling their products abroad. Mizuno and Daiwa Seiko both make clubs in the U.S. Mizuno also plans to open a plant in England in 1987. As Japanese manufacturers gain additional recognition abroad, predictions are that they will see appreciable growth in their share of the world market.

The influence of Japanese manufacturers is also growing among tennis buffs worldwide because of the new technology being offered and the professional endorsements that have resulted from it. Since professional champion Martina Navratilova began playing with Yonex's graphite racket and acting as its spokesman, the company has become a world-scale manufacturer. Also under development by Japanese manufacturers are ceramic rackets. Already on the market are rackets incorporating boron, aramid fibers, and carbon and glass.

In the sport of skiing, American and European manufacturers currently maintain market dominance in Japan. While Japan's Yamaha skis are competitive, the combined sales of France's Rossignol, Olin of the U.S., and Austria's Kneissel account for 45% of the Japanese market. In ski boots, Italy's Nordica and France's Salomon control the market with 60–70%, and in bindings, Salomon accounts for 80% of the Japanese market. Two of the European manufacturers—Nordica and Salomon—are particularly successful because they have created Japanese subsidiaries fully capitalized by the parent companies.

Competition among brands of sports shoes is severe in Japan. Foreign brands such as Nike from the U.S. and West Germany's Adidas and Puma are popular. But Japanese manufacturers like Mizuno and Asics are developing shoes using new materials with superior shock-absorbing properties to compete with the imported products. Nike has also had a checkered past in Japan, an indication of the degree of competition in the market. In 1981, it established a local corporation, Nike Japan, to handle sales of the American product here. But in 1986, after a period of poor management, Nike Japan became a subsidiary of Nissho Iwai, a general trading company.

Among manufacturers of musical instruments, Japan has been the production center for the world since the 1960s. Nippon Gakki with its Yamaha brand and Kawai Musical Instruments hold first and second place both on the domestic market and internationally, with Yamaha accounting for 30% of the world market.

Japan has some areas of the domestic market all to itself. For example, Japan has a monopoly in the market for electronic instruments such as electronic keyboards and synthesizers. But a monopoly does not mean an easy time for individual manufacturers. With the entry into the market of Casio Computer and its SK-1 keyboard (see pp. 42–43), competition is becoming increasingly intense.

The trend in the toy industry in the 1980s is toward more and more joint ventures between Japanese and American companies for larger sales in the U.S. In 1986, Japan's Bandai joined with Mattel of the U.S. to market Barbie dolls.

Takara has made an agreement with the No. 2 American toy company, Hasbro, for the sale of war toys. In October 1986, America's third ranked toy company, Coleco, linked itself with Japan's Tomy for product development, manufacture, and sales. Early in 1987, SEGA Enterprises, the Japanese amusement equipment manufacturer, bought Time Out Family Amusement Centers of the U.S.

Like many industries recently, leisure products have been affected by the steep rise of the yen since the autumn of 1985. Japanese manufacturers have begun moving their factories to cheap-labor locations such as Taiwan, South Korea, and Singapore to make products that are then imported for the domestic market.

The bicycle industry in Japan is one of the chief examples of the effect of cheap labor in the newly industrializing nations of Asia and the Japanese response to it.

The U.S. is the world's largest market for bicycle parts. In 1985, Taiwan held 81.7% of that market, with Japan coming in second at 9.6%. South Korea was close behind, however, with 5.5%. The aggressive business practices of Taiwanese and South Korean manufacturers are also directed at Japan itself, particularly in the area of the inexpensive ¥10,000 bicycle. During the first half of 1986, the number of ¥10,000 bicycles sold in Japan was 54,114—triple that for the same period the previous year. Most of these came from Taiwan, and they put a large dent in the sales of Japanese brands, particularly the ¥20,000 bicycles usually sold in supermarkets.

Japan has been known as the world factory for bicycles, but change is not far off. Taiwan is expected to become preeminent in the field in the near future. As happened in the U.S., the change will leave the one-time champ with a number of bicycle-trading companies, but few manufacturers.

The onslaught by the Taiwanese and South Koreans against Japanese manufacturers is even greater in leather goods than in bicycles. The export of leather handbags from Japan has virtually ground to a halt. As a result, Ace, Japan's largest bag maker, is taking its production abroad. In November 1985, it began production in the People's Republic of China, making leather goods both for Japan and foreign markets.

In the shoe industry, the strong yen, coupled with a liberalization of trade regulations on leather and leather products, has caused a doubling of shoe imports—to 1.8 million pairs—for the first half of 1986 as compared with the same period in 1985.

To counter the competition, Japanese shoe companies have adopted a policy of importing low-priced styles and manufacturing higher-priced shoes domestically. Union Shoe actually began providing technical help to two South Korean factories twenty years ago. Five years ago, it built a factory in Singapore, and it now has plans to expand its overseas operations in Southeast Asia.

Writing equipment manufacturers in Japan export 30–50% of their production and have been seriously affected by the strong yen. In addition, the domestic market has cooled considerably.

The country's three major manufacturers—Sailor Pen, Pilot Pen, and Mitsubishi Pencil—have attempted to remain competitive by producing ink ribbons for use in office-automation equipment such as word processors, but the results have not been completely satisfactory. The saviors of the industry have been the stationery kits—such as Team-Demi, a set of miniature desk-top supplies (see p. 188)—and the felt-tip pen that writes with little pressure on the point. Domestic demand is good, and exports remain satisfactory. Indeed, it is estimated that 90% of the water-base felt-tips used in the world today are Japanese made.

Pen manufacturers are also looking to possible production in Taiwan and South Korea, but more than that, they hope to develop new big-selling products such as the stationery kits. And once again, whether the industry is sports equipment or writing instruments, the key to the future appears to be the establishment of overseas production for low-priced goods and the development of high-value products appealing to the consumer.

T·E·M·A·K·I: Paper-Thin Speaker
Mitsubishi Petrochemical/Yonmarugo

The T·E·M·A·K·I speaker looks like a sheet of paper. About 0.01 mm thick, it is made of a piezoelectric macromolecular substance in which the macromolecules vibrate in resistance to the flow of electric current, producing sound from the front surface of the speaker. The flexible speaker can *be rolled up and even printed upon, breaking all stereotypes of speakers as being boxy. The speaker alone sells for ¥25,000, and a special amplifier, adapter, and other pieces are sold separately. A range of products combining the speaker with other elements is expected in the future.*

This is a success story involving an industrial giant and a fledgling design firm. Mitsubishi Petrochemical is the largest petrochemical producer in Japan, with sales in the billions of dollars and operations overseas. Yonmarugo is a small, newly founded company specializing in illuminated

A stylish accessory piece for a modern room

advertising devices. While Mitsubishi Petrochemical was able to offer expertise at the leading edge of today's technology, it had to rely on Yonmarugo for the necessary sensitivity to style and form in marketing this product. Cooperative attempts between such industrial giants and tiny start-up firms are not uncommon in Japan, but this is one of the few truly successful cases. It is often difficult for firms of such radically different scales to put their skills to work in joint ventures. The large firm tends to control the small one or treat it cavalierly, while the small firm is apt to find itself going along with its partner's wishes instead of asserting an independent approach. In the case of Mitsubishi Petrochemical and Yonmarugo, a factor in their success was the former's openness to its smaller partner's opinions.

The origins of this product go back to 1973. At that time, Mitsubishi Petrochemical began researching piezoelectric macromolecular materials, and within a year had developed a sample that was 0.1 mm thick. Its efforts continued, and in 1983 it succeeded in increasing its piezoelectric constant and perfected the basic pattern for a 0.01-mm sheet-form speaker. Espying a commercial possibility, the company approached an audio manufacturer with the goal of developing the sheet-form speaker into a marketable product. The latter proved incapable of finding the right niche for the speakers in the audio market, and finally gave up.

This left Mitsubishi Petrochemical with no market for its new material. The company's Electronic Materials and Devices Department, which was involved in finding possible commercial applications, felt that it needed to adjust its approach. It attributed its failure to having clung to preconceived notions about what audio products should be. It was proposed that a better approach would be to make the speaker into a stylish and very decorative device that could even be used as an advertising and publicity tool. Thus began the search for a partner with strength in design. At a product exhibition in March 1985, Hiroyuki Aoki, head of the EM&D

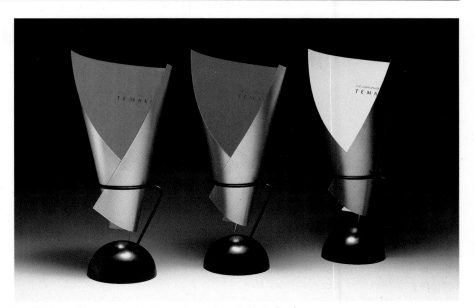

T·E·M·A·K·I and its special stand come in a set, available in 3 colors

Department, came across Thin Light Sign System, a surface-light source developed by Yonmarugo. Unlike a conventional surface-light source, in which the combination of linear light sources produces uneven lighting, the Yonmarugo system made clever use of prisms to create a product that was slim and gave off light evenly. Aoki, who had long been interested in combining light and sound, was thrilled by the product. He called at Yonmarugo's tiny office in Tokyo just two days later. Tatsuji Mizobe, president of Yonmarugo, was quick to respond when Aoki presented his proposal. This, he thought, was a material that everyone would snatch up. But he could well imagine the difficulties of making it into a commercially viable product. Thus, Mizobe agreed to take part in the project, but he countered Aoki's urgency with a proposal for a three-year project. Yonmarugo succeeded in convincing Mitsubishi Petrochemical of the importance of taking their time on the project, and three months later a three-year joint development plan had been established, according to which Mitsubishi Petrochemical would provide the material and Yonmarugo would turn it into an interior decor product. Yonmarugo's strategy was to aim initially for a simple design and presentation that would widen consumers' expectations of speakers, and

then to follow that up by combining the speaker with other products.

In March 1986, the speaker, in a loosely rolled sheet form, was unveiled at the Japan Shop Exhibition in Tokyo. As expected, it caused a great stir. Six months later it went on sale under the name T·E·M·A·K·I, so called after a type of sushi rolled in sheets of dried seaweed. Numerous inquiries were received from companies, and sales were predicted to reach 10,000 sets within the first year, making it a hit product.

Work on the project is far from finished, however. The two companies have high expectations for a recently developed, translucent piezoelectric macromolecular sheet. Time will be needed before it can be mass-produced, but a translucent speaker would be perfect for realizing the integration of light and sound. A further advantage of the sheet-form speaker is that it does not produce electromagnetism, unlike conventional speakers. This permits combining the speakers with computer displays, presently impossible with conventional speakers, which require a shield to protect the computer and all disk-stored data from their magnetic fields. Together, Mitsubishi Petrochemical and Yonmarugo are working on these new possibilities, inspired by their previous success.

1986 High Award for Excellence

Casio SK-1: An Electronic Sampling Keyboard
Casio Computer

The SK-1 is a popular sampling keyboard available at ¥16,000, an extraordinarily low price compared to that of sampling keyboards for professionals, which retail for ¥1–10 million. A human voice, an animal cry, a rushing river, or indeed any sound can be entered into the keyboard's memory. When the user strikes the keys, the instrument plays back the sound at appropriate pitches. If a dog's "woof" is recorded, for example, the user can play a melody in "woofs." The keyboard also incorporates certain preset tones as well as the usual complement of keyboard functions, including a selection of rhythms.

In the summer of 1984, Casio was in the process of developing a sampling instrument commissioned by composer Isao Tomita for a performance at Ars Electronica, a festival of electronic arts to be held in Linz, Austria, that September. The synthesizer created for Tomita had a sampling function that allowed the performer to play melodies using sounds from nature as a source—a waltz of "woofs," for example. Intended for professional use, the instrument was large, expensive, and difficult to operate. Nevertheless, it was fun to use. Casio felt that a similar product might be created for the world of amateur music, with special appeal for young children.

Setting to work, the staff who had received the development order spent the first three months in a room at Casio's research and development

Everyday sounds can be recorded and played back

Beginning in September, the development staff went to work on the design of the instrument and the layout of the electronic circuitry. The architecture for the sampling was not particularly difficult. The analog sound that entered the microphone would be converted into digital form and stored

headquarters, considering the basics of the technology for the instrument. This covered a range of issues, such as the sampling time, the scale of the electronic circuits, and the functions that should be added to the instrument. They decided that the sampling time—the interval in which a sound is entered into the memory—should be 0.8 seconds, with "one-touch" recording into a microphone. The team considered some fifty combinations of additional functions, such as automatic play.

in the memory; when the user played the keys, the sound would be retrieved from the memory, treated with the proper tone, converted back to analog sound, and played.

The company wanted an instrument that would be small and light. This would be impossible, however, if all three functions—conversion from analog to digital sound, the addition of tone, and reconversion from digital to analog—were to be performed by integrated circuits, since the print board

Sampling is initiated automatically

would have to be 1m² in size. The team was thus forced to design its own LSI for the instrument. By the end of December, it had come up with an ultraminiature chip (49 mm²), permitting a major reduction in cost. To make it distinctive and elegant, the board was given gold sampling keys and a shiny body, even though this increased the cost.

In July 1985, members from Casio's development, production, and sales divisions gathered for an Instrument Promotion Conference, at which they exchanged views on the best way to make the new instrument succeed as a

sounds were good but the quality of the preset tones was terrible—and the sales people were doubtful that it would sell. Obtaining an extension of two months, the development team set about reviewing all its work.

The first change made was to lengthen the sampling time to 1.4 seconds, long enough to record "Hello, how are you?" in Japanese. Next, the print sounds were changed from electronically synthesized ones to PCM (pulse-code modulation) sound sources from acoustic musical instruments. This was a difficult matter, however. One PCM sound source that

first year reached 1 million units. The instrument has been very popular overseas, with exports accounting for 80% of sales. To sell a million of one kind of musical instrument was a first for Casio, and indeed unprecedented for the industry as a whole. In Japan, the keyboard has been retailed through musical instrument stores and the music sections of department stores. The keyboard sections in such stores are normally quiet places, but the popularity of the SK-1 with young people has changed that.

1986 Award for Excellence

consumer product. Since the LSIs, commissioned from a subcontractor, were still not ready, the development team used a printed integrated-circuit board to demonstrate the instrument, and drawings to illustrate what it would look like. Nevertheless, Casio was confident from the test model that it was a good product.

But the critiques were harsh. The technical people had a number of complaints—the sampling time of 0.8 seconds was too short, the sampling

gave them trouble was the brass ensemble, which had excess noise that was hard to remove. The designers rewrote the program over and over, however, until the problem was finally resolved. At the next Instrument Promotion Conference the instrument was approved, and Casio unveiled the product in December 1985.

The initial production rate of the keyboard was 20,000 units per month, yet this soon proved inadequate. Production was increased, and sales for the

Keyboard: 32 keys, max. of 4 sound harmonies
Preset tone colors: 8 PCM tones (piano, trumpet, flute, pipe organ, etc.)
Auto rhythms: 11 rhythms (disco, rock, waltz, 4-beat, etc.)
Speaker: 8.0 cm (output power: 1 W)

Pecera "Paper Ceramic"/Tomita Furnace
Tomita Sogyo

The Tomita Furnace fires paper ceramic to glasslike hardness at a temperature of nearly 900°C. It can be operated at home on an ordinary gas range, with easy temperature control. Paper ceramic can be fired in this kiln in only thirty minutes, while the firing time in electric kilns is usually two hours. The paper ceramic Pecera represents an improvement over previous paper ceramics, since it shrinks less and does so in the same ratio vertically as horizontally. This improved material, together with the low price of the kiln, holds the promise of giving rise to a new kind of handicraft.

At first glance Pecera looks like ordinary drawing paper from a sketchbook. It has a distinctive feel—as though lightly coated with powder—but it can be drawn on with ordinary writing implements, as well as cut or folded. Fire it in a kiln to 900°C, however, and it will turn as hard as glass.

First developed around 1980, paper ceramics attracted considerable attention for their paperlike form and ceramic properties. Some predicted that they would open up a new handicraft field, while others pointed to their promise as an industrial material. They were finally judged a mere passing novelty, however, and interest in paper ceramics soon waned.

There were two reasons for this. First, paper ceramic shrank more than 40% in firing. Composed of a mixture of clay and pulp, to which were added a fixative and a low-temperature-sintering agent, it was inevitably given to shrinkage. It shrank so much, however, that designs on its surface were severely distorted during the firing process, particularly because the horizontal and vertical shrinkage ratios were different. The second drawback was the lack of a specialized kiln suitable for home use. It was possible to use electric kilns, but at more than ¥30,000 apiece they were too expensive. Furthermore, electric kilns need a long start-up time, and cannot fire paper-ceramic pieces in under two hours. This is too long for most crafts lessons, making it impossible to finish work in one lesson. Temperature adjustment is also difficult, and during tests many pieces cracked under conditions of rapid heating and cooling.

To overcome these obstacles, Shikoku Paper, the manufacturer of Pecera, consulted Tomita Sogyo, a firm with experience in firing technology for paper ceramics, for assistance. Tomita began by developing a special glue for use with Pecera. In handicraft use, craftsmen would often cut Pecera with scissors and then glue the pieces together. Until the special glue was available, they had been forced to use ordinary epoxies, but these often peeled off during the firing process. Tomita Sogyo joined forces with an epoxy manufacturer to develop a new epoxy that not only would adhere well to both clay and pulp but also would not peel off in firing.

Next Tomita approached the problem of shrinkage. By distributing the pulp uniformly throughout the paper and changing the fixative and sintering agent used, it cut shrinkage to 32% and equalized the horizontal and vertical shrinkage ratios. The new fixative gave the fired material the strength of glass. Pieces made of fired Pecera were so strong that even if dropped from a height of over 10 cm they would not break.

Yet these improvements were of no avail without the development of a kiln suitable for home use. Kilns with a built-in heat source are prohibitively expensive, and this prompted the novel idea of using the gas-range burners present in households as a heat source.

Since it is translucent, Pecera gives a stained-glass effect

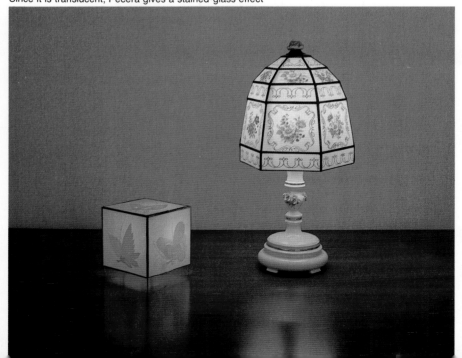

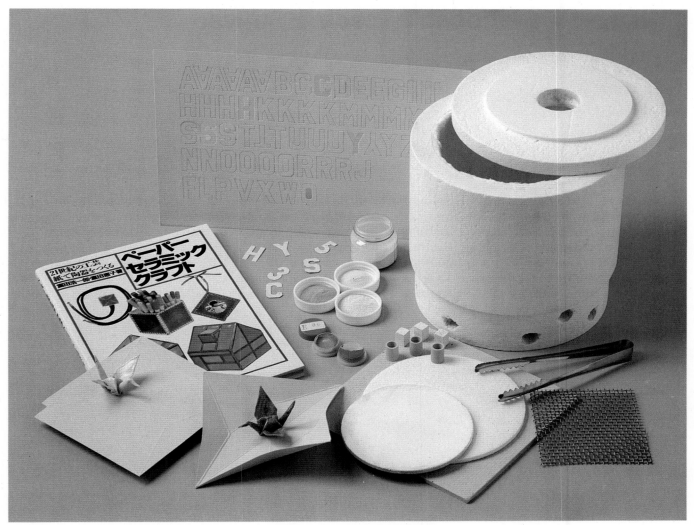

Paper ceramic can be treated like paper—folded, cut, and colored (ceramic kiln is shown at right)

The developers set about designing an appropriate oven. They made one using an alumina-silica ceramic as the basic material, melting it at high temperatures and then resolidifying it into fine fibers. However, after repeated firings cracks appeared in the kiln walls, and eventually developed into chips. The kiln material seemed unable to withstand rapid temperature changes, and Tomita made numerous attempts to improve the kiln by changing the thickness of the walls and altering the relative densities and proportions of the inner and outer layers. Its efforts proved fruitless for several months, and it found itself stumped. Kōichirō Tomita, president of the company, explains: "We were stuck for several months. Then somehow we chanced upon the idea of not hardening the ce-

ramic fibers used in the kiln walls but applying them like wool to the inner surface of the walls." This turned out to be the perfect solution. The ceramic wool worked so well as an insulator that it proved safe to touch the outside of the kiln even during firing. Small holes were made near the bottom of the kiln to keep the internal temperature uniform, and the ease of temperature adjustment on a home gas burner allows even a beginner to operate the kiln correctly and safely.

The perfected kiln went on sale in July 1986, affordably priced at ¥15,800 for the home-use model and ¥21,000 for a larger model. By the end of the year the company had sold 200 kilns, with sales figures of more than 1,000 predicted for 1987. Long-term success, however, depends on the

growth of interest in this new craft. Tomita has been training teachers for paper-ceramic classes since 1985, emphasizing the variety of applications of the material. The number of paper-ceramic hobbyists in Japan jumped to nearly 3,000 in 1985, an increase of 50%. Tomita has announced its goal to increase that figure to 30,000, and is developing a marketing strategy to help meet that goal.

1986 Award for Excellence

Kiln (gas burner)
Standard measurements: 20 (ø) × 20 (H) cm;
  wt: 1.2 kg
Maximum temperature: 950° C
Usable thermal power: City gas and propane gas
Material: Alumina-silica ceramic
Price: ¥15,800

Choysol: A Disposable Electric Shaver
Minimum

Choysol is an ultrasmall, battery-powered shaver that became something of a mass-media topic in Japan. Its name is a compound of a slang word for "a little" and the verb "to shave." It is about the size of a disposable lighter and costs only ¥500.

Soon after it went on sale it became a popular topic of conversation. By the end of 1986, some one million shavers had been sold, making it a hit in a country where demand for electric shavers is around 600,000 units annually. Symbolic of its times, the

Choysol shaver has been carried along by the current popularity of disposable products of all kinds.

The Choysol electric shaver was inspired by the unshaven face of Eiji Okada, founder and president of Mini-

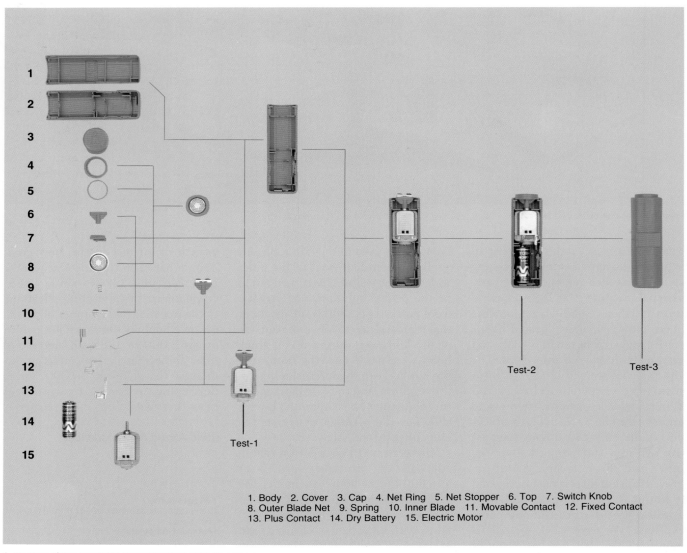

1. Body 2. Cover 3. Cap 4. Net Ring 5. Net Stopper 6. Top 7. Switch Knob
8. Outer Blade Net 9. Spring 10. Inner Blade 11. Movable Contact 12. Fixed Contact
13. Plus Contact 14. Dry Battery 15. Electric Motor

A diagram of the assembly process which uses no screws

mum. While employed as a salesman at a company that manufactured small parts, he frequently stayed at the office until late at night and then rose early in the morning to call on customers. Having often forgotten to shave, he found clients pointing out that he looked unkempt.

Various possible solutions to his problem presented themselves, but were found wanting. What he really needed was a small razor that could fit easily into his pocket and that he could use on the commuter train in the morning. Thinking there must be many people with the same problem, he decided to make one himself. Although he had absolutely no technical know-how, he was confident of success. Fond of making things on his own, he soon became absorbed in designing the shaver. In fact, he left his job in February 1985 in order to devote himself to full-time development of his miniature shaver. It took him until September to produce a prototype, supporting himself all the while with meager unemployment insurance benefits. In January 1986, he set up Minimum and started shipping samples of his miniature shaver, christened Choysol ("little shaver").

However, it proved no easy matter to make a product that was small, inexpensive, and of high quality. It took an assiduous search of numerous parts manufacturers to obtain elements that were small and could cut well, such as the ultrathin net and the surgical steel blades. Great attention was also paid to the structure of the shaver. By making it of fifteen parts that could be snapped together, with no need for screws or solder, Okada simplified the manufacturing process and thereby kept costs down. His attention to detail was evident in such additions as a prop built into the body to stabilize it when placed on a table, and a cap with a notch to make it easy to open when replacing the battery. Since convenience was of utmost importance, the shaver was made to run for fifteen to twenty minutes on one 1.5-V manganese battery. In recognition of its clever design, the product was awarded a Good Design Prize by MITI (Ministry

of International Trade and Industry). This is a great distinction, because the shaver fell into the "articles for daily use" division, in which fewer than 8% of the entries win prizes.

Having achieved sales of over one

Actual size of Choysol

million units in less than a year, the shaver was a great success. Much of this can be attributed to its superior design and consumer demand for convenience in an increasingly hurried world. Nevertheless, an element which cannot be overlooked is the appearance of this shaver at a time when the market for disposable products was booming. Gadgets such as disposable cameras and disposable radios have made a great impact in Japan. Choysol rode on this wave, and was taken up by the media. Its position in the market was then solidified by steady advertising.

The product's success is not due solely to the research and development that went into it, nor to the media coverage that it enjoyed, but also to the intelligent marketing strategies that Okada developed. He selected as his first outlets shops like Tokyu Hands, which carries a wide range of trendy products, and Ito-ya, a graphic-arts and stationery supplier. Okada thought that his Choysol might catch on very quickly among young customers who are always on the lookout for some

With the company president at the head of the test force, all merchandise is fully tested before being shipped

new, unique product. He was right. He next set his sights on Kiosk, the network of small shops found in railway stations and even on railway platforms all over the country. This gave Choysol nationwide exposure and made it an instant hit. Soon, orders started coming in for Choysol to be used as sales-promotion gifts, prizes at golf tournaments, and party favors. Sales through these channels equal those of ordinary retail shops.

Hoping to avoid the pitfalls of excessively rapid expansion, Okada follows a prudent, conservative management style. Despite increasing demand, the production rate has been kept at a steady 150,000 units per month. Okada still uses a room in his own home as company headquarters, while production is carried out in an apartment across the street. Such a small scale is quite remarkable for a company anticipating revenues of ¥500 million a year.

1986 Award for Excellence

In-Card (TIC 502): Personal-Seal Card
Tango

The In-Card is a personal seal built into a credit-card-sized piece of plastic. This presents a challenge to conventional seals, which are usually small cylinders on one end of which one's family name is carved. Slightly smaller than a bank cash card, the In-Card fits neatly into a wallet or calling-card holder. The seal face is 3.5 mm thick, while the rest of the card is a mere 1.5 mm thick. The seal is covered by a sliding door that is saturated with thick red ink on the reverse side. Sliding open the door inks the seal, preparing it for impression on a document. Each card is good for about 200 uses.

In Japan, a personal seal functions much as a signature does in the Western world. Impressing one's seal is an indispensable procedure in attesting that one has received money or merchandise, or in indicating that one has understood a document. The formal use of seals is a traditional Japanese custom that extends into all aspects of one's life—from serious matters such as having certificates of residence or copies of family registers issued at government offices, to such everyday events as accepting a delivery at the door.

But the use of personal seals is a nuisance. Seals are normally small, hard cylinders shorter than a regular cigarette and a little thicker. Walking with a seal rolling around in one's pocket is inconvenient, and one can easily lose it. Seals are not used every day, yet when one is needed nothing can get underway without it. Many people have trouble keeping track of their seals and are reduced to turning out cupboards and scrabbling through desk drawers looking for one when they need it. Since people do not usually carry their seals with them all the time, they are sometimes unable to take advantage of a bit of unexpected spare time to handle personal business at a government office or a bank. No seal, no deal.

The In-Card is a product that cleverly surmounts the distinctive problems posed by personal seals. It turns the seal into something one can carry routinely. While there have been improvements in cylindrical seals, including the development of a self-inking type and a combination seal and pen, the In-Card is the first seal developed in card format with an eye to carrying convenience.

Although simple in appearance, the product was difficult to develop. It took twenty months to produce a finished version, after considerable trial and error and dozens of improvements on the test version. The biggest obstacle to collapsing a seal into a card was the problem of thinness. First, Tango struggled with the face of the seal itself, and the depth of carving. Too thick and the seal impression would be blotched; too thin and the ink would cover it only scantily, producing a faint, indistinct impression. Tango made a set of seal faces of 0.1-mm gradations in thickness, testing again and again to see which gave the clearest impression, necessarily taking into account the fact that there would be some differences in the force with which the user pressed the seal.

Having settled on the thickness for the face of the seal, the company then turned to incorporating it into the body of the card. It was found that a round seal inserted into the card with a slight skew produced a crooked impression. This led the designers to abandon the usual concept of a seal face as round, and instead mount it on a rectangular chip that was easier to line up in the card. The card was then designed to allow the seal to spring back into place after being pressed, and a sliding door for the seal face was added to avoid inky fingers. The work involved taking out three related patents and four utility-model rights covering the clever design features of the card.

In developing this product, Tango was well aware of a potentially strong source of demand: the market for

Cards are available in many colors

48

In-Card employs a square stamp face, eliminating slippage and smudging

promotion-related novelty items. Since the In-Card is a flat surface, it is possible to have it imprinted with a design of a company's choosing—such as its name or logo—and then to give it away as a promotional gift. A seal with one's own name is a highly useful item, and thus the targeted recipient is quite likely to retain the gift In-Card. This enhances its advertising value, making it more desirable than most novelty items, which people soon dispose of as junk.

The In-Card was put on sale in November 1985, at a price of ¥800.

Cards with uncommon surnames were also made available on special order, costing ¥2,000 each. At one point, demand outstripped supply by 100%, and sales reached almost 2.5 million cards in the first year on the market. Tango has not made a serious effort to advertise the card, allowing word-of-mouth to do the job instead. Strong sales of the card opened up new sales routes. Not only stationery stores, but also supermarkets, department stores, mini-marts, tobacconists, and even gasoline stations and film-processing shops now carry the new cards. Card-

format products continue to appear in Japan. The card boom began with credit-card-sized pocket calculators in the early 1980s and gathered momentum with the introduction of NTT's enormously popular telephone cards in 1984. In 1986, these were joined by ball-point pens, mechanical pencils, and universal cutting blades in card format. The In-Card's timely appearance at the crest of this boom is a large factor in its success.

1986 Award for Excellence

Toy Cat's Paw
Bandai

In the fall of 1985, an employee in the development section at Bandai came up with the idea of toys with a cat theme. "I once had a cat, and also worked in a pet shop," she said, "so I

fad might be coming to an end, and that consequently it would be too late for these products to be successful. Nevertheless, the decision was made to proceed with the manufacture of a toy cat's paw as a test item.

Bandai's development section tries to create fun products that are not limited by traditional concepts concerning toys. In order to gather as many ideas as possible, the section holds weekly meetings, for which the participants have to prepare proposals.

For the meeting where the idea for the Toy Cat's Paw was presented, each planner was assigned to come up with five proposals. Tomoyo Mitani had three ideas about which she felt fairly

confident, but she had trouble coming up with two more. The day before the meeting, while racking her brains for ideas, she thought, "Wouldn't it be fun if people could lead the life of cats.... Cats spend a great deal of time just sunning themselves without a thought in their heads." And onto her note paper, she wrote, "Paws, ears, tails..."

Despite the simplicity of the toy, it was half a year from the initial go-ahead before it was put on sale. Reorganization within the company after Bandai was first listed on the Tokyo Stock Exchange impeded development, and the idea lingered for several months. Responsibility for developing the product was finally assigned to a newly created division for toys for girls. The idea for the toy was that it should combine mechanical movement with the texture and appearance of a stuffed toy.

was quite familiar with cats. The image of cats sitting around sunning themselves without a thought in their heads appealed to me. And I thought it might appeal to others, too." While there was hardly a desperate need for such products on the market, her coworkers considered it an "interesting" idea. At the time Japan was experiencing something of a fad for cats. Women's weekly magazines were featuring cat specialty shops in their pages, and young women in particular were showing interest in cats. Additionally, there is a popular comic strip about a tabby cat named Michael, who also appears in a video and in numerous commercials. Some trepidation was expressed that this

The first prototype developed was short and fat and looked like a real cat's paw, but the originator of the idea rejected it as inappropriate. She insisted that since cat gestures were feminine and seductive, the paw should be long and slender, with a sleeker look. It was redesigned to meet these specifications, and in the spring of 1986, the Toy Cat's Paw was put on the market.

The time for its appearance could not have been more propitious. Comic books, cartoons, and even feature films with feline themes were appearing all over Japan. The cat obsession has gone so far that there is even a Cat Day. The Cat's Paw acted as a further stimulus to this trend, and became a fad of its own. At the beginning of sales, a single toy store in Tokyo's trendy Harajuku, a dis-

trict where students frequently gather, sold 240 items in a mere two hours. Within six months sales had reached 980,000 paws, far exceeding the company's target of 200,000. Its unprecedented success was accounted for by its popularity among university students. The company had intended the paw to be sold to younger schoolgirls, but unexpectedly the college set began buying it, too.

The success of the Cat's Paw prompted further development by Bandai. The first paw produced was brown and white, but the company later introduced such variations as black, grey, and all-white ones, as well

as an all-black paw with a white tip at the end. To these were added stuffed Cat's Ears and Cat's Tails, creating a

"Cat's Meow" series. The Ears and Tails were not as successful as the Paws, achieving sales of 40,000 and 100,000, respectively.

1986 Award for Excellence

CLOTHING, FOOD, AND HOUSING

TRENDS IN THE 1980s

The Japanese apparel industry, spurred by a high yen and a rising international reputation, is venturing overseas more than ever before. —— *Clothing*

Like the West, Japan has learned the dangers of an unhealthy diet. And like Westerners, Japanese are demanding healthful, convenient, gourmet foods. —— *Food*

The technological achievements of Japan are now being applied to its construction industry. The results will change the nation. —— *Housing*

Clothing

Apparel companies have become the focus of much attention in Japan during the 1980s for their high earnings compared with other textile-related industries. Unlike the high-profile companies of the Japanese economy—such as electronics or car manufacturers—clothing manufacturers have not made their earnings from exporting high-quality domestically made products. Success has come through sales at home and licensing agreements and manufacturing ventures abroad.

Indeed, exports of Japanese apparel, ¥300−400 billion a year since 1981, have dropped slightly in recent years. In 1985, exports declined 5.4% from the previous year. Imports of clothing, by contrast, generally have been over ¥400 billion annually since 1981, and have shown an upward trend. Imports for 1985 totaled ¥497.7 billion, up 3.0% over the previous year.

Many Japanese apparel companies are small. Others are world-class in size. Renown, for example, had 1986 sales of approximately ¥215 billion, and Kashiyama of around ¥178 billion. Yet Renown and Kashiyama have virtually no overseas sales. Even among apparel companies that pursue an export market, the percentage of sales is small. Exports, chiefly to the U.S., accounted for 7% of the 1986 sales of Sanyo Shokai, another large clothing manufacturer, whose sales during the first half of that year totaled ¥36.5 billion.

The rise in imports began in the 1980s, with products such as underwear, polo shirts, and acrylic sweaters from the People's Republic of China, Taiwan, and South Korea. The variety of products is now increasing steadily. In recent years there has also been growth in imports of high-quality, name-brand clothing from the U.S. and Europe. Some Japanese manufacturers such as D'URBAN and Renown have also taken advantage of cheap labor in textile factories in Southeast Asia to produce low-cost products there for import into Japan.

The most conspicuous developments in the industry in 1986 were the purchase of some foreign companies and the establishment of joint ventures with others. In April, Kashiyama began a joint venture in Milan with Italian designer Luciano Soprani. It obtained the rights to wholesale and retail sales of Soprani items not only in Japan but also in the U.S., including the opening of direct-management boutiques.

In October, Kashiyama purchased J. Press, the American manufacturer of traditional men's wear. For more than ten years, Kashiyama had had a licensing agreement with J. Press, and the brand had become Kashiyama's third largest seller among its men's apparel lines in Japan.

Itokin, a large manufacturer of women's clothing, now owns and operates fourteen stores in major cities in the U.S., including New York. It opened five stores in 1986. As has become customary with several Japanese manufacturers, Itokin licenses the name of a famous designer—for example, France's André Courrèges—for clothing made and sold in Japan as well as for imports.

Sanyo Shokai, with a relatively high rate of exports among Japanese manufacturers, has joined Mitsui to establish a raincoat-manufacturing business on the outskirts of New York. Operation began in the spring of 1987. The move is particularly bold since it is unusual for a foreign company to enter the American men's wear market as a domestic producer.

While they are not apparel manufacturers, the Japanese high-fashion designers Hanae Mori and Issey Miyake are becoming leaders in the international fashion world. The two operate boutiques in the U.S. and Europe, and show their spring and fall collections in both places. A recent Miyake coat design made use of Toray's Furtastic, an artificial, Japanese-made fur fabric that has already been used by international couture designers such as Karl Lagerfeld. Indeed, the Japanese apparel industry as a whole is growing more international. The appreciation of the yen is forcing the prices of Japanese clothing up, making it necessary for Japan's manufacturers to shift more and more production overseas to hold down costs. This will ensure their expansion worldwide.

Food

The food industry in Japan is a giant one, with production totaling ¥30 trillion in 1985, or about 10% of the nation's GNP. While big companies such as Kirin Brewery, Ajinomoto, and Snow Brand Milk Products loom large in the market, they also coexist with more than 50,000 small food producers. A cornucopia of products pours out from these companies—from traditional foods such as miso (soybean paste) and soy sauce to Western-style frozen foods, soft drinks, and alcoholic beverages.

Demand within the Japanese food market has generally been stable over the years. Now, however, the food industry is undergoing a major transition. The change is being forced on it from within and without—at home, by a rising standard of living and changing consumer tastes, and abroad by a muscular national currency.

So what are Japanese consumers looking for in food

products these days? As the national diet reaches what some have called "the age of gluttony," trends are toward nutritious, low-calorie, gourmet, and easy-to-prepare foods. Aiming for better eating habits, consumers are looking for healthy, low-calorie foods, particularly dietetic sweeteners such as aspartame and low-cholesterol products such as safflower oil.

The gourmet trend has made pasta, bread—especially freshly baked bread—and imported alcoholic beverages increasingly popular. In addition, more and more Japanese are attempting to make authentic, if expensive, epicurean dishes at home.

And, finally, as it becomes more common for both husband and wife to work outside the home, there is growing demand for easy-to-prepare foods. The marketplace is offering increasing numbers of frozen foods and products for microwave cooking, such as House Range Gourmet, a series of food products designed to be prepared in microwave ovens.

Since the autumn of 1985, the Japanese food industry has been highly vulnerable to fluctuations in the currency exchange rate. A strong yen allows food manufacturers to buy raw materials such as wheat, soybeans, corn, and sugar cheaply on the world market and make a profit on the finished product. But at the same time, a corresponding drop in prices for the finished product has meant that the companies cannot expect an overall increase in revenues. In fact, revenues among some major manufacturers actually decreased during fiscal 1986.

As a result, competition within the industry is growing stiffer. Some large manufacturers flood the market with as many as 300 new products each year. The annual success rate for such products is 5–10%, about the same as in the U.S.

Major domestic agricultural products such as rice, wheat, and sugar are increasingly more expensive in Japan than on the international market. The difference comes from Japan's agricultural policy, which limits imports in order to protect the country's farmers. The situation, coupled with a strong yen, is developing into a problem for the food industry. While Japanese food-processing technology is high and provides quality products, imports such as inexpensive instant ramen (noodles) from South Korea and Taiwan, and chocolates and cookies from Europe, are taking an increasing share of the market.

The challenge to the Japanese food industry, particularly from inexpensive South Korean and Taiwanese food products, is to devise ways to compete by creating products especially suited to domestic tastes, or products that are more highly refined, such as Kikō Ramen, an instant noodle with gourmet appeal. A stabilization of the high yen rate could also lead to an expansion of Japanese food enterprises abroad.

Housing

In Japan, a country whose tiny, cramped houses have often been called "rabbit hutches" by Westerners, the trend in housing in the 1980s is toward construction appropriate to the nation's new economic power. Housing of that scale often means high-rise, multiunit construction, luxurious, hotellike services, interesting architectural design, and sensitivity to the structure of the Japanese extended family.

Some of the new high-rise residential construction is as much as 100 meters high, or about thirty-one floors, and builders are devoting considerable effort to developing technology that will make the buildings safe and livable, as well as tall. Ohbayashi, for example, has finished technical development on a proposed fifty-story, reinforced-concrete residential building that will be highly resistant to noise and shaking from wind, and from the earthquakes that frequently make Japan tremble.

All major construction companies, including Shimizu, Taisei, Kajima, and Takenaka, have in hand the technology to build reinforced-concrete buildings of up to thirty stories. They are also developing better systems for fire prevention, information distribution, and refuse disposal. This derives from the recognition that peripheral technology, such as the creation of special dust chutes so residents do not have to ride elevators to dispose of garbage, will eliminate many of the problems associated with high-rise living.

Japan is also now seeing the growth of housing developments that offer services similar to hotels. In April 1986, Seiyo, a member of the Seibu Saison Group, completed Villa Saison, a 294-unit development in Tokorozawa near Tokyo. At its center is a "Community Forum" reception area that offers services ranging from kitchen cleaning and car rental to wake-up calls. The service even makes reservations for theater and airline tickets.

The single-family dwelling has not been forgotten amidst apartment construction. Sekisui House commissioned talented young architects to design an experimental line of houses called Is Pret-a-Porter, using some prefabricated modular units as well as some on-site construction. The idea was to bring artistic flair to prefabricated-housing design, usually known for its uniformity.

An understanding of the multigenerational structure of the Japanese family living situation also appears in the development of new housing products. Projects for two-family dwellings show a trend toward structures that allow two households of three generations—grandparents, parents, and children—to maintain privacy while living together under one roof. Some of these houses emphasize the independence of the two households with a separate, easy-to-use kitchen for the elderly couple. Others concentrate on the special needs of the elderly by eliminating stairs, adding wheelchair ramps, and installing emergency call buttons in toilets and baths.

Japanese builders and real estate companies are not confining their efforts only to Japan. Armed with an overall command of the new technology, they are moving overseas. Aoki, for example, is building a 1,000-unit housing development in Raleigh, North Carolina. It is also constructing a complex of seven new office buildings on nearby land, with the intention of making a community where residents can live close to their work.

Similarly, several years ago, Sunrise, a U.S. business, began large-scale, comprehensive development of a combined housing and leisure project on a 700-hectare site in the Los Angeles suburbs. In October 1986, the Japanese company Mitsubishi Estate joined the Sunrise project. The project, funded with Sunrise capital, also makes full use of high-quality housing-construction techniques nurtured in Japan.

A few manufacturers of prefabricated housing are also looking for markets abroad. Misawa Homes, for example, is working in the People's Republic of China. The company is eager to take the technology it has developed to please the demanding Japanese consumer and put it to use in production and sales overseas.

Furtastic: A Polyester-Fiber Artificial Fur
Toray

Furtastic is an artificial fur made of special polyester fibers that resemble mink. Although fake furs of acrylic fibers are common, Furtastic is the first polyester artificial fur. Mink consists of long guard hairs with short underfur; a similar structure was achieved using polyester. General sales of Furtastic began in 1986, but as early as April 1985, Toray was providing this new material exclusively to fashion designer Karl Lagerfeld. Sales totaled 4,800 m² in fiscal 1986. In fiscal 1987, exports are expected to remain at 3,000 m² and domestic demand is predicted to rise to 15,000 m².

The initial research and development that resulted in Toray's Furtastic began in its laboratories in the early 1960s. Real mink hairs are tapered, and a technique for making such fibers existed. At that time researchers posed the question of whether or not it was possible to create a furlike material out of these synthetic fibers.

In April 1979 a new project team was formed. In order to develop a fur fabric with the same structure as mink, the group had to examine every technical possibility, including previous Toray research. They found, for example, that in 1977 pulsating spinning, a technique for producing tapered fibers continuously, had already been perfected, and that in 1978, production of a pile fabric using these fibers had been considered.

Pile fibers must be implanted into the base fabric to create a fur. There are four methods of forming fabrics with pile: double weaving, pile weaving, sliver knitting, and needle punch. With double and pile weaving, a high pile density is possible, but implanting the long fibers is difficult. With sliver knitting and needle punch techniques, the opposite is true. Implanting is simple, but high pile density is difficult to achieve. Although the demerits of all the methods were apparent, Toray took out patents on all of them to prevent competing companies from developing a similar product sooner. The method Toray eventually used in developing Furtastic remains a company secret.

Furtastic is a product based on a thorough analysis of real mink and perfected by concentrated application of Toray's synthetic fiber technology. The finished Furtastic has 17,000 strands of pile implanted into each square centimeter of the polyester backing. The pile density matches the density of hairs in actual mink. The implanted pile has guard hairs and underfur, as is the case with mink, and the guard hairs are 26 mm long and 40–90 μm in diameter. Both the guard hairs and underfur have tapered tips. The underfur is 18 mm long and 10 μm in diameter. There is a bundle of sixteen underfur fibers for each guard hair, with 1,000 bundles per square centi-meter, a structure reproducing that of mink.

The density required to recreate the structure of mink presented certain problems. With 17,000 pile fibers per square centimeter implanted, the base fabric becomes very stiff. In order to soften it and achieve the suppleness of real mink, Toray used techniques and knowledge derived in the development of its hit Ultrasuede brand of

Furtastic can be dyed any color

Comparison of various types of fur

Mink

FURTASTIC

Other Synthetic Fur

synthetic suede. A range of ingenious methods were invented, such as using special resins to make the fibers slimmer and stabilize the pile. One hundred and ten of these innovations have been made public through patents.

In December 1983, when the techniques and product concept had been determined, a development group was established, and in September 1984, a pilot facility to turn out 300 m^2 of Furtastic per month was established. At the end of 1984, Toray's marketing division clinched a major contract with fashion designer Karl Lagerfeld. The new artificial fur made its public debut on April 30, 1985, at the Lagerfeld fashion show in New York.

Furtastic has many distinctive features: the beauty and high density of its pile, the luster of the fibers, and its realistic feel. The use of artificial fibers enables it to be dyed in many shades. These visual attributes are reinforced by the texture—a combination of a minklike touch and suppleness. A highly practical fabric, it is lighter than mink, retains its shape when worn, has no odor, and does not fade or shed. Mothproof and resistant to mildew and soiling, it is easier to maintain and store than mink and can be dry-cleaned.

In July 1985 Toray established facilities to produce 1,200 m^2 a month. In July of the following year, a Furtastic marketing department was formed to begin full-scale marketing. The sales plan for fiscal 1987 predicted no increase in export sales, but a fivefold increase in domestic demand compared with the previous fiscal year. The domestic expansion is due to the decision of designers such as Issey Miyake and major women's wear manufacturers to use Furtastic. Since the fabric is priced at about ¥16,000/m^2, a Furtastic short coat is about 60% less expensive than mink.

Toray is wary of competitors manufacturing imitative products, as was the case with its Ultrasuede. Although they were the first in the world to manufacture this artificial suede fabric, within a very short time other companies introduced similar products. When Karl Lagerfeld's Furtastic designs went on display in a leading Japanese department store, the first customer was from a major synthetic fiber manufacturing company. Toray spent eight years developing Furtastic, but it expects that its rivals will catch up in approximately three years.

1986 Award for Excellence

Senposai: A New Nutritious Hybrid
Kirin Brewery / Tokita Seed

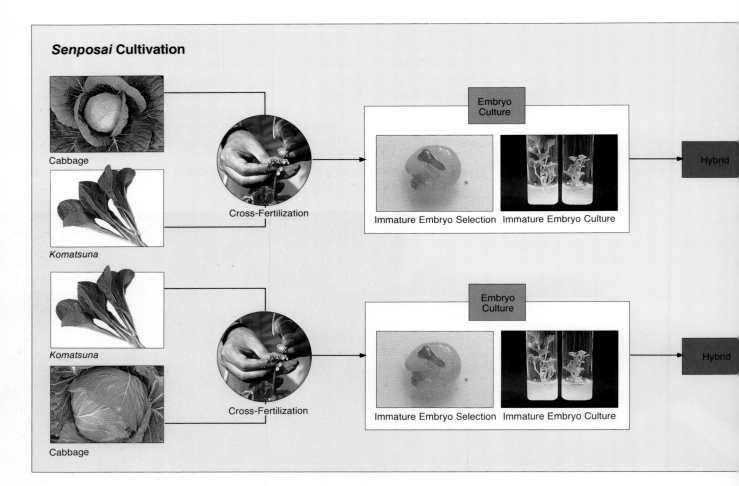

Senposai Cultivation

Cabbage

Komatsuna

Cross-Fertilization

Komatsuna

Cabbage

Cross-Fertilization

Embryo Culture

Immature Embryo Selection   Immature Embryo Culture

Embryo Culture

Immature Embryo Selection   Immature Embryo Culture

Hybrid

Hybrid

Although common cabbage and komatsuna, a hardy spinachlike vegetable of the rape family, cannot be crossed by conventional breeding techniques, Kirin Brewery, using a new biotechnological technique known as embryo culture, has succeeded in creating a hybrid and raising a new vegetable, Senposai, from the resulting seed. This hybrid Senposai has the sweetness of cabbage and the tenderness of komatsuna. Since it is resistant to heat, it can be cultivated year-round, even in the summer when most other leafy green vegetables are in short supply. Senposai is the first new bioengineered vegetable to be developed by the private sector.

Kirin Brewery, the largest Japanese brewery, first showed interest in the development of new vegetables as part of a diversification program in 1981. The company had considerable experience in improving varieties of hops and barley, but realized that it required the cooperation of a seed specialist company in order to develop and market vegetable varieties. Kirin decided to

approach Tokita Seed, a seed company with expertise in the techniques of varietal improvement for such vegetables such as the common cabbage, Chinese cabbage, and giant radish. The two companies formally signed a cooperative agreement in February 1982, formed project teams, and commenced research. The goal of the project was to produce a vegetable that could be cultivated all year, especially in the summer when leafy green vegetables are scarce, and that would not be susceptible to soft rot, a disease common in *komatsuna*, in which the plant loses turgidity and rots.

Between March and May of 1982 they made as many crosses as possible between common cabbage and *komatsuna*, turnip and giant radish, and Chinese cabbage and *komatsuna*. Since the flowers of these plants are complete, with both stamens and pistil, they self-fertilize if left to themselves. Thus, in order to hybridize, the stamens must be removed from the plant

Initially Kirin researchers considered using simple ovary culturing but were not successful. They next tried ovule culturing, and then went into embryo culturing. To illustrate the process, if Kirin had been using a pea, it was as though they first placed the pea, still in its pod, on the culture medium and next tried shelling the peas and culturing them. Finally they used only the embryo, the tiny sprout that even-

rapa var. *pervidis*), was created. It was named *Senposai* (lit., "thousand-jewel vegetable"), after the thousand *(sen)* leagues the mythical *kirin*, the brewery's mark, flies across the skies, and the jewel *(hō)* used in Tokita's trademark.

In 1984, Kirin and Tokita met to evaluate the new vegetable. *Senposai* met their four criteria for evaluation: disease resistance, flavor, ease of cultivation, and seed-production efficiency. After they determined that it was not only heat resistant, tender, and soft like *komatsuna*, but also sweet like cabbage, and required only thirty-five days from seeding to harvesting, they decided to proceed with commercial development.

Three farms, with which Tokita had friendly relations, were given seeds in the summer of 1985. They were not told that this was a new variety, but were simply told to grow it as though it were a new type of *komatsuna*. It was too early to sell the seed since they had not officially registered it yet with the Ministry of Agriculture, Forestry, and Fisheries.

In September the first crop reached the Tokyo market. Two of the farmers shipped the new crop to Tokyo's Kanda wholesale market, the other to the Tsukiji wholesale market, also in Tokyo. At the Kanda market, the jobbers said that the vegetables were tastier than standard *komatsuna*. At Tsukiji, they were priced at ¥60 a bunch, ¥10 more per bunch than standard *komatsuna*. When the Kirin and Tokita project members heard this news, they gained confidence and prepared to market *Senposai* commercially.

Enough seed to cultivate about ten hectares was ready for the summer of 1986, but since many research institutes and amateur horticulturalists all over Japan requested seeds for test plots, commercial sales were limited. In 1987, Kirin and Tokita plan to prepare ten times as many seeds to market throughout Japan.

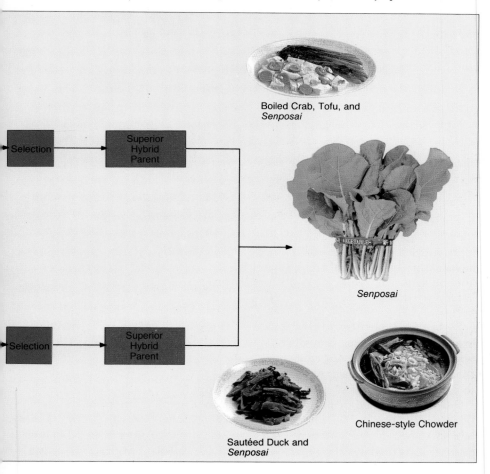

Boiled Crab, Tofu, and *Senposai*

Senposai

Sautéed Duck and *Senposai*

Chinese-style Chowder

to be the mother before it flowers, and then when it does flower, it must be fertilized with pollen from another plant.

In many cases, fruit was not produced since the parent varieties are different. Tokita Seed identified those crosses that did set fruit, and brought the seed pods to the Kirin Brewery Plant Laboratory. For a single set of crosses, there would perhaps be 20,000 fruits, but on opening the fruit, the researchers found that many contained no seeds. Only one in several hundred to several thousand fruits could produce a viable new plant.

tually grew into a new plant.

Embryo culturing is a tissue-culture technique to excise out of a pod an immature embryo obtained after a wide cross. It is cultured on an appropriate medium with nutrients, and grown into a whole plant. Without this process, embryos usually die shortly after the cross.

After three years of trial and error, this technique was perfected, and the resulting new vegetable, a hybrid of common cabbage *(Brassica oleracea* var. *capitata)* and a spinachlike plant known in Japan as *komatsuna (Brassica*

1986 Award for Excellence

Karamente:
Spicy Instant Noodles
Bell Foods

Karamente is a series of spicy instant cup noodles. Introduced to the market in January of 1986, they have been particularly popular among teenagers and young adults. The success of these noodles has prompted other leading instant-noodle manufacturers to produce new spicy noodle lines. The noodles, whose dough and soup both contain hot peppers, were a surprise success for Bell Foods. First available in miso (soybean paste) and soy sauce flavors, the product line has been expanded to include curried and yakisoba noodles. All four flavors retail at ¥140 per pack. In one year, the total sales of these noodles were ¥3.5 billion.

Instant cup noodles are a very popular and inexpensive snack food in Japan, accounting for ¥300 billion in domestic sales annually. Bell Foods, a medium-sized instant-noodle manufacturer, is unusual in that its instant noodles are nonfried. Although nonfried noodles account for only 5–10% of sales, Bell adopted its policy because nonfried noodles are healthier. It was this policy that led to the development of Karamente.

Bell Foods has been involved in the development of low-sodium foods for a number of years. Although the normal intake of sodium derivatives should be restricted to 10 g per day, one portion of instant cup noodles already contains 6 g of salt. Bell Foods, with the hopes of appealing to an increasingly health- and diet-conscious consumer market in Japan, decided to create noodles low in sodium content.

The company initially began with development of two types of noodles—low-sodium "bio-noodles" and "super-hot" noodles. The problem with the latter was that in Japan, consumers have in the past tended to believe that hot spicy foods are not healthy. Since instant noodles are a common snack for children, Bell Foods was concerned that parents would react negatively to spicy instant noodles.

Bell Foods decided to introduce the "bio-noodles" first. In these noodles, a biotechnological method where yeast gave off a salty taste was developed. The noodles therefore had a salty taste but low sodium content. Bell Foods, confident of its product's success, introduced its new noodles under the product name Hontsuru to the market in August 1985. Initially the noodles received positive response from retailers, but sales were poor, and the noodles were taken off the market in the fall of that year. Bell Foods believes that one reason the noodles did not do well was that their taste was too bland.

All the while, Bell Foods continued its development of the spicy hot noodles. There were many difficulties in developing the noodles. Should the hot taste be achieved by using red peppers, or a combination of spices? How should the red pepper be incorporated into the noodles? In order to answer some of these questions, Bell even sent some researchers to Mexico to study chili sauce production. The soup, alone, took one year to develop and is a blend of twenty ingredients, some of which had to be obtained in the People's Republic of China. The development process lasted a total of three years, although Bell is secretive about the details.

Even when the noodles were ready to be marketed, Bell had reservations about its new product. The noodles were placed on the market in December 1985, shortly after the "bio-

Nonfried noodles are used in Karamente

Cup noodles generally have a short product life span and few brands manage to stay on the market for five years. Bell Foods, however, is confident that the popularity and acceptance of hot foods is not a temporary phenomenon, and that Karamente will be around for some time to come.

1986 Award for Excellence

Noodles in miso-flavored broth

Noodles in curry-flavored broth

Yakisoba: Japanese-style chow mein

noodles" failure. Bell, therefore, was conservative with its marketing, and the initial production run was a mere 72,000 packs.

Karamente was specifically targeted to young customers, in the age range of thirteen to twenty, and was initially only sold in convenience stores that are heavily patronized by young customers. From the very start, sales of Karamente were overwhelming. In most convenience stores cup-noodle sales are considered to be good if a pack a day is sold, but Karamente sold as many as five or six packs a day.

With this positive response, Bell Foods stepped up production and expanded its sales network to include major supermarkets and grocery stores. In 1986 the company launched a television advertising campaign. An indication of the success of Karamente is the speed with which other makers quickly introduced their own spicy noodle product lines, but according to a Bell Foods spokesman, the imitations are inferior. According to Bell Foods, one major difference is in the color of the noodles. Other manufacturers fry noodles, a process which turns the red pepper in the noodles black, but because Karamente are not fried, the noodles retain a red color.

Research conducted by Bell Foods showed that although young people were the first customers, housewives and young working men are also buying Karamente. Bell Foods attributes its success in part to the fact that ethnic foods, especially hot spicy cuisines, have recently become extremely popular in Japan, and people are more willing to try new and unusual tastes. In addition to spicy instant noodles, other hot foods such as instant curries and spicy rice crackers have deluged the market.

Range Gourmet: Instant Microwave Food
House Food Industrial

A new cooking package that is heat-resistant and does not get hot

Range Gourmet is a line of processed foods for the microwave oven. By simply adding water and cooking as is, foods like steamed bread, cake, or boiled rice can be ready to eat in three to seven minutes. At the end of 1985, twenty-three different items were put on the market, and the one-touch home-cooked food became an instant hit, with sales totaling ¥4 billion in just one year. In late 1986, the product line was expanded, adding new items like fondant cake. The standard retail price of a package of boiled rice is ¥220; the most expensive item, fondant cake, costs ¥300.

Range Gourmet is a pioneer product that introduced to Japan a new kind of food product exclusively for the microwave oven. Process research developed a new polypropylene foam, high-heat-resistant container that can withstand temperatures of 130–140°C. Throughout the development process, a total of twenty-four patents were obtained to cover all aspects of the new design technology.

House Foods wanted to develop dry products that were nonfrozen and therefore distributable at normal temperatures. Personnel from the head office research laboratory in Higashi Osaka City were engaged in the development program for five years. Over-

seeing and guiding the program was former president Ikuo Uragami, who, prior to his death in the tragic aircraft accident of a Japan Air Lines flight on August 12, 1985, was personally interested in the success of this product line.

Uragami appointed as Tokyo manager Tatsuya Minewaki, formerly head of retort food products (pasteurization through heating under pressure), and ordered the start of the commercial production of microwave foods. Immediately after taking charge, Minewaki established a committee that included Uragami to taste-test the products developed by the research laboratory.

Developing a suitable product container proved a formidable problem. It

needed to be not only heat-resistant, but also comfortable to handle when removed from the microwave oven. Great efforts by the development team finally resulted in the design of a new material made from polypropylene foam. The merchandiser of the materials section suggested also using paper for package containers. He himself created the design. As a result of these experiments with packaging, a decision was reached in early 1985 to use polypropylene foam containers for *zōsui* (a stew of rice and vegetables with salmon), *gomoku-soba* (mixed noodles), Chinese rice stew, and others, but paper containers were to be used for chocolate and fruit cakes. Minewaki detailed final production plans to President Uragami on August 10, 1985, only two days before the fatal accident. After the accident, the realization of Uragami's dream through "House Range Gourmet" became a company goal, and their efforts produced the original twenty-three-item line of products that included boiled rice, porridge, steamed bread, cake, popcorn, and noodles. Sales began in October, and wholesalers and supermarkets greeted the new line favorably.

First-year sales reached ¥4 billion. Behind this large-scale success were

marketing strategies. Initially, the printed media conveyed information on these new products and their preparation to the public. Sampling-sales displays were also set up in supermarkets and department stores. After consumers understood the basic concept behind the products, television advertisements were used to promote House Foods' Range Gourmet.

The company later introduced over twenty new products and a new striped packaging design, to consolidate the product line image. Special display sections that featured panel photographs, and attention-getting streamers were set up in larger stores.

House Foods has no qualms about altering its original ideas. As an example, it canceled its scheduled introduction of a new line of cooking sauces. Since they are items that would be added to food, they did not fit the original Range Gourmet concept, which

was to create an entire product line of ready-to-eat foods.

Future plans call for semiannual (spring and fall) product revisions and new additions, snack and staple items in particular. Sales promotion includes monthly themes such as "Hot Breakfast Foods," "Christmas Party Foods," "Night Foods" for students preparing for examinations, and others. Television advertisements promote these special products.

As of November 1984, 51.6% of Japanese households were microwave-equipped. While previously the microwave had been used primarily to reheat already-cooked food, or for thawing frozen food, House Foods' product line

has opened a whole new world of home microwave cooking. Since the manufacturers of home electrical appliances have been open to these modified uses of their products, this new line of foods is likely to further increase the popularity of microwave ovens.

As microwave usage grows, other food makers are producing similar products. Nevertheless, House Foods' Range Gourmet can be considered the pioneer product for the new age of microwave cooking in Japan.

1986 High Award for Excellence

Cakes from the Range Gourmet line

Honjitsu Kaiten Panya San: Refrigerated Bread Dough for Home Use
Amfresh

5 varieties of refrigerated bread dough

Honjitsu Kaiten Panya San is refrigerated bread dough, easy to bake in a home oven. The dough is packaged in cylindrical cardboard containers. Once removed from the containers, the dough is shaped by hand and requires only fifteen to twenty minutes of baking. This convenient product is available in five varieties—croissants, cinnamon rolls, cocoa rolls, butter bread, and Danish rolls. Each package contains enough dough to make five or six servings, and retails at ¥370. Honjitsu Kaiten Panya San was introduced to the market in September 1986. Monthly sales have reached 500,000 packages, or ¥200 million.

Amfresh was established in December 1985 as an equal partnership between Morinaga Milk and Asahi Chemical. Their goal was to combine the powerful sales network of Morinaga Milk and the technical expertise of Asahi Chemical to produce and market new products. Their debut product is Honjitsu Kaiten Panya San, a refrigerated bread dough. Similar chilled dough products are sold in the United States, but the same products cannot be marketed in Japan due to standards outlined by the Food Sanitation Act regulations.

The main difference between Honjitsu and standard bread is that it does not use yeast fermentation. Fermenting yeast produces carbonic acid in the bread, causing it to rise. The dough, however, cannot be stored for long when yeast is used, even under refrigerated conditions. This product uses baking powder, which produces CO_2 gas. When this is combined with the steam given off by the dough, the bread rises naturally. Butter and other flavorings render it as tasty as bread made with yeast. The dough for Honjitsu bread is quite sophisticated. The croissant dough, for example, consists of twenty-four thin layers, resulting in a light, crispy texture.

In developing this product, Amfresh's biggest problem was with packaging. When the product leaves the production plant, the dough fills the container loosely and is easy to remove, but by the time it reaches stores it has risen, and presses against the sides of the container. The dough must have these expansion properties, or it will not rise sufficiently while baking. Too much pressure, however, would cause the container to split with the slightest touch. If the can were too sturdy, it would be difficult for consumers to open.

Eventually, Amfresh decided to use a conventional cylindrical cardboard can, whose sides can be be peeled away. The cardboard surface of the can has a spiral seam, and a light touch of a spoon anywhere along the seam causes the can to pop open. This design was chosen over conventional cans with top openings that would cause the dough to be damaged during removal.

The can must be chilled throughout the distribution chain, since at room

Bread made from refrigerated dough

temperature the dough rises and would eventually cause the can to burst open. Honjitsu therefore uses the distribution system of Morinaga Milk, one of its parent companies, and retails only in stores where the product can be refrigerated. Product life is sixty days, and following the expiration date, the product is retrieved.

Honjitsu bread is actually produced and packaged at a plant of Asahi Foods, a subsidiary of Asahi Chemical, and Amfresh handles product planning, market research, and publicity. Before the product was introduced nationwide, Amfresh conducted marketing tests. Research was conducted to determine whether the bread should be located in stores in the bread, refrigerated foods, or prepared foods sections. Amfresh eventually decided to place it among other refrigerated products such as ready-made pizza. Because prepared refrigerated dough was a new concept for the Japanese consumer market, a television advertising campaign was launched to introduce and explain the product.

Initial sales were positive, but research indicated that more varieties of bread were needed, particularly a type where the consumer could add something to the dough. This led to the development of the Danish-roll dough, a plain dough to which jam or fruit can be added to the customer's liking.

First-year sales are expected to exceed the initial ¥2 billion target, and should reach the ¥3−5 billion level annually in three years. It is unusual for a new food product to result in sales of ¥2 billion. Although other frozen or partially baked bread doughs have been available for some time, they have not been successful. Thawing out frozen dough requires considerable time, and prepared doughs, available at bakeries, have already gone through the yeast fermentation process, and home bakers cannot enjoy watching the bread rise in their own ovens.

Honjitsu Kaiten Panya San is convenient and simple to bake, and the homemade bread that results is delicious. Although ovens play a limited role in traditional Japanese cooking, recently approximately 50% of Japanese households have ovens. As a result, the debut of this refrigerated dough was well timed. It is particularly popular with housewives and high-school girls, and is catching on with working men and women. Amfresh is now considering the addition of other types of bread to its product line, and in future plans to develop refrigerated cookie and pie doughs.

1986 Award for Excellence

A just-opened can

Tenkaramon: *Shōchū* Created by Cell Fusion
Nishikinada Shuzō

The new Tenkaramon, which combines the best qualities of both saké and *shōchū*

Tenkaramon is a shōchū, *inexpensive distilled Japanese liquor, that is manufactured by cell fusion of* shōchū *and saké molds to create a new mold. One common type of* shōchū *is made from a sweet potato* (imo), *and is known as* imoshōchū. Imoshōchū *has a disagreeable smell, but Tenkaramon is manufactured by a cell-fusion technique that does away with the unpleasant odor. It was first introduced to the market in July 1986, and by the end of that year some 25,000 gallons were manufactured. The product has sold especially well in Tokyo and Kagoshima, the main* shōchū-*producing prefecture of Japan.*

Shōchū is inexpensive distilled liquor, native to Japan, made from grain, sweet potatoes, or other starches. Tenkaramon is a new type of *shōchū* produced by Nishikinada Shuzō, located in Kagoshima prefecture. Kagoshima, the southernmost prefecture of Japan's four main islands, is the largest *shōchū*-producing area of Japan. Since Kagoshima is also the major sweet-potato-producing region of Japan, *shōchū* made in this area is made from sweet potatoes and is called *imoshōchū*. Although *shōchū*, usually a working-class drink, enjoyed a surprising surge in popularity in the early 1980s, many customers dislike the strong odor emitted by *imoshōchū*, preferring other types. Tenkaramon is a potato-based *shōchū* that does not have an unpleasant odor due to its unique cell-fusion process, which retains the delicious flavor of this drink.

Tenkaramon is produced by Nishikinada Shuzō, whose parent company, Kawauchi Gen'ichirō Shōten, is a well-known name in the *shōchū* business.

Based in Kagoshima, it produces approximately 85% of the mold spores that are used in *shōchū*-brewing equipment, including automatic mold-producing, *shōchū*-distillation, and ion-reciprocation machines.

The idea behind the cell-fusion technology used in Tenkaramon was initiated in 1977 by the son of the president of Kawauchi Gen'ichirō Shōten, Masaaki Yamamoto. The son, Masahiro, first developed an interest in cell-fusion in *shōchū* production during his student days at the University of Tokyo's Agricultural Department Graduate School, where he studied biotechnology.

Kawauchi Gen'ichirō Shōten hoped to promote the popularity of *imoshōchū* by a cell-fusion method. In this method, a new mold is created via cell-fusion of white mold from *imoshōchū* and yellow mold from saké. A special enzyme melts the membrane of the white and yellow molds, turning them into photoplast. The combined new mold breaks down the excess material from the sweet potato, often the cause of the disagreeable smell of *shōchū*, resulting in a product that retains only the best qualities of *shōchū*.

It was only after eight years of intense research that the new mold was selected from tens of thousands of types in February 1985. Despite its years of experience in the industry, Kawauchi Gen'ichirō Shōten had never actually brewed *shōchū*. In order to brew *shōchū* a government license is necessary, and obtaining such a license takes a great deal of time. Kawauchi Gen'ichirō Shōten decided instead to find a brewery that would be willing to use its new mold, but everyone it approached was skeptical. By chance, a *shōchū* brewer, Nishikinada Brewery, asked President Yamamoto if he were interested in purchasing the company. Negotiations ensued, and Kawauchi Gen'ichirō Shōten bought Nishikinada Brewery.

Kawauchi Gen'ichirō Shōten had to exercise caution in opening a brewery lest it encroach upon its many saké- and *shōchū*-producing customers all over Japan. In order to avoid any difficulties it made clear that its purpose for

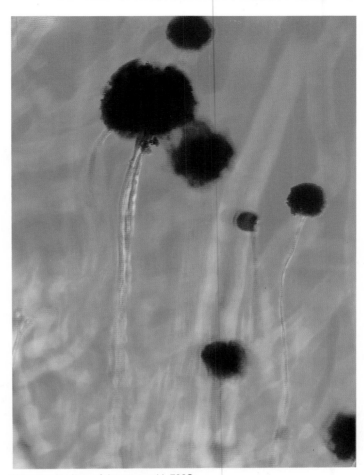
Microscopic photo of the new mold, 706C

opening this brewery was to produce *shōchū* using its new mold.

Kawauchi Gen'ichirō Shōten placed Tenkaramon on the market in July 1986. The retail price for a 1.8-L bottle is ¥1,050 in Kagoshima and ¥1,200 in Tokyo. According to President Yamamoto, although some locals from the Kagoshima area complain that the new product lacks the unique qualities of *imoshōchū*, general response to the new *shōchū* is favorable. The October 1986 Tokyo International Bio Fair indicates that his opinion is sound. Nine thousand taste-test cups of Tenkaramon quickly disappeared, and the company had to quickly produce another 6,000 cups.

The *shōchū* boom began to slow down in 1985, but President Yamamoto is optimistic regarding further growth. In his view, new products are necessary to revitalize the industry. Kawauchi Gen'ichirō Shōten is already

working toward developing other new molds with the hopes of introducing yet another innovative product.

1986 Award for Excellence

Kanban Musume: Self-Heating Saké in a Can
Toyo Jozo

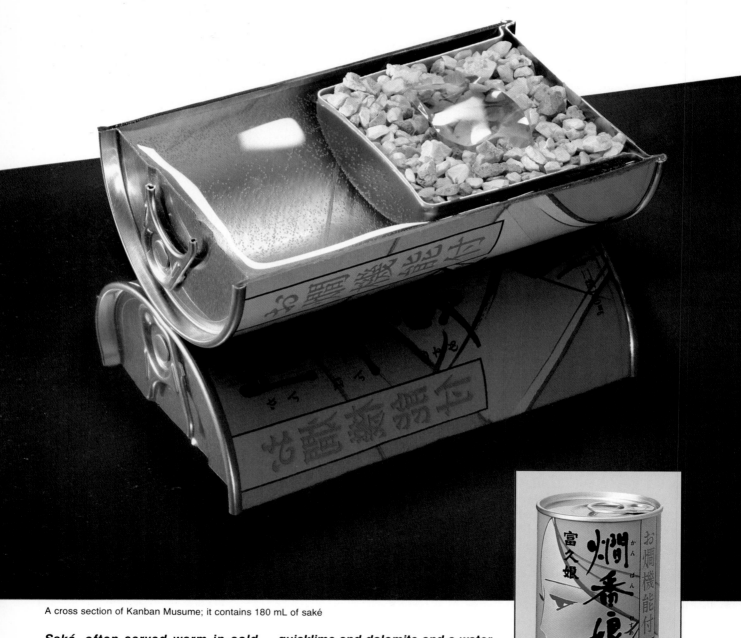

A cross section of Kanban Musume; it contains 180 mL of saké

Saké, often served warm in cold weather, is heated by placing a saké container in boiling water, a time-consuming and bothersome process. Kanban Musume is saké in a can that has a self-heating function. The 350-mL can holds one serving, 180 mL of saké, and has a concave bottom section that contains both a mixture of quicklime and dolomite and a water compartment. The saké is heated by an exothermic reaction between the quicklime and water. When the water bag is pierced by the attached pin, a convection current is induced, resulting in heated saké. Retailed at ¥260, since its debut in late 1985, it has had total sales of 7 million cans.

Reaches drinking temperature in 3—5 min

Kanban Musume is a one-serving can of saké with a self-heating function. In order to activate the heating process, the can must first be turned upside down, and the bottom side pierced with the attached pin. The pin is then immediately removed, a lid placed over the bottom surface, and the can returned to its upright position. The warmed saké is ready in three to five minutes.

When Kanban Musume was first marketed in November 1985, many in the saké industry were skeptical about its potential success for several reasons. Although one-serving or "one-cup" saké containers are fairly common in Japan, Kanban Musume has a markedly different appearance from standard one-cup saké. In general, saké is warmed by placing a saké container in boiling water, or is prewarmed in automatic vending machines. In addition to its unique appearance, Kanban Musume is priced at ¥260, whereas standard one-cup saké is only ¥170.

Despite the initial skepticism, Kanban Musume became a top-selling product in the saké industry, appealing particularly to outdoor enthusiasts interested in sports such as fishing and mountaineering, in addition to those who buy it for home use. According to Toyo Jozo, during its peak demand in the winter of 1986, wholesaler allotments were initiated due to limited supply.

Saké is Japan's traditional liquor, and as a result, the saké industry is often conservative and resistant to change. Until now, marketing changes have centered around refining the content of the saké itself, or in altering slightly the traditional container. With the success of Kanban Musume, it has become apparent that consumers are responsive to functional innovation.

Kunihiko Higaki, manager of sales planning for Toyo Jozo, is responsible for the development of this product. Although he did not have a technical background, he had once seen an aluminum saké-heating device that used gunpowder, marketed by a fireworks manufacturer. This particular product was smoky and dangerous, but set Higaki thinking about the possibility

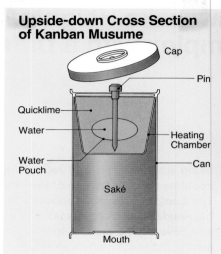

Upside-down Cross Section of Kanban Musume

Cap
Pin
Quicklime
Water
Heating Chamber
Water Pouch
Can
Saké
Mouth

Pull out the pin, put the cap back on, and turn it right-side up

of a self-heating, one-cup saké mechanism.

Higaki took his idea to the chemical and pharmaceutical division of Asahi Chemical, which is an affiliate of Toyo Jozo and where he had once worked as a salesman. Together with a former colleague, Masafumi Hamazaki, he began developing the product. Initially he considered gunpowder, iron oxide, quicklime, and other chemicals as heating agents, and ultimately decided on quicklime in granular form. Since quicklime alone is designated a dangerous substance according to government regulations, dolomite was added. Where to attach the water bag inside of the can also required considerable attention.

Higaki took his prototypes to Fukumusume Shuzō, an affiliate of his company, but encountered resistance from the saké-manufacturing technical staff, who were afraid that the heating mechanism would not meet industry requirements for new products.

Test marketing began in February 1985, but unexpected problems arose. The actual use of the product, entirely new in nature, was difficult for some customers. Many made mistakes in executing the heating function, and some complained that the saké did not get warm, or that the quicklime powder leaked. A nine-month delay resulted while more comprehensible instructions were prepared and other minor changes implemented.

Higaki still believes that there is

further room for improvement, but for all his reservations, Kanban Musume's sales have grown at a remarkable pace. Sales for 1986 are estimated to be 6 million cans and 8 million in 1987. The heating function has succeeded in penetrating the outdoorsman's market, an area where saké is weak in comparison to whiskey and beer. There has been great demand, unexpectedly, from middle-aged workers, who, because of their work, live far away from their families. These men, accustomed to having their saké heated by their wives, appreciate the convenience of the self-heating function. Continued sales growth is expected and other manufacturers are already marketing imitative products.

Toyo Jozo plans to continue introducing products with innovative functions, and thereby gain a competitive edge over its rivals. Higaki feels that "in the future the saké industry in general will broaden its scope in marketing with regard to content, containers, and functions," further adding that "those who are innovative and aggressive in research and development, those who are not limited by the boundaries of traditional attitudes and concepts, will succeed." Kanban Musume is not only a successful saké product; it is also an indicator of the direction of new product development in this field.

1986 Award for Excellence

Kami Meguro Ogawazaka Heights: A Rebuilt Condominium Complex with a Difference
Nippon Steel

The residents of Kami Meguro Oga-wazaka Heights are in a unique position. They live in recently renovated and enlarged condominiums, but bore none of the expenses of this process. The former condominium, Kami Meguro Housing, was first developed in 1957 by the Japan Housing Corporation (now the Housing and Urban Development Corporation). Nippon Steel recognized that the space was being underutilized and rebuilt the complex to make full use of the land. The company thereby rehoused the old residents in more spacious units, and covered the rebuilding costs by selling the remaining new units.

Kami Meguro Housing, the predecessor of Kami Meguro Ogawazaka Heights, was developed in 1957 by the Japan Housing Corporation. According to the Architectural Standards Law, all land in Japan has a designated floor-area ratio. This site was rated at a capacity ratio of 150%, in other words, with a floor area-to-land area ratio of 1.5 to 1, but it had been developed with only a 52.7% capacity ratio. It consisted of sixty-eight condominium units in three four-story buildings in poor condition. The condominiums were small, 35 m² each, and consisted

The new and improved Kami Meguro Ogawazaka condominium complex

Front entrance after rebuilding

of two rooms plus a kitchen. The electrical capacity per unit was only 10 amp. As the number of residents grew, the units not only became increasingly cramped, but the old 10-amp service could not accommodate the increased use of electrical appliances.

The new condominium buildings are four stories tall, modern in design, and surfaced with white tiles. The complex has undergone a remarkable metamorphosis from the undistinguished original buildings. The number of total residential units has increased to ninety-eight, and each unit is more spacious, with floor spaces ranging from 48 m² to 97 m². The electrical capacity has been increased to 40–60 amp.

The main point of this rebuilding project was using the permissible capacity ratio to the maximum. Kami Meguro Housing was rated at 150% but actually had only 2,900 m² of floor space for its 5,500 m² of land. Nippon Steel, in rebuilding, utilized the capacity ratio to the maximum, putting up new structures with a total area of 6,900 m², a 140% increase.

Thus, the residents were able to make effective use of their asset, the land, by an equal value exchange formula with Nippon Steel. The landowners and the builder divided ownership rights in the new building according to the value of the land and the cost of construction. The condominium owners received the right to 51 m² of the new building for one of the old units. Those who wanted a larger unit paid the additional cost in proportion to the space of the unit they wanted. Nippon Steel sold the remaining new units and used the profits to cover the construction costs.

There were several factors behind the success of this project. One was the enthusiasm and commitment with which the condominium owners themselves tackled the rebuilding project. In October 1981, two housewives who owned units called together six other owners and discussed other rebuilding projects. When they surveyed other condominium owners in December, of the thirty-three original owners, nine were opposed. Thereupon, the two women who had initiated the effort visited every household to convince them of the plan's merits. Three months later, they received the unanimous approval of the owners.

Once rebuilding had been decided upon, the owners had to state their preference for new units. Naturally, all residents wanted the units with better sunlight and location. The two women, once again, had to try hard to find a solution acceptable to everyone. One of the women, Yoko Yoshimura, recalls the period as being exasperating. Eventually their hard work paid off, and agreements were reached regarding most of the units. The remaining three were allotted by lottery.

By late 1984, the basic agreement for the rebuilding had been reached. The accord was reached only after the Nippon Steel people had visited the owners on a daily basis for two and a half years. Kazuaki Yashima, senior manager of the Urban and Housing Division of Nippon Steel, which was designing the new complex, comments that listening to and incorporating the residents' preferences as much as possible led to redrawing the plans entirely six times. Actual construction began in May 1985 and it was completed in March 1986.

There have been, however, surprisingly few similar rebuilding projects. The only other example began in May 1986, when Towa Real Estate Development Corporation, one of Japan's largest condominium developers, began work on Kotakidai Condominium in Nakano Ward, Tokyo. The three-building, sixty-unit, 2,600-m² complex developed by the Japan Housing Corporation in 1982 will be rebuilt as two buildings with eighty-one units totaling 6,700 m² by October 1987.

After the Kami Meguro project was completed, Nippon Steel received seven proposals for rebuilding projects, none of which was successfully negotiated. Yashima's view is that landowners overestimate the value of their land, and therefore distrust the conditions offered by Nippon Steel.

Both Yoshimura and Yashima believe that the success of their rebuilding project was due to the faith between the landowners and Nippon Steel. Similar projects will succeed only if such mutual trust can be achieved.

1986 Award for Excellence

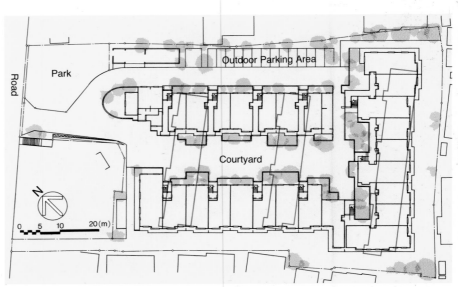
The section outlined in red indicates the floor space of the original Kami Meguro complex

Ark Hills: Joint Office, Residential, and Hotel Development
Mori Building

An overall view of the Ark Hills complex in which

The Ark Hills urban complex consists of a high-rise office building, residential towers, a modern hotel, a television studio, and a concert hall. Located in central Tokyo between the Akasaka and Roppongi districts of Minato Ward, it occupies a 56,000-m² site. Equipped with the latest communications technology, the office building provides tenants with access to a TV conference system linking Tokyo and Osaka, a high-speed digital-circuit network, and other advanced information and communications systems. The residential towers are luxurious, and the international-oriented complex provides unparalleled services and facilities.

Mori Building first began plans for redeveloping a large tract of land in the Akasaka and Roppongi districts of Minato Ward in central Tokyo in 1967.

The starting point of the intricate project was simple: Taikichiro Mori, president of Mori Building, purchased a small tract of land in Akasaka, the location of a public bathhouse. At that time he planned to construct a building on about the same scale as Japan's first high-rise building, the Kasumigaseki Building, a thirty-six-story high-rise office building, built in 1968.

When Mori went to apply for permission to develop this site, however, the official in charge of development in Minato Ward suggested that he instead redevelop a larger 56,000-m² tract that was occupied by old residential houses. Living on the site, however, were some 220 families with claims to the land. In Japan, rights to land ownership, to rented land, and to rented dwellings are protected under the Rented Land and Rented Dwellings Law, a complicated law regarding the purchase of and rights to land.

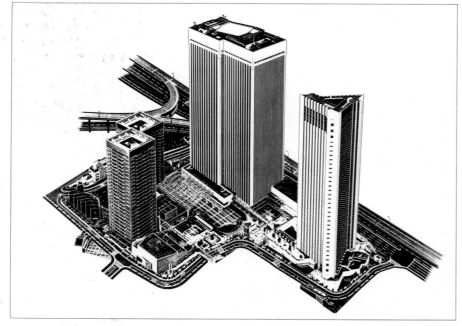

Ark Towers (residential wing), the Ark Mori Building (office wing), and the ANA Hotel

Minoru Mori, Mori's second oldest son and a managing director of the company, opened an office in the area, and spent considerable time cultivating mutual trust and understanding between the company and the local residents. Several Mori Building employees actually moved into the district to encourage their new neighbors to support the development project.

In Japan, relationships concerning rights to residential land are highly complex. Since selling land affects inheritance, entire families were involved in the decision-making process, and were often divided. Mori Building sometimes acted as an arbiter, mediating between family members over their shares in the inheritance. In one extreme case, a Mori Building employee had to fly to the United States and search coast-to-coast to find

working, living, and cultural spaces are unified

speed-circuit leasing service for tenants were started. These pioneering services are the responsibility of another Mori son, Akira, an executive director of Mori Building.

Ark Hills has received recognition as an innovative urban complex, fulfilling the functions of an office, residential, and cultural arena. The high-rise office building, in particular, is attracting many foreign firms.

President Mori is firmly committed to his unique view of city planning. In his words, "The 24-hour city is incomplete unless offices and homes are concentrated together in a contiguous work-residential pattern. We expect cities to provide opportunities, for free moments from busy work schedules, for superior cultural experiences. Moreover, cities must provide places for human interaction."

In keeping with his personal views, Mori convinced Suntory to build a concert hall (see pp. 110–11), All Nippon Airways to build a major hotel, and TV Asahi to establish a television studio, all in the Ark Hills complex.

Mori Building is already in the process of planning its next large-scale redevelopment project. It has acquired land in the vicinity of the former headquarters of TV Asahi, a 10,000-m² lot in Roppongi, and is considering negotiating with TV Asahi over jointly redeveloping the site. Another future project involves the former Forestry Agency housing site, an 11,000-m² lot in Minato Ward that it purchased in December 1986 in cooperation with a major real estate company's housing department. The site, including the surrounding area, is about 40,000 m² in total area. A second Ark Hills is being planned for this lot.

1986 High Award for Excellence

Ark Hills construction site size: 41,186 m²
Actual building area: 22,853 m²
Extended building site size: 360,608 m²
Volume ratio: 739.6%
Completion of construction: End of March 1986
Ark Towers: East Tower—2 basement floors and 25 aboveground floors; West Tower—2 basement floors and 22 aboveground floors; Ark Mori Building—4 basement floors and 37 aboveground floors; ANA Hotel—3 basement floors and 36 aboveground floors

the right person with whom to negotiate.

In 1978, the landowners finally unanimously decided in favor of development. At this point eleven years had passed since Mori's first land purchase in the district.

The problems were far from over once actual redevelopment began. Two in particular presented difficulties. One was responding to the increasing internationalization of Japan, especially Tokyo. The other was in deciding how to deal with high technology in the telecommunications and information fields. It was President Mori's idea to plan an urban complex that was not simply office buildings, but one with residential towers, a hotel, and a concert hall as well. It was his personal belief that in the future, urban planning must not only consider the workplace, but also other aspects of life such as cultural activities and leisure.

The plans for telecommunication and information facilities in the building were altered repeatedly. Efforts to improve on the building continued. In December, a TV conference service linking Tokyo and Osaka and a high-

The building site prior to construction

INDUSTRIAL AND CONSUMER MATERIALS
TRENDS IN THE 1980s

Undergoing severe contraction, the metals industry is pinning its hopes on high-value-added products and new alloys. —— Metals

Though small by international standards, the Japanese chemical industry is competing through consumer-oriented products. —— Chemicals

The production of finished textiles has been hurt by the rising yen; Japan is concentrating instead on the export of raw materials. —— Textiles

Metals

In 1986, for the first time in three years, the production volume of crude steel in Japan dipped below the 100-million-ton mark to a total of 95.5 million tons. It appears that this tendency will continue in 1987, when the total is expected to drop to about 93 million tons.

Though it is experiencing such production volume decreases, Japan's crude steel production volume still holds first place in the free world, far ahead of the U.S. in second place with 80 million tons. Also, in terms of iron-manufacturing technology, Japan maintains a standard that is far superior to that anywhere else in the world. With this technology, steel makers in Japan are attempting to develop high-value-added materials to push through the industry slump.

Of particular interest in the attempt to put steel to new uses are vibration-control steel plates, which act to keep down vibrations and noise. They employ a sandwich-type construction in which micron-thin resin is inserted between two steel plates. The new product is being produced by three major companies—Kobe Steel, Nippon Steel, and Nippon Kokan. The present market volume is around ¥20 billion per year. About 80% of this is used for automobile oil pans. Along with the growth in the automobile industry, this figure is expected to expand to ¥120 billion in ten years. There is also great enthusiasm for the development and increased utilization of high-strength and rust-resistant steel plates.

The rising value of the yen is also exerting a strong influence in the nonferrous metals industry. Up until ten years ago, Japan's aluminum-refining industry boasted second place in world production with a volume of 1.1 million tons, but this will drop to

35,000 tons after April 1987. The nonferrous metal mines still in operation number only in the teens, and it has become absolutely necessary for copper and other metal refineries to decrease their facilities, reorganize, and move to foreign countries.

As a countermeasure, these refineries are joining forces with various manufacturers to improve the materials they produce for use in electronic and electrical parts. Showa Electric Wire and Cable and Sumitomo Light Metal Industries have developed an aluminum alloy for use in VCR cylinders and for which they hold 90% of the world market. Nippon Mining and Sumitomo Metal Mining have developed 99.9999% pure metals, and now lead the world in the field of high-purity metals.

Alongside this competition to develop new materials and pioneer their uses through extension of original technology, competition in the practical application of new metal materials—a field which had remained at the stage of research and development until now—has entered the steel and nonferrous metal industries, where it is arousing great enthusiasm. Titanium, for example, is now seeing applications in more familiar goods. Originally, the main use for titanium was for chemical- and desalinization-plant pipes. But the strong yen has cooled the facilities-investment enthusiasm of chemical manufacturers, and the low prices of crude oil have upset the water-distillation-plant plans of the Middle Eastern nations. This demand slump has spurred competition to develop new uses for titanium. Nippon Steel was the first to make titanium sheets for general use in roofing. Toho Titanium has put a shockproof titanium attaché case on the market. Other uses of titanium, such as for glasses frames and tennis rackets, are appearing one after another.

The industry is placing its greatest hopes on expanding the use of titanium in airplanes and submarines. Such companies as the top domestic producer, Kobe Steel, along with Sumitomo Metal Industries and Nippon Mining, have succeeded in supplying titanium for use in the new V2500 airplane engine and the deep-sea submarine research vessel Shinkai 2000 (completed in 1981), indicating that the demand for titanium is destined to grow vigorously in the near future.

Another field of interest is the applications of shape-memory alloys. The 1986 world market volume of shape-memory alloys was around ¥7 billion. About ¥5 billion of this was taken by Lakum of the U.S., and in second place was Japan's Furukawa Electric, with about ¥1.2 billion. More than 90% of Lakum products are put to military use as pipe joints in fighter planes. Furukawa, on the other hand, holds by far the largest share in the area of articles for everyday use such as brassieres, eyeglasses, and home electrical appliances.

Shape-memory alloys consist of nickel-titanium alloys, copper alloys, and steel alloys. Nickel-titanium alloys are used by both Furukawa Electric and Lakum. However, the cost of the copper and steel alloys is expected to go down in the future. Already, Mitsubishi Metal is beginning to put copper alloys to practical use, and Dowa Mining and Nippon Steel are getting ready to challenge Furukawa Electric, with low cost as their main weapon.

Chemicals

World chemical production in 1985 was valued at US$690 billion. Japan held a 13% share of this total with $87 billion, placing it second behind the U.S. with a total of $220 billion. The figure for Western Europe stands at $178 billion, meaning that the U.S., Japan, and Western Europe now lead the world in the chemicals industry. However, compared with Europe and the U.S., both of which have a long history of technology buildup and gigantic enterprises that have undergone long development on the world market, Japan's chemicals industry is extremely small-scaled. It is also generally lagging behind in terms of internationalization. In the future it will become increasingly important for Japan to nurture the production of sophisticated products, such as fine chemicals, that take advantage of high-level technology.

Even on the scale of individual enterprises there is a large difference between Europe and the U.S., and Japan. In the U.S., there exist such giant chemical companies as Du Pont (with a sales volume of $35.9 billion in 1984), the largest chemical company in the world; Dow Chemicals ($11.4 billion); and Union Carbide ($9.5 billion). The 1984 situation in Western Europe is similar, with three large West German companies, Bayer ($15.1 billion), Hoechst ($14.5 billion), and BASF ($14.1 billion); one British firm, ICI ($13.4 billion); and Belgium's comparatively small-scale Solvay ($3.9 billion). All of these concerns are larger than Japan's major company in the field, Mitsubishi Chemical Industries ($3.3 billion). The situation in Japan is such that there is a large number of enterprises involved in chemicals when compared with the relatively small scale of the chemical industry.

Due to this weak point, it is more difficult for Japan to make large investments for research and development than it is for European and U.S. companies. The European chemical companies have concentrated on innovation, and the American companies have concentrated on establishing mass-production technology, and it is with these two pillars that they have supported the development of the world chemical industry. On the other hand, Japanese manufacturers have specialized in developing products that have direct consumer appeal, such as electrical appliances and automobiles, but this does not necessarily indicate that Japan is being eclipsed in terms of international cooperation. To take just one example, when the export and import prices of synthetic resins to and from Europe and the U.S. are compared, it can be seen that although the import price per ton is less than $2,000, the export price is around $3,000. This means that Japan has a powerful competitive edge even when compared with Europe and the U.S. in terms of such expensive products as high-function resins.

The leadership of Japan, the U.S., and Europe in the chemicals industry is being threatened by other countries' advances. One of these is the entry into the field of petrochemical products by Saudi Arabia and other countries that have their own petroleum resources. Other challenges are the movements in this direction by such NIC nations as South Korea, Taiwan, and Singapore. The Saudi Arabian petrochemical industry, which produces an annual 1.6 million tons of ethylene, began production in 1985. The Asian NICs are also working toward building up their petrochemical industries. Thus, it appears that the lead maintained by the industrialized nations in the field of everyday chemical products will gradually break down in the future.

In the midst of this situation, the chemical manufacturers of the U.S., Japan, and Europe are racing toward higher quality and the development of new types of enterprises. The key to their future growth lies in such new materials as high-function polymers, advanced ceramics, and compound materials, and biotechnology as well. New materials hold especially great promise for the future, and there are estimates that place the growth of the new materials market as high as the $5 trillion level by the year 2000. At present, the Japanese industry is ahead of its competitors in the application of fine ceramics, but if it is to maintain a strong position internationally it will have to diversify production of high-value-added, high-technology materials.

Textiles

The textile industry falls into two categories: synthetic textiles and cotton spinning. Since the G-5 meeting of September 1985, the industry has been faced with such problems as an export slump and sluggishness in the domestic market due to the rapid rise of the yen. All companies involved in both synthetic textiles and cotton spinning consider the state of the high yen to be inevitable, and as a result are beginning to decrease their scale of business and reorganize.

While the synthetic textile industry is avoiding the building of additional facilities based upon rules of organizational improvement, such nearby nations as South Korea and Taiwan are making broad-scale additions to strengthen their synthetic textile production facilities. At the end of 1985, the daily production capability of long synthetic textiles was 1,350 tons in Taiwan compared with Japan's 1,192 tons, and the total of Taiwan and South Korea added together comes to almost double that of Japan. In terms of product quality Japan is several levels higher than these countries, but the difference in production capacity brought about by their up-to-date facilities is putting great pressure on Japan. The soaring value of the yen makes the situation graver. Synthetic textile manufacturers are trying to survive by shifting their production focus to high-value-added products that have greater competitive strength than the products of nearby nations.

Even in the cotton-spinning industry, reduction of facilities is proceeding steadily. There were 8.2 million spindles at the end of 1983, but by the end of 1985 this number had dropped to 7.8 million and six months later stood at 7.6 million. Factories have closed one after another since 1986, and the industry is facing a severe situation. On the other hand, in Pakistan, where the spindleage at the end of July 1985 was 4.4 million, there is a 5-year plan to build an additional 1 million spindles.

However, in spite of the high yen, exports from Japan of textile raw materials are increasing in terms of volume. Exports to South Korea and Taiwan are particularly favorable, with the January to September 1986 total already exceeding the performance results for the entire year of 1985. The reason for this situation is that the export from Japan of textiles and clothing has decreased due to the high yen. Developing countries in Asia, moving to fill the resulting gap on the world market, do not have an adequate supply of textile raw materials. They have thus turned to Japan to supplement supply, creating a vertical division of labor in the international textile industry.

Three-Dimensional Fabric
Arisawa Manufacturing

Three-dimensional fabric, a structural material that can be used in buildings and airplanes, is made of carbon, aramid, and silicon-carbide fibers woven in three directions—lengthwise, side-to-side, and perpendicularly. Resins, metals, and ceramics are used to create a stable, advanced composite fabric with great tensile strength in all directions. The fabric was developed by the Research Institute for Polymers and Textiles of the Agency of Industrial Science and Technology, a section of the Ministry of International Trade and Industry (MITI). Arisawa Manufacturing received rights on the basic patent in 1984 and began its own development of the product. In 1986, Arisawa began mass-producing the fabric for the first time.

"When fibers are woven three-dimensionally, the resulting fabric has great resistance to exfoliation and shearing," according to Kenji Fukuda, chief of the Research Institute for Polymers and Textiles. In the early 1970s, when Akitsugu Nakafuji, Arisawa Manufacturing's carbon-fiber project team leader, heard Fukuda talk about a three-dimensional fabric, he thought, "This is it!"—a structural material strong in all directions was something he had sought for years.

A fiberglass called FRP, or fiber-rein-

This 3-dimensional fabric is an advanced composite material that combines resins, metals, and ceramics

forced plastic, already existed. It was made by weaving threads in two directions on the flat, stacking the resulting fabric in several layers, and then binding them together with adhesives such as resins. The resulting material had no resistance to exfoliation and shearing. Users such as automotive parts manufacturers repeatedly asked for a material without these disadvantages.

Nakafuji thought, "If we could produce a three-dimensional fabric with superfibers based on the findings of the Research Institute for Polymers and Textiles, I am sure there would be a great demand for it, not only for automotive parts but for use in airplanes and spacecraft, too. Fibers would be an excellent structural material if the problem of exfoliation and shearing were solved, since fiber has high tensile strength and flexibility. To overcome the problem of instability, all we need to do is harden it with resins, ceramics, and carbon to make a composite material."

When Arisawa Manufacturing obtained rights on the basic patent in 1984, it sent technicians to the MITI research institute for instruction in weaving techniques for three-dimensional fabric and composite materials. It also made its own prototypes, seeking ways to convert the research lab's ideas into practical manufacturing and marketing methods.

There were two technical problems to be solved. One focused on the addition of perpendicular weaving to the woof (side-to-side) and warp (lengthwise) threads—an untried idea at the time. If warp and woof threads are loosened, a third thread can be easily introduced. The problem lies in binding the three firmly together. "It was no problem to create a rough, loose material,"

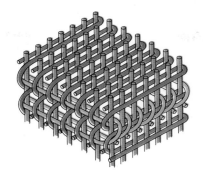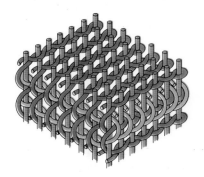

The structure of the 3-D fabric, showing both the direct (left) and the entwined (right) weaves

said Norifumi Oikawa, of the carbon-fiber project team, "but such a material is of inferior strength."

The rate of the weaving presented the second problem. Three-dimensional weaving is possible if done slowly, but speed is needed for a commercially viable product. "We worked by trial and error," Oikawa remembered, "both changing the shape of the thread and using different raw materials."

A year after the experiments began, a machine to weave the special three-dimensional fabric was developed. Arisawa Manufacturing enlisted the support of Mitsubishi Electric and Toyota Automatic Loom Works for the mechanical, electrical, and weaving technologies. In 1986, company president Eiichi Arisawa made the final decision to proceed with manufacture of this three-dimensional fabric.

The first product was a fabric with threads crossing in three directions in straight lines. The threads created a flat fabric of very high density. Arisawa Manufacturing began production upon receiving orders from aircraft, spacecraft, and construction industries.

The second stage was development of an entwined gauzelike fabric. In it,

threads from all three directions are intertwined and are not in straight lines, causing a knitted effect. This weave results in a low-density fabric where the threads do not move as much as in the fabric developed in the first stage. Machines to produce this new type of fabric will be installed in factories in mid-1987, and the company anticipates working on fabric for large-scale architectural and oceanic construction projects. If these two types of fabrics are successful, the company plans to manufacture other types as well.

Reaction was strong when production of the three-dimensional fabric began. Kajima Corporation quickly joined up for joint research on architectural structural materials. Product choices range from super to conventional fibers. Raw materials such as resins, ceramics, and metals can be combined to create any kind of composite materials.

If, for example, urethane foam is added to a three-dimensional fabric, the product's strength is increased, making an adiabatic, insulating, lightweight structural material. A product appropriate for use in high-speed automobile emergency brakes or punctureless tires is created.

Three-dimensional fabrics for structural use are attracting attention outside of Japan, too. Production plans are under way in a number of countries and competition is expected to increase substantially in the near future.

1986 High Award for Excellence

Detail of right-hand section of photo at left

Advanced composite material

Pichit: A Sheet for Long-Term Food Storage
Showa Denko

Pichit is a dehydrating sheet with an edible sugar and a polymeric water absorbent between two layers of a semipermeable membrane of polyvinyl alcohol. When fish, meat, or other fresh food is wrapped in this sheet and stored at low temperatures, excess water content in the food is extracted in a simple osmotic dehydrating process. Unlike dehydrating methods used in the past—such as salting, drying, and pressing—with Pichit there is no dripping or structural destruction of the food. Available to the general market since June 1986, Pichit's sales in the first six months after its debut passed ¥50 million.

The low-temperature osmotic dehydrating sheet Pichit, now attracting worldwide attention, was originally created to preserve the quality of frozen foods. When fresh foods are frozen, their cellular structure breaks down, with a resulting decline in flavor and quality. As early as 1980, Masatake Segawa, head of the New Products Division at Showa Denko, began to experiment with methods of drying foods at low temperatures, with the hopes of making a discovery about maintaining the quality of food.

In the course of his research, he learned that the greatest enemy in food-quality maintenance is the water content of the foods. For instance, in fish and shellfish, the water content stimulates oxidation and produces peroxide compounds that are believed to be a health hazard for humans. Segawa's team of researchers decided to first remove the excess water content by osmosis and a macromolecular absorbent (a polyacrylic soda) and then freeze the food. In 1983, at the annual Japan Home Economics Conference,

Kobe Women's College students presented data on peroxides in dried fish, broken down according to the drying method used. Their results gave fresh sardines a peroxide rating of 24.5. The same fish processed with Pichit at 5°C had a rating of 27.3. In contrast, fish dried by heat at 35°C had a peroxide rating of 57.9, and sun-dried fish, a rating of 180.7. These figures underlined the effectiveness of Pichit.

To use Pichit, the fish or meat is wrapped in cellophane, then in the Pichit sheet. If the food is then refrigerated, not only the surface moisture but also the excess water content from within will be absorbed. For instance, a fish wrapped in the sheet and kept between 0°C and 5°C will lose 3–5% of its water content in two hours. The sheets swell up in absorbing the moisture, but they can be dried and reused up to fifteen times.

Before the product was put on the market, Showa Denko asked a first-class Japanese restaurant to try using the sheets and comment on their effectiveness. According to Segawa, "They said that with Pichit, the ingredients did not suffer the usual drop in flavor—the real seal of approval."

After these careful preparations, Showa Denko took the major step of announcing the commercial version of Pichit (sheets of 50 × 70 cm) in April 1986. Department stores and consumer cooperatives are using the sheets in making what they call "healthy dried foods with low peroxide levels." An upscale supermarket in Tokyo processes fresh fish in Pichit and has it delivered straight from the fishing areas to the store, where it is sold as "frozen fresh fish." Delivery services have also begun using Pichit so that they will not have to worry about dripping perishables.

Dehydration results in two cuts of beef

An item that has been covered with commerical wrapping and refrigerated for 2.5 days at 5° C

Dehydration carried out at 5° C with Pichit, after which it was refrigerated for 2 days at 5° C

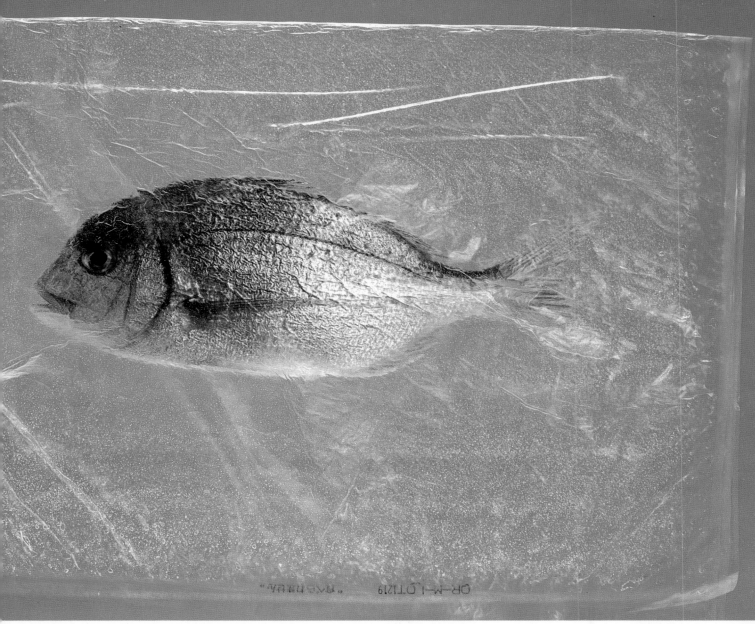

Fish is wrapped in cellophane, enclosed in Pichit, and refrigerated; stored at 0—5° C, 3—5% of its moisture will be absorbed in 2 hours

Marketing of the family-size Pichit (35 × 35 cm sheets) has been assigned to Showa Aluminum, an affiliate of Showa Denko. Using Showa Aluminum's existing distribution channels for household products, Showa Denko expects to be able to sell the sheets in a wide general market. At present, sales are concentrated only in department stores. Nationwide sales are the goal for the near future, and the company is also planning to announce a slightly modified version for more extensive home use.

Sales are not confined to Japan. Inquiries from abroad have been increasing rapidly, and Pichit is already being used in Norway to make smoked salmon in a fifth of the time required by conventional methods.

Pichit is a revolutionary force in food distribution. Since the new material can be applied in the initial, secondary, and tertiary processing of fish, shellfish, and meat, its effects can already be felt. At the major Japanese fishing ports of Sasebo, Wakkanai, and Kushiro, the transaction volume of fish fresh-dried with Pichit has been growing rapidly due to increasing orders from department stores. The product's appeal, given today's preferences for fresh foods, is overwhelming. In the year since the creation of Pichit was first announced publicly, the selling points have been amply supported by sales figures that tripled the company's initial goals. Showa Denko is now predicting annual sales of ¥4 billion after three years and ¥10 billion within ten years.

Pichit is now covered by one patent in Japan and two in the United States, but forty-one others are pending. Professional chefs are rating it as one of the greatest modern cooking equipment discoveries. In order to take advantage of Pichit's distinctive feature of preventing destruction of the structure of fresh tissues, the company is working with university research institutions to consider medical applications, such as in storing internal organs. It is also, in cooperation with a chemical company, considering applications in household goods. There seem to be no limits to the potential for new applications of the Pichit technology.

1986 High Award for Excellence

Laser Mirror: Highly Reflective Sheet Steel
Kawasaki Steel

This brilliantly reflective sheet steel has remarkable clarity of reflection after painting. Laser processing of the rollers used in cold rolling permits a microsurface roughening treatment to create sheet steel with a regular motif invisible to the eye; this gives the sheet metal outstanding formability as well as more clarity and brilliance after assembly and painting. When used in automobile bodies, it can produce a brilliant finish comparable to that of luxury-class European automobiles. Laser Mirror sheet steel, which is already being used in Nissan Motors' and Mazda's new models, costs only ¥3,000 a ton more than ordinary cold-rolled sheet steel.

On the left is the Laser Mirror, and on the right is a conventional cold-rolled steel plate

Japanese automobiles have a well-deserved reputation for quality. The long-established European automobile manufacturers, however, still create an impression of superiority in the quality of their paintwork and the luxurious feel of the surface of their bodywork. Equaling that quality finish is the final hurdle Japanese automobile manufacturers face today, when style and surface finish matter so much. The phrase "brilliant reflectivity," expressing the quality sought in exterior finishing, has become a key word in automotive technical development.

Japanese automobiles are given three coats of paint: the base, the middle, and the finish. European luxury automobiles, in contrast, are painted four times and sandpapered. The intermediate sandpapering is thought to be the key to enhancing brilliant reflectivity. It is, however, an extremely time-consuming process. Thus, Kawasaki Steel decided that it should aim for a product that could achieve brilliant reflectivity without the sandpapering step by developing a sheet steel that could achieve the same luster with the standard three coats of paint, and no loss in production efficiency.

Bright sheet steel already existed, but it was not suitable for use in automobile bodies. To prevent fusion of the sheets of steel to the molds, the surface of the sheet steel must be saturated with lubricating oil. Bright sheet steel, however, is too smooth for lubricating oil to saturate.

The molding process requires that the sheet steel must have some degree of surface roughness. Thus, fine irregularities of micron magnitudes are deliberately produced on the surface. In the shot-blasting method, fine steel powder is blown with tremendous force against the roller. The electric-discharge method produces the same effect by sending current to the roller, which transfers its irregularities to the surface of the sheet steel.

These methods open small pores at random in the surface of the metal. A sheet covered with such holes, however, is unlikely to manifest brilliant reflectivity. The next problem was to achieve a steel sheet with a certain degree of surface roughness while retaining its potential for brilliant reflectivity. It was at this stage that Kawasaki Steel engineers showed their own brilliance.

They decided to use lasers as an alternative processing method to the shot-blasting and electric-discharge methods. They hoped that shining a

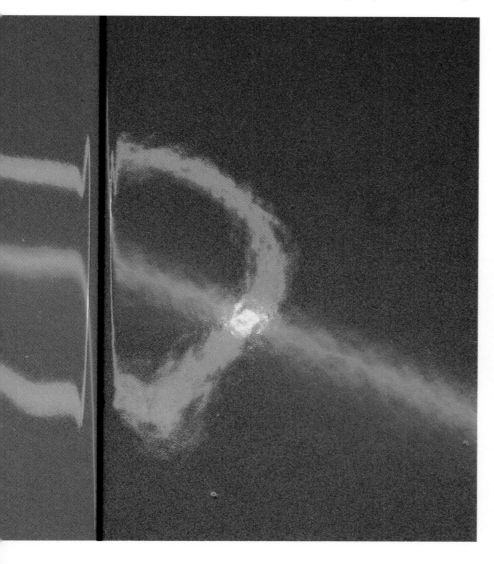

Laser Mirror

Conventional sheet steel

fine laser beam on a rotating roller would produce small pores at regular intervals.

With the laser technology available at that time, however, it was extremely difficult to apply a regular pattern to the rollers efficiently, and the research project kept running into obstacles. Thus, Kawasaki Steel attempted to gather all technical information on the subject. It unearthed a research report by CRM Laboratories, a Belgian institute for metallurgical research on the development of a unique processing technology using a CO_2 laser. Kawasaki Steel immediately sent engineers to the Belgian laboratory and decided to try using the CRM equipment for laser processing their rollers. The experiments gave highly promising results: with that equipment, they could produce pores spaced at fixed intervals with almost exactly the same size, depth, and shape.

Beginning in the spring of 1985, Kawasaki Steel began developing the processing equipment jointly with Miyama and with Okura and Co., which had introduced the laser-processing technique from CRM Laboratories. They experimented with dozens and then hundreds of regular patterns. The results showed that pores of a diameter of 150–200 μm and a depth of 5 μm spaced about 300 μm apart were ideal. The new sheet steel was ready to market in the spring of 1986.

An examination of a cross section of this steel through a microscope reveals that Laser Mirror has a considerably greater proportion of flat areas than does shot-blasted or electric discharge processed sheet steel. Results of evaluative testing carried out by Nissan Motors showed that the new sheet metal meets requirements for both brilliant reflectivity and ease of processing.

Full-scale use of Laser Mirror began with the exterior bodywork of new models of Nissan's Laurel Sprit and Nissan Exa and Mazda's Luce. In addition, applications are expected in home electrical appliances and architectural materials. Fujio Yamaguchi, the thin-sheet technologies section manager in charge of Laser Mirror's development, says he now wants to initiate development of a brilliantly reflective sheet steel that will need only two coats of paint instead of the usual three. The battle for brilliant reflectivity has only begun.

1986 Award for Excellence

Acklam—FS/MS: A Building Material Lighter and Stronger than Stone
Asahi Composites

Acklam—FS/MS are two forms of a material made of aluminum sandwich panel with 3-5-mm slices of marble or granite bonded with adhesive. Used as an interior decoration item, in comparison with natural marble paneling of the same thickness, it is one-fourth lighter and three times stronger. It is extremely lightweight and has a specific gravity of only 0.6. Marble and granite are popular materials because of their textures, but due to their weight they are unwieldy. Acklam, in addition to having the beauty of natural granite and marble, is easy to install. This innovative material was created by Asahi Composites, a joint venture of Asahi Chemical, a general chemical firm, and Ciba-Geigy, a Swiss chemical company.

When Isao Mizuno first became manager of Asahi Composites in September 1984, he tried to think of useful and practical applications for materials developed by Ciba-Geigy, a parent company of Asahi Composites, along with Asahi Chemicals. Among these products was a honeycomb core, usually used in aircraft interiors.

In November 1984, Mizuno went on a trip to Europe and the United States with the hopes of being inspired with new ideas. During his trip he passed through London's Heathrow Airport and saw internal wall cladding made of aluminum honeycomb materials skinned with aluminum sheeting. He at this point decided that this was the best use for honeycomb cores, despite the fact that Asahi Composites had no experience whatsoever in building materials. Immediately upon returning to Japan, he began discussing

Only ¼ the weight of natural rock material of the same thickness, this material has a specific gravity of 0.6 and floats in water

these ideas with company members. Their conclusion was that they needed to create a lightweight panel by attaching stone to the surface of a honeycomb core, but technically they did not know how to develop such a product.

It was by chance that one of the employees of Asahi Composites brought an interesting newspaper clipping dated February 4, 1986, from the *Nikkei Sangyo Shimbun* newspaper, to the attention of Mizuno. "Production of an extremely thin stone material has been initiated by three new companies in Yamaguchi prefecture." Mizuno immediately telephoned one of the companies, Purecoat, spoke with its president, and arranged to visit the following day. After confirming the newspaper's report, and determining that Purecoat had indeed developed a technique to cut marble to 0.5 mm, a tenth of what had been possible in the past, Asahi Composites began to negotiate the possibilities of joint develop-

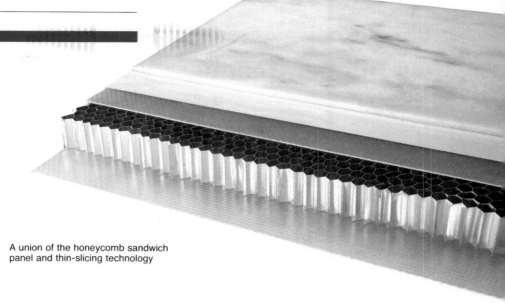

A union of the honeycomb sandwich panel and thin-slicing technology

ment. A contract was signed on April 1, 1986.

With this arrangement concluded, Asahi Composites then looked for a stone supply source. It approached Japan's leading stone supplier, Sekigahara Stone, and in July 1986, formed a Stone Panel Tri-Company Group. Sekigahara Stone would supply the raw materials and develop a production technique for the stone panel, Purecoat would cut the stone, and Asahi Composites would attach the honeycomb to the stone and market the finished product. This project could not have been executed by one company alone, and according to Mizuno, one of the important aspects of the project's success was mutual understanding and cooperation regarding distribution of profits.

Before Acklam−FS/MS could be marketed, there were some development problems, particularly with judging the proper thickness for the stone. The thinner the stone is, the lighter the finished product, and the easier the installation. However, if the stone is cut too thin, the honeycomb inside can be seen. After considerable research, Asahi Composites determined the best thickness for marble to be 4.5 mm, and for granite, 3.0 mm.

The first customer was a yacht design company building for an Australian the Southern Cross III, a luxury yacht that cost several hundred million yen. Acklam−FS/MS lines the wall of the entrance hall of the yacht.

The buyer specifically requested natural stone, and the yacht design

company wanted to use the largest possible pieces in order to have as few joints as possible. In order to accommodate the specifications of this first order, Asahi Composites worked with Sekigahara Stone to develop panels measuring 1.2 × 2.4 m. Until then they only had 30-cm² prototypes. Asahi Composites realizes that since Acklam−FS/MS will in the future be used for interior walls, it will have to adjust to the conditions determined by architectural and construction designs.

At present, Acklam−FS is produced at a rate of 15,000 m² per month. It is hoped that by lowering costs through automation of the polishing process, it will be the same price as natural stone. Acklam−FS/MS is mostly used for interior walls, but Asahi Composites hopes that as it gains more experience in installation and as the durability of the product is increased, Acklam−FS/MS will some day be used for outdoor walls and tables as well.

1986 Award for Excellence

Multi Rubber Bearings: Vibration and Shock Absorbers
Bridgestone

Multi Rubber Bearings (MRBs) absorb shock and vibrations, particularly of earthquakes, in buildings and machinery and instruments. They are cylindrical structures made up of numerous, alternating, thin layers of rubber and steel, and are designed to be placed between a building and its foundation. They prevent earthquake shocks from striking the building directly. The unique feature of the MRB is a life-expectancy approximating that of a building—sixty years. A single bearing of 80 cm in diameter can support a 250-ton building. In an apartment house with twenty units, only fifteen bearings are needed.

Earthquakes are common in Japan. Nearly 10% of all the seismic energy of the world is concentrated in and around Japan. In the past, most large, earthquake-resistant, high-rise buildings featured "flexible structure" architecture. That is, the foundations were made particularly strong while upper floors were given flexibility to sway with the shock. Medium- and low-rise buildings were designed with thick walls and other reinforcements so they would not collapse during earthquakes. Recently a "vibration-absorption style"—using MRBs—has been attracting attention.

In buildings with traditional earthquake-resistant construction, shocks are conveyed directly to the structure, resulting in an impact several times stronger than the earthquake itself and causing secondary damage. The new shock-absorbing method of construction allows for rolling during an earthquake, but the movement is very gentle. As a result, there is little danger of the breaking of glass or the collapse of the building.

In the new method of construction, the MRB is the center of the vibration-absorbing device. With its alternating layers of rubber and steel plating, it is extremely rigid on the vertical plane to support the weight of the building, and elastic on the horizontal. It functions as a spring to slow down the rolling of the building and lessen the sudden earthquake shock.

The major focus of Bridgestone's work on MRBs since 1981 has been on increasing life expectancy to match that of the building they support. In foreign countries, there had been similar work using vibration-absorbing rubber in buildings, but no one had ever proposed guaranteeing the rubber for the life of the building.

When an earthquake happens, warping occurs in many locations inside the rubber bearings. Through sectional changes, the location of the warping and the size of the area varies. Also, when exposed to the elements, the rubber deteriorates. If a bearing were to collapse, it would occur when an earthquake was so violent that the warping exceeded the shape-changing capacity of the rubber or the seams between rubber and steel.

To reduce warping to a minimum, the Bridgestone development team set up a system called LALDA (Life Assurance with Large Deformation Analysis). Using LALDA, they simulated warping and succeeded in making a comprehensive analysis of durability.

At that time, the product had a thirty-year life expectancy, but this was extended, based on the LALDA test results. The Bridgestone development team experimented with materials, mixing natural rubber and zinc-plated copper, for example, and covering them with a special durable rubber. Eventually, the team arrived at a material with a sixty-year life expectancy.

The new MRB was recognized by the Building Center of Japan, an orga-

This structure of rubber and steel plates resists and prevents vibration and absorbs displacement

A test that confirms the force capabilities of multi rubber bearings

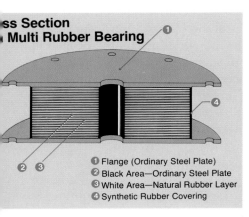

**ss Section
Multi Rubber Bearing**

① Flange (Ordinary Steel Plate)
② Black Area—Ordinary Steel Plate
③ White Area—Natural Rubber Layer
④ Synthetic Rubber Covering

nization that advises the Ministry of Construction. But it is still necessary to obtain the ministry's permission for each project using earthquake-resistant methods.

Even so, general construction companies made numerous inquiries about the MRBs. As a result, vibration-absorbing rubber is being used by several companies throughout Japan.

Shimizu Construction, in cooperation with the Engineering Department of Tōhoku University, built two buildings of the same structure in Sendai, but vibration-absorbing rubber was used in only one. Since May 1986, comparative experiments have been carried out, but a true test took place on January 9, 1987, when Sendai was hit by a major earthquake measuring four points on the Japanese seismic scale. The shock sustained by the building with the MRBs caused only a quarter that of the oscillation suffered by the other building.

Since there is no need to make the upper part of a building using MRBs strong with construction devices such as thicker walls, the overall cost of such buildings is far lower than that of the older earthquake-resistant method of construction.

Bridgestone expects that MRBs will

be used in buildings where it is particularly important to prevent secondary earthquake damage, such as computer centers, hospitals, art museums, clean rooms, biotechnology research wings, and atomic energy generators. They are also appropriate in places that need to avoid vibration such as integrated-circuit and laser-processing plants. If regulations governing architectural standards are revised to facilitate the use of the vibration-absorbing structure system, it seems certain that this method of construction will spread to residential dwellings and medium- and low-rise buildings.

1986 Award for Excellence

MACHINERY

TRENDS IN THE 1980s

In a tightening world market, Japan's machinery industry is relying on joint ventures to pull it into the future. —— Machinery

Japan's unparalleled manufacturing prowess depends on more than sweat. Domestically produced machines and robots keep the factories going. —— Machine Tools and Industrial Robots

Machinery

In the early phase of Japan's economic growth in the 1950s and 1960s, Japanese machine manufacturers relied heavily on technology from the U.S. and Europe. But as they grew, they dissolved their cooperative agreements with foreign companies and began to make their own inroads into the markets of the U.S. and Europe.

These incursions caused friction over trade between Japan and its trading partners. Then, in the fall of 1985, the yen began to rise in value, and with it came a decline in Japan's competitive position abroad. As a result, a number of companies have begun to rebuild their cooperative relationships with the major companies of the U.S. and Europe.

Orders of Japanese industrial machinery peaked in 1981 at ¥5.9 trillion, according to the Japan Society of Industrial Machinery Manufacturers. Since then they have slumped, dropping to ¥4.9 trillion in 1985. The first half of 1986 was heavily affected by the strong yen and orders totaled only ¥2.0 trillion, a 28.8% decrease from the same period in 1985.

In the midst of this harsh business climate, the construction machinery industry has engaged in a fierce sales war. In 1985, Japanese manufacturers were charged with dumping hydraulic shovels in Europe. Trade disagreements with the U.S. also began to smolder, particularly because Japan's Komatsu was beginning to catch up in sales with Caterpillar, the U.S. construction machinery company. Komatsu has now even built its own production plants in the U.S. and the U.K. for the manufacture of wheel loaders and hydraulic shovels.

Other Japanese manufacturers adopted a different strategy; they sought joint agreements with European and U.S. companies. In 1984, Hitachi Construction Machinery, the industry's second largest manufacturer, began supplying hydraulic shovels for Deere & Company of the U.S. to sell under its own brand name. In 1986, Hitachi joined with the Netherlands' Fiat-Allis B.V., the largest construction machinery manufacturer in Europe, to build Fiat-Hitachi excavators in Italy. Hitachi supplied hydraulic machines and electronic control devices and manufactured the hydraulic shovels in the Italian factory. In addition, Hitachi dealers began selling Fiat-Allis bulldozers and wheel loaders.

Caterpillar did not accept the competition from Komatsu with its arms folded. It made plans to strengthen its cooperative ties with Mitsubishi Heavy Industries (MHI), Japan's third largest manufacturer, in July 1987. The agreement will unify Caterpillar-Mitsubishi, a joint venture company for building bulldozers, with the construction machinery department of MHI. The new company will focus efforts on design of the hydraulic shovel, a piece of machinery in increasing demand. MHI technology will be used to produce hydraulic shovels in Caterpillar factories in the U.S. and Europe.

The use of electronics such as microcomputers is proceeding as rapidly in the construction machinery industry as it is in other industries, and it is in electronics that Japan excels. It appears that a number of the country's smaller manufacturers will use their expertise in electronics to strengthen cooperative relationships with businesses in Europe and the U.S.

Japan's plant-engineering companies also find themselves in a hostile business climate. Over the past few years, the companies have suddenly increased in strength. The three top plant-engineering companies—Chiyoda Chemical Engineering & Construction, JGC, and Toyo Engineering—and heavy machinery manufacturers such as MHI have become keen competition for the leading companies in the U.S., the U.K., France, and Italy.

Japan's engineering companies have expanded their business by exporting chemical plants, oil-refining facilities, and desalinization plants, particularly to developing countries and the oil-producing countries of the Middle East. However, as both crude oil prices and prices for raw materials have slumped, the market has shrunk. Japan's exports of such facilities peaked in 1981 at US$17.4 billion and then became stagnant. Exports are expected to be about $7 billion for 1986.

As a result, competition over these plants has intensified, and as prices drop, so do profits. For this reason, the world's leading engineering companies have begun forming consortia for each new project. MHI is promoting an alliance with Westinghouse Electric in the U.S. to build electricity-generating plants. It appears that a rapid increase in such cooperative ventures will occur in the future.

The future of Japan's engineering companies is not all dark. Although there is a general slump in the demand for chemical and oil-refining plants, developing nations still have a need for them. In addition, advanced-technology areas such as nuclear power, biotechnology, and factory automation require a new type of engineering to develop. On the domestic scene, public works projects such as the New Kansai International Airport and the Tokyo Bay Bridge and Tunnel are providing business. The Japan Machinery Federation and the Japan Society of Industrial Machinery Manufacturers predict that "by the year 2000, an engineering demand of around ¥39 trillion will be born."

The industry that is expected to see the most new

growth is aerospace. Production in Japan's aircraft industry came to a complete halt after the country's defeat in World War II, but is now gradually regaining strength. Since 1979, Japan has began production of the F-15 jet fighter plane, under license from the United States, and Boeing's 767 aircraft, jointly developed by the United States, Japan, and Italy. Five nations, including Japan, have also joined to develop the world's most advanced jet engine, the V2500. The development of new types of aircraft requires such large amounts of funding for research that international cooperation is a necessity. Countries have already begun working together, and the biggest companies in Europe and the U.S. have high praise for the power of Japanese companies in such areas as production technology.

Japan's space development industry works from a small annual budget of about ¥100 billion, but its persistence and success in satellite launching and related activities have placed Japan among the world's major space-researching nations. Based on its success in launching the H-I rocket in 1986 (see pp. 92–93), development of the Japanese-produced H-II rocket is slated for completion in 1991. These launches will set the stage for a two-ton stationary satellite, an unmanned space laboratory, and Japan's version of the space shuttle. There are also plans for a Japanese manned space lab that will dock with a U.S. manned space station.

Machine Tools and Industrial Robots

Machine tools, also known as "mother machines," make parts for other machines. Japan leads the world in the production of machine tools, a lead that has in turn contributed to Japan's competitive performance in other industries, including automobiles and electrical equipment. Japan's export of machine tools also has increased so rapidly that it has become a cause of international trade friction.

Japan's machine tool production increased by 19% in 1985 over the previous year and totaled ¥1.5 trillion in sales, topping ¥1 trillion for the first time. Japan has maintained the lead in machine tool production for four consecutive years since 1982, and now holds more than 20% of the world market.

Machine tools were developed in the U.S. and Europe, and until the 1970s, Japan's role was chiefly that of an importer. The transformation from importer to exporter occurred in a little more than ten years, and now Japan exports at a rate ten times greater than it imports.

This growth has been possible because of the development of numerical-control (NC) technology that uses computers to facilitate machine positioning and improve the precision of machined products. The basic NC technology was pioneered in the U.S., but was transformed into commercially viable production methods by the ever-adaptive Japanese.

A particularly successful example of Japan's approach is the cost-efficient, concentrated production of general-purpose tools such as machining centers (MC) and NC lathes. Productivity has been increased by introducing such labor-saving systems as flexible manufacturing systems (FMS) on a scale far wider than that of Japan's European and American competitors. More than 70% of Japanese machine tool production uses NC—a much higher percentage than found in other countries.

The introduction of NC technology did more than reverse Japan's position in relation to the West. It also had a great impact on the relative positions of companies domestically. Two of the three largest machine tool manufacturers—Mori Seiki and Yamazaki Mazak—owe their recent rise to the efficient mass production of MCs and NC lathes and their export to the U.S. and Europe. In contrast, highly respected companies such as Ikegai and Hitachi Seiki were late in converting to NC systems and suffered from outdated facilities, preventing them from maintaining their traditional excellence. Okuma Machinery Works, one of the older companies that managed to survive the transition, did so by developing and producing the NC devices that form the brain of the NC machine tools.

Machine tool companies, most notably Mori Seiki and Yamazaki Mazak, have increased their exports rapidly, entering markets in the U.S. and Europe. Their combined exports in 1985 totaled ¥395 billion, a 26% increase over the previous year. Exports accounted for nearly 40% of total sales.

In factory automation, industrial robots have played an important role, together with machine tools, in improving the productivity of the Japanese manufacturing industry. Robots are used for a wide range of jobs including welding, painting, transport, precision fabrication, and inspection.

The Japanese robotics industry got its start using technology borrowed from the West, but has developed in about a decade into the world's leading producer. Thanks to original-equipment-manufacturing practices, relationships with robot manufacturers in Europe and the U.S. are amicable and friction over trade competition virtually nonexistent.

The year 1980 is generally thought of as the Year of the Robot, since it was the first year that saw widespread use of the machines. From 1980 to 1985, production grew by nearly 400%, and in 1985 totaled ¥300 billion. Observers predict that Japan's share of the international market will eventually exceed 50%. Japan is currently not only the world's largest producer of industrial robots, but also the world's largest user of them. Eighty percent of the robots made in Japan in 1985 were for domestic use.

There are many reasons for the growth of the robotics industry in Japan. Demand was created first by the oil shocks of the 1970s; they created a pressing need for labor-saving production methods to reduce costs. The second impetus was a labor shortage in jobs that involved monotonous tasks or unfavorable working environments. On the supply side, automation caused prices to fall. Large manufacturers, realizing the potential of the industrial robot market, also made substantial investments in research.

Fanuc leads the list of Japanese companies that successfully rode the wave of robot technology. Although a relatively new company, it was second among Japanese companies in robot production in 1985. Fanuc specializes in marketing NC and servomotor technologies and has set up a distribution and engineering subsidiary in the U.S. with General Motors, a venture that has allowed Fanuc to expand exports greatly. The subsidiary has received a substantial order from GM to help it upgrade automobile production facilities.

The market for industrial robots both in Japan and elsewhere will almost certainly continue to expand. Manufacturers are now developing intelligent robots with visual sensors that will permit them to perform more complicated tasks. Although certain sectors of the robot industry are still led by U.S. technology, Japan's overall position as the world's leader is likely to remain unchallenged for the next several years.

LE-5 Engine: An Engine for the H-I Rocket
Mitsubishi Heavy Industries/Ishikawajima-Harima Heavy Industries/National Space Development Agency

The LE-5 is Japan's first rocket engine powered by liquid oxygen and hydrogen, and it was used in the second stage of the H-I rocket. This has increased the launch capabilities for putting satellites into geostationary orbit from the 350 kg of the N-II rocket to the 550 kg of the H-I rocket. Japanese rocket-engine technologies for such elements as the thrust chamber, the turbopump, and the gas generator were integrated to permit smooth operation of the H-I rocket in August 1986, all the way from engine start to cut-off during flight. The same engine was extremely successful in reignition in its very first launching.

On August 13, 1986, eleven years after the initiation of research and development of Japan's first rocket technology using liquid-oxygen and -hydrogen fuel, the H-I rocket was successfully launched from the Tanegashima Space Center in southern Japan.

The central moving force in the project, for everything from the overall organization and promotion to the actual manufacture of the LE-5, was Mitsubishi Heavy Industries (MHI), Japan's largest comprehensive heavy machinery manufacturer. A world leader in such fields as shipbuilding and plant operation, it has recently been prompted by structural changes in the international economy to consider other endeavors for the future. A major thrust is now under way to make expertise in aerospace the main pillar of its business. Thus the successful launch of the LE-5–equipped H-I was a significant test of the company's technological strength as it enters the twenty-first century.

Another key player in the project was Japan's National Space Devel-opment Agency (NASDA), the parent body of Japan's space development. NASDA's Launch Vehicle Program Department was responsible for coordinating the entire project, from developing the LE-5 to launching the H-I.

One of the essential technologies that NASDA worked on was a hydrogen-bleed ignition system, which is the first of its kind in the world. It relies on the operation of the hydrogen-bleed cycle only at the time of ignition; as soon as ignition is effected, the gas-generator cycle turns on to return to a normal cycle. Considerable doubt was expressed concerning the system, since it involved technology that was unknown at the time. Together with MHI, NASDA collected data on the hydrogen-bleed cycle and put great efforts into the establishment of conditions for shifting to the gas-generator cycle. After repeated test failures, the technology for the switch-over was established. This involved slowly

changing the flow rate of the ignition valve, with careful confirmation of the thrust buildup during switch-over.

Development and production of the liquid-fuel-related turbopump system, which was one of the key technologies in the development of the LE-5, was entrusted to heavy machinery manufacturer Ishikawajima-Harima Heavy Industries (IHI), Japan's top jet-engine maker. IHI carried out test-manufacture, research, and prototype development of both the liquid-oxygen and the liquid-hydrogen turbopumps, and manufactured the entire system.

As Akira Okayasu and Ken'ichi Fukui, leaders of IHI's part of the project, point out, this system presented "far greater difficulties" in the developmental stages than any they had faced before. The rotational speed of the liquid-oxygen turbopump is 16,500 rpm, and that of the liquid-hydrogen turbopump is more than 50,000 rpm. Compared to similar devices such as industrial-machinery engines and jet engines, these are incomparably higher speeds.

One of the most difficult technological problems to be solved was the vibration of the hydrogen pump. The turbopump is a combination of a turbine and a liquid-hydrogen pump, and at the point where the two are joined vibration occurs. Test operations for confirmation of efficiency produced vibration that made it impossible to achieve the required 50,000 rpm. The cause of this problem was the imbalance of the rotor and the lack of bearing preload. The team managed to solve this problem by correcting the axis balance, and effecting precision control of the running gap around the bearings.

A further serious problem was the practical application of the bearing

The LH$_2$ turbopump developed for the LE-5 engine

The H-I Rocket No. 1, with its LE-5 engine (insert), was launched from NASDA's Tanegashima Space Center at 5:45 AM on August 13, 1986

retainer that holds the rotor. In order to make it answer the demands of high rotor speed, it required a self-lubricating ball bearing. For this, IHI turned to Teflon as a suitable material. To increase the strength of the Teflon, glass-fiber cloth was mixed in, but it was found that this brought about resistance between the retainer and the ball during high-speed revolution. In order to solve this problem, the company developed a method for dissolving the glass fiber on the retainer surface.

The success of the H-I with the LE-5 is a significant benchmark for Japan, proving that Japan can now develop liquid-oxygen and -hydrogen rocket technology on its own. The next step after the H-I is the development of the large-scale H-II, produced entirely in Japan, and the accompanying liquid-oxygen and -hydrogen engine, the LE-7.

1986 High Award for Excellence

Type: Gas-generator cycle
Propellant: Liquid oxygen/liquid hydrogen
Thrust: 10,500 kg · f (vacuum)
Specific impulse: 450 sec
Mixture ratio: 5.5
Combustion pressure: 36.8 kg · f/cm^{2}a
Overall length: 2,548 mm
Maximum diameter: 1,643 mm
Weight: 255 kg
Gimble angle: 3.5°
Nozzle throat diameter: 136 mm
Nozzle expansion ratio: 140

Progressive-Wave Ultrasonic Motor
Shinsei

Shinsei's Progressive-Wave Ultra-sonic Motor features small size combined with high-power output. Its structure consists of an elastic body, a movable body, and a piezoelectric ceramic that vibrates at high speed when infused with a high-frequency electric current. Its drive system is a progressive-wave type, in which the vibration of the piezoelectric ceramic is changed into a progressive wave by the elastic body, which, in turn, rotates the moving body. Sample shippings at a price of ¥30,000 each (including the high-frequency electric power source) were made available in September 1986.

In 1975, Shinsei, a manufacturer of lapping machines, initiated the development of a new type of motor for use in the actuator of an auto-handler. This was prompted by the absence of small, high-power output motors that could execute complicated motions with precision. Conscious of the need to develop a new small-sized actuator that would take the place of other motors, such as those using oil and air pressure, Toshiiku Sashida, the president of the company, was inspired by an idea he had encountered in an academic thesis that had been written shortly after the war. The thesis stated that it was theoretically possible to produce 400–600 W per square cen-

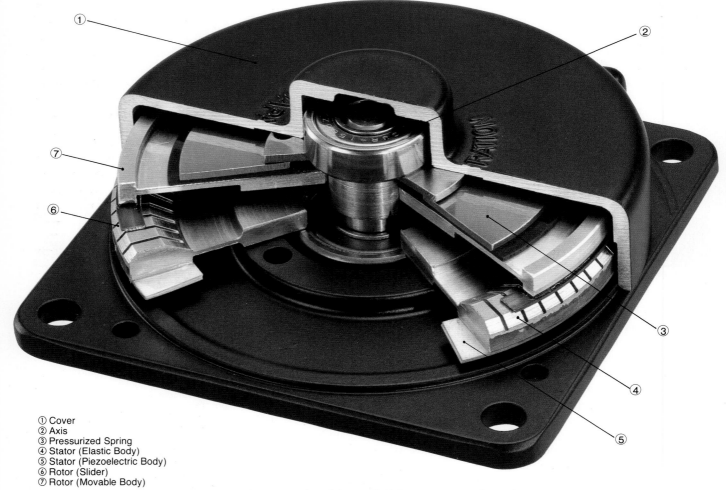

① Cover
② Axis
③ Pressurized Spring
④ Stator (Elastic Body)
⑤ Stator (Piezoelectric Body)
⑥ Rotor (Slider)
⑦ Rotor (Movable Body)

A cross section of the small, high-power-output ultrasonic motor

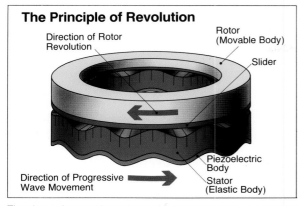

The Principle of Revolution

Direction of Rotor Revolution

Rotor (Movable Body)

Slider

Piezoelectric Body

Direction of Progressive Wave Movement

Stator (Elastic Body)

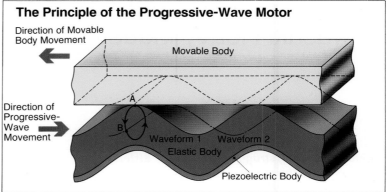

The Principle of the Progressive-Wave Motor

Direction of Movable Body Movement

Movable Body

Direction of Progressive-Wave Movement

A

B

Waveform 1   Waveform 2

Elastic Body

Piezoelectric Body

The ultrasonic motor is made up of 3 basic elements—a piezoelectric body, an elastic body, and a movable body. As is seen in the diagram on the right, the vibration received by the elastic body converts into a traveling wave that goes in the direction indicated by the arrow, and changes from Waveform 1 to Waveform 2. At this time, Point A moves to Point B, giving birth to circular movement. The power thus generated causes the movable body to move in the opposite direction. The diagram on the left expresses this in the shape of a ring.

timeter with ultrasonic wave vibrations produced by the magnetostriction of nickel. This, he felt, might be the key to the technology for a new motor.

Proceeding along these lines, he began research on converting the ultrasonic vibration to a specified direction of a movable body. This produced a method in which a vibration chip attached to the end of a ceramic piezoelectric element puts out a periodic amplitude to activate the moving body. This became the driving system known as the stationary-wave type, and application was made for a patent in 1979.

This kind of ultrasonic motor proved to have low durability, however. Since the part of the vibration chip that comes into contact with the moving body is always stationary, the chip is subject to a great deal of abrasion; a full day of operation causes efficiency to drop significantly. Thus, despite its high conversion efficiency, the motor did not attract much attention.

In searching for an improvement over this kind of motor, Sashida next drew inspiration not from an academic thesis, but from an ordinary toy of the 1960s, the Hula-Hoop. The image of the Hula-Hoop moving back and forth and side to side around the axis of the body gave him a new idea in his search for directional conversion. He realized that if the shaft of the motor is skillfully vibrated and causes the outer ring to rotate, the point of contact constantly changes, greatly reducing the wear and tear on any single point. This led to the birth of the progressive-wave type of motor.

However, the actual creation of the progressive-wave motor was indeed a difficult process. In the case of the linear motor, the wave produced by applied vibration at one end is reflected to the other end and returned. This presents a considerable problem, since the coming wave and the returning wave combine and give birth to a standing wave. It was thus necessary to absorb the wave on the opposite end of the elastic body. A viscous fluid and other similar devices were tested but found unsatisfactory. Finally, when one end was coated with rubber, a clean progressive wave was produced.

A further problem was that even when a slider was placed on the thin plate that produces the wave, it could not move. A theoretical analysis revealed that the points on the surface described an ellipse, yet in the case of a thin plate, the ellipse was so small that the slider could not move forward. However, this could not simply be resolved by increasing the thickness of the plate, since the resulting rigidity would prohibit effective vibration. Instead, the slider was placed on a 3-mm-diameter bar, and this produced extremely smooth movement.

After a long series of trial-and-error experiments, the linear-type motor was perfected. This was then followed by the rotating type, which underwent repeated structural improvements. The appearance of the progressive-wave type generated a great deal of interest in the ultrasonic motor, but its conversion efficiency was still too low to make it a marketable product. At

only 5% efficiency, there was no way to make it practical. Efforts were made to bring the average efficiency of the motor to over 30%. This was finally achieved with such improvements as the use of a fiber-reinforced plastic on the friction surface. In September 1986, the product was put on the market.

Today the ultrasonic motor has gained recognition as a motor ahead of its time. It is being commercialized now by more than fifty major manufacturers including Matsushita Electric Industrial. It holds almost limitless potential applications in such products as actuators, cameras, and home electrical appliances.

Shinsei, however, is a tiny company with only six employees. Even if it were to engage in mass production, it would be unable to keep up with the major manufacturers. Instead, Shinsei has made technical agreements with five major manufacturers, including camera makers, and is continuing application development. This approach of building a network for technology offers to increase profits is the most sensible strategy available to a small company in a field of giants.

1986 Award for Excellence

Input voltage: 100 V rms
Rated current: 53 A
Drive frequency: 40 kHz
Rated revolutions: 100 rpm
Rated torque: 3.9 kg-cm
Rated output power: 4W
No-load current revolutions: 130 rpm
Starting torque: 6 kg-cm
Rotor inertia: 72×10^{-3} g-cm/sec^2
Efficiency: 38%
Repeat life span: More than 1 million

Ceranozzle: Ceramic Nozzle for Welding
Kawasaki Heavy Industries

Welders have long struggled with the problem of spatter (small metal droplets) adhering to the welding nozzle during gas-shielded arc welding. Spatter left sticking to the nozzle clogs the nozzle's mouth, making it impossible to carry out effective welding. In such cases, welding work must be stopped in order to remove the spatter, a particularly troublesome problem when such work is performed by robots. Kawasaki Heavy Industries has solved this problem by changing the old nozzle material from copper alloy to silicon-nitride ceramics, producing a nozzle whose life span is eight to fifteen times longer than that of older ones.

For Kawasaki Heavy Industries, a comprehensive heavy machinery manufacturer involved in making ships, aircraft, and industrial machinery, welding is a mainstay technology. Throughout its long history, it has tried a number of different welding methods, but the problem of nozzles being blocked by spatter during arc welding had continued to be troublesome. Despite progress made in robot welding, full automation has been prohibited by the need to interrupt the work process to remove the spatter stuck to the nozzle. Workshop technicians agreed that welding work would become much more efficient if there were a nozzle that was easy to clean even if spatter stuck to it.

The need for such a nozzle was obvious, and pressure from Kawasaki's Technology Research Center was all that was necessary for development to get under way. An order came to devise a new product in a short amount of time at as little cost as possible, and it appeared to those concerned that development of an effective nozzle would not cost all that much.

Actual development work was initiated in January 1985. It was quickly decided to utilize a silicon-nitride ceramic as the material for the nozzle. Ceramics have superior heat resistance, and a high melting point of 1,900°C. Only a small amount of spatter will adhere to ceramics, and any that does collect on the surface can be removed very easily. Functionally speaking, therefore, ceramics are the perfect material, but they are very expensive. The sales price of a copper nozzle is ¥700 and its actual cost is about half that. The cost of the first prototype, however, was ¥70,000. At this price, no matter how long the life span, it would be extremely difficult to sell.

The main reason for such a high cost was the difficulty of processing the ceramics. The part where the nozzle attaches to the welding machine has to be thread cut, and it was far more troublesome and time-consuming to carry this out than had been expected. Furthermore, costs could not be reduced by making the nozzle thinner, since this would make it too fragile. Also, since about twenty nozzle sizes are necessary, no simple countermeasure would fill the bill for reducing cost. The company's technicians instead hit upon the idea of using a connecting part made of brass, which is mechanically attached

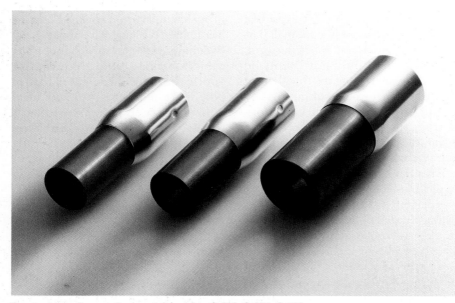

Standard-type Ceranozzle; from left to right—C-300, C-350, C-500

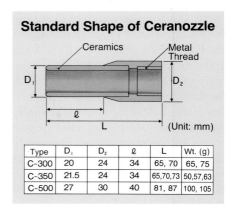

Standard Shape of Ceranozzle

(Unit: mm)

Type	D_1	D_2	ℓ	L	Wt. (g)
C-300	20	24	34	65, 70	65, 75
C-350	21.5	24	34	65,70,73	50,57,63
C-500	27	30	40	81, 87	100, 105

to the ceramic body. Since a simple cylindrical shape is all that is necessary for the ceramics, no additional mechanical processing is needed. The part to be attached can be made with existing processing technology by simply setting the measurements and shapes necessary. In this way, it became possible to bring the cost down to under ¥10,000 apiece.

The company immediately began using the new product experimentally in such places as its motorcycle factories, and in the summer of 1985 began experimental sales. While taking orders from users, it was simultaneously conducting checks on the product, such as durability tests. With a price of around ¥7,000, which is a good ten times that of its copper counterpart, the new nozzle was put on the market in July 1986.

The reputation of the ceramic served the product well, and soon after it was put on the market, sales began to grow. During the first six months, around 8,000 nozzles were made and 5,000 sold. Mass production lowered the price to between ¥4,500 and ¥5,500, which still furnished a profit.

The arc-welding-nozzle market shows annual sales of nearly 2 million units. The major users are manufacturers of such large-scale items as automobiles and construction machines. The nozzle's reputation among the users' production workshop engineers is high, but volume sales can only be generated if production technology chiefs are interested. For this reason, positive sales promotion is being carried out, with a target of obtaining a 30% share of the market by 1988.

The nozzle's reputation is also high in foreign countries. Since it was introduced at the International Institute of Welding in July 1986, it has become the subject of numerous inquiries from European and American enterprises, and export of samples has been initiated. The company is setting its sights on gaining a large share of the foreign market, and promotional campaigns are being carried out in the People's Republic of China.

The high performance of the ceramic nozzle is undisputed. Demand is

sure to increase rapidly if the price is brought down further, since the automation of welding work is expected to grow. However, the market is not infinitely elastic. In Kawasaki's own factories, the nozzles have already been in use for over a year, and it is clear that

the nozzle has such a long life that sales will ultimately bottom out.

1986 Award for Excellence

Ceranozzle keeps spatter adherance to a minimum and has a maximum life span 15 times that of older products

Nara Hybridization System: Powder Surface Modification Technology
Nara Machinery

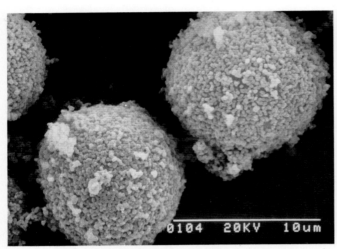

An electron microscope photo of an ordered mixture of a core powder of Nylon-12, with particles of an average diameter of 5 μm, upon the surface of which titanium dioxide particles of an average diameter of 0.3 μm have been attached by means of static electricity

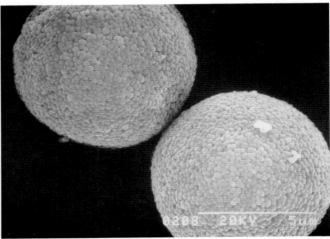

An electron microscope photo of the ordered mixture at left after it has had its surface texture altered by means of a 3-minute hybridizer fixing process; this process is used in the making of materials for cosmetics and other products

Nara Machinery has developed powder surface modification technology that embeds the surface of a core powder of microscopic size with even smaller powder particles of as little as 0.01 μm in diameter. Treating the core powder with static electricity causes the finer powder to adhere to the core's surface. The surface powder is then stabilized in its position by application of physical force. The ultrafine powder can also be melted and then coated onto the surface of the core powder.

Nara Machinery is a manufacturer of such equipment as powdering machines. In about 1981, the company began trying to produce increasingly fine powders with drying-system and shock-system powdering machines. Its target was production of powders of less than 1 μm in diameter. During the experimental process, however, the number of successful trials was half the number of failures. It did not bother the researchers that the number of failures began to mount, as this is a natural part of experimentation. But since a great deal of money was spent on the experiments, the company began to consider seriously just how to profit from them.

Recent research at the Science University of Tokyo on smearing tiny particles on the surface of powders provided an important lead in this direction. These research efforts had been directed to making tiny particles adhere to a powder surface by means of static electricity. The method employed had not proved entirely satisfactory, since the particles were not firmly stabilized and could easily come loose and fall off. If pounded with shock treatment, the particles could be firmly stabilized, but there was a strong risk of crushing them in the process. In searching for successful stabilization technology, the university recognized that the failure data accumulated by Nara Machinery constituted a potentially important body of information.

It was felt that the failures of this method might provide clues to the conditions necessary for successful stabilization of small particles. Thus, a professor of pharmacology from the university joined with the development group of the company's technology department to undertake analysis of the four years of accumulated data. It was discovered that making tiny particles successfully adhere to a core powder without crushing them did not depend only on applying sufficient shock force. Other factors in the process included temperature, the proper mixture of particles and air, and the period of application of the force. To develop a machine that could perfectly balance all four of these conditions, it was necessary to completely redesign part of its internal mechanism.

Drawing on the accumulated data of

previous tests to establish the suitable temperature range and the appropriate concentration of particles that would permit the particles to be pounded but not crushed, the team began work on a new machine. In less than a year and a half, the researchers came up with a commercially viable product. The machine they made was capable of surface modification not only by using force, but also by skillfully exploiting a ble-covered microcapsules by enclosing a layer of tiny particles in a membrane, and research was continued to develop three-layer and four-layer capabilities.

The range of applications for the Nara Hybridization System covers all fields related to powders. Since it is possible for the machines to create entirely new materials, they have drawn considerable attention from ferent companies. By improving the powders used as ingredients of such products, the Nara Hybridization System allows companies to differentiate their goods from those of their competitors. Cosmetic powders, for example, can be enveloped in tiny particles that are water-resistant in order to make the cosmetic adhere more securely to the skin over a longer period. Also, medicines can be made more palatable and

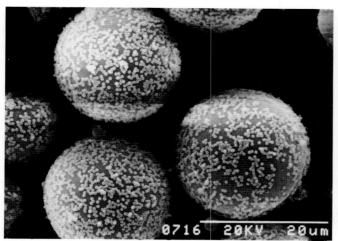

An electron microscope photo of an ordered mixture of a core powder of styrene resin, with particles of an average diameter of 17 μm, upon the surface of which acrylic resin particles of an average diameter of 0.45 μm have been attached by means of static electricity

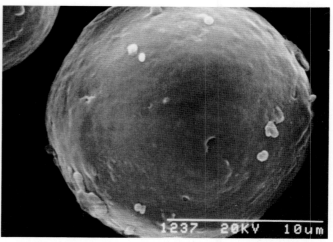

An electron microscope photo of a microcapsule of the ordered mixture at left, which has had its surface texture altered by means of a 2-minute filming process

property of the particles. If a powder is bombarded by particles the resultant heat energy causes them to melt and form a membrane covering the core powder. This process uses the drying system and is particularly useful in making microcapsules for medicine. It is also economical in that it can be completed within two to ten minutes.

The machine was put on the market in April 1986, and within five months twelve units had been sold. The company made five types of machines featuring different processing capabilities available, with a price range of ¥15–60 million. The NHS-1 is capable of processing 3.5 kg per hour using 3.3–3.7 kW of power. The largest machine, the NHS-5, can handle 50 kg per hour and uses 55–75 kW of power.

After sales began, efforts to make the tiny particles adhere to the powder surface more evenly, and to create multiple layers of particles, continued. It had already been possible to form dou-

research departments of companies that deal with such materials as ceramics, electronic materials, and powdered metals. In such industries as chemicals, foods, and cosmetics, technological uniformity has resulted in considerable uniformity in the products of dif-

effective. Nara Machinery is considering making this new technology a main pillar of its future enterprises.

1986 Award for Excellence

The Nara Hybridization System NHS-1 model

Seiki FA-Card System: An IC-Card System for Machine Tool Programming
Hitachi Seiki

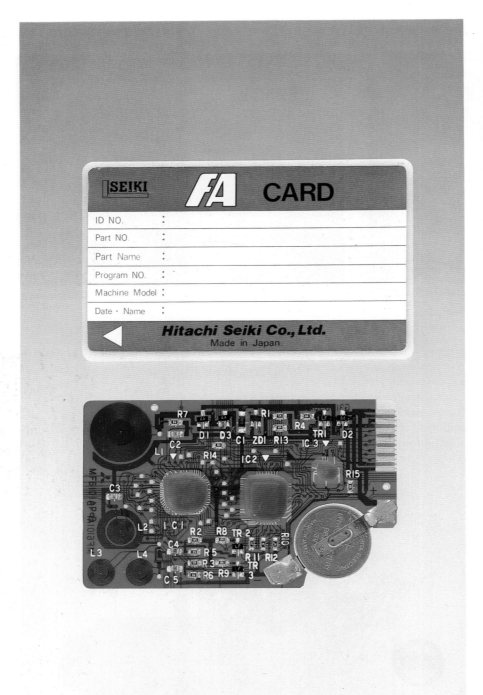

The FA-Card and its inner structure (2-K card, shown actual size; thickness is 3.5 mm)

This system embodies an innovation in numerical-control (NC) program-transfer systems for machine tools by using a nonplug IC card as the data medium. Use of IC cards simplifies storage and saves space, and the cards can be reused by writing different programs on them. Hitachi Seiki was the first to employ such IC cards in the machine tool world, and other manufacturers have been catching up with imitative products. The system consists of a portable read/write device and the IC cards. The standard price for ten 8-K cards and one read/write device is ¥320,000. Sales, including exports, total thirty sets a month.

Numerical-control technology has been progressing in the machine tool industry since the mid-1960s, providing increased savings in energy and improved precision. Despite this progress, for two decades the data medium of NC processing has remained, in the majority of cases, paper tape. A number of alternative methods have been developed, including on-line direct numerical control (DNC), magnetic tape cassettes, and floppy disks, but none has been effective enough to replace paper tape.

To increase the competitiveness of its machine tools, Hitachi Seiki began to develop ways to reduce energy costs and simplify the programming requirements for operating them. Among the areas of possible improvement discussed was the processing of NC data. This in turn prompted analysis of users' needs, and it became clear that the necessary requirements of the data medium were judged by two criteria, physical and sensory. Among the physical qualities required, users wanted an inexpensive data medium that

25M/ATC Turning Cell
controlled by the FA-Card System

would not become soiled or damaged, and would be resistant to oil and water. In sensory terms, they required a medium which would allow them to examine each program physically by touch and sight. The lack of popularity of magnetic tape cassettes and floppy disks in NC applications appeared to be due in part to their having failed the requirement of sensory accessibility.

At the same time that Hitachi Seiki was studying possible data media, the development of intelligent IC cards attracted attention, and in January 1984, an engineer at the company proposed using IC cards as NC-data media. Initial response, however, was unenthusiastic. No IC cards suitable for such applications were found, and the idea was shelved. Instead, the firm marketed a system that used a portable read/write unit that recorded NC data in its internal memory. With this system, the user attached the read/write unit to an automatic programming system. After the NC data was recorded in the read/write unit, the user would then transfer the NC data to the machine tool by carrying the unit over to the tool and plugging it in. The system attracted praise for being considerably cheaper than conventional systems using personal computers, but its inability to store NC data was a serious drawback.

Since the response to the potential of this product's portable read/write unit seemed promising, Hitachi Seiki

resolved to perfect it. For this it turned, a year after the engineer made his original proposal, to the idea of replacing the internal memory with an IC card. After completion of a prototype, the product was put on the market in the fall of 1985, using a domestically produced plug-type IC card. Such a card had the one disadvantage that it does not provide the immediate sensory access that seemed to be important in an NC-data medium, and thus the company was not entirely confident of success. As a result, it adopted a strategy of shipping five of the new sets as samples to domestic and overseas customers in order to evaluate users' needs.

Users' responses were highly favorable, and their requests served to clarify the company's goals. Users indicated that they wanted a nonplug IC card that could withstand factory handling, and they also suggested that a built-in microprocessor was unnecessary—memory alone was sufficient. It was also felt that the expensive IC cards should be such that one could write more than one program on each, unlike a roll of paper tape for a program. Finally, users indicated that convenience and flexibility of use were less important than cost performance, a result which the company had not expected.

Based on its revised impression of users' needs, the company switched from the plug-type to nonplug format

and worked on revising software for multiple program use. The final product was ready to market in May 1986. Setting the price, however, was a headache. Users had suggested a maximum of ¥1,000 per card, but that price was too low for production costs and the pace at which the IC cards were expected to be adopted. Ultimately, the company priced each 8-K card at ¥5,800. The issue the company now faces is price reduction. It has set itself a target of ¥1,000 or less per card, and is working with the card manufacturer to reduce both design and production costs. At such a price, it is expected that demand will reach approximately 50,000 cards a year.

Moreover, the actions of other firms in the industry are a major factor in the spread of IC cards. Rival companies have begun employing IC cards, albeit of the plug type, to catch up with Hitachi Seiki. Although this generates competition in the short run, in the long run it helps the company by expanding the use of IC cards.

1986 Award for Excellence

Connection with a portable read/write unit

SERVICES: FINANCIAL, INSURANCE, AND ENTERTAINMENT

TRENDS IN THE 1980s

Emerging from a past of heavy regulation, Japan's banks are quickly coming up with innovative services and are venturing overseas. —— *Banking*

With huge capital surpluses, Japanese investors are helping the nation's securities firms become world-class forces in international markets. —— *Securities*

Like the banking and securities businesses, insurance has been propelled into the age of innovation. New products are appearing rapidly. —— *Insurance*

Japan's increasing affluence has spawned a host of service industries, some Western-style, some particularly Japanese. —— *Entertainment*

Banking

The liberalization and internationalization of Japan's financial markets in 1986 has brought major changes to the Japanese banking industry. No longer able to depend simply on accepting deposits and making loans for their business, banks today must innovate, and new ideas for managing money will be the key to success in the financial marketplace of the future. More and more, profits will be made from commissions, foreign exchange, and bond dealings, as well as enterprises in equity sharing and international financing.

The banking industry in Japan has been quick to respond. In March 1986, Sanwa Bank developed a new type of account that is composed of a mix of time deposits, government bonds, gold-investment accounts, and mortgage securities. The attraction of this kind of account is that it can be expected to offer a higher rate of return than ordinary accounts.

Banks are also engaging in new cooperative ventures with other kinds of financial institutions. In January 1987, for example, Mitsubishi Bank and United of Omaha Life Insurance of the U.S. marketed a so-called Health Time Deposit, a savings account that combines medical insurance and a time-deposit account. This kind of product diversification is gearing banking services toward more specific needs. Large-scale loans for individuals, or products targeted solely for women or particular age groups—such as the Ladies' Card Loan of Mitsui Bank and Fuji Bank's Let's Card—are manifestations of this trend.

These changes are not limited to customers in the general public, however. Banks have also developed financial products with bank-determined (as opposed to government-determined) interest rates, such as large-scale time deposits aimed primarily at businesses. At the end of 1986, 25% of the total deposit balance for thirteen major banks in Japan was in the form of floating-interest-rate products.

While successive interest rate reductions have decreased the costs of raising money for banks, interest on loans remains high, ensuring large profits. Banks are now keenly interested in expanding their commission income. In April 1986, Daiwa Bank established a medium-term management program whose costs, including personnel expenditures, are completely covered by commission income.

The international strategies of Japan's major banks now involve the participation in or purchase of foreign financial institutions. In April 1986, Sanwa Bank acquired Lloyds Bank of California, obtaining its excellent personal finance division. And in August of the same year, Sumitomo Bank purchased a part of Goldman Sachs, one of the world's most prestigious investment banks. The thrust into foreign exchange and foreign bond dealings has encouraged banks to build firm footholds overseas, thus assuring strong positions in the marketplace of tomorrow.

Securities

The Japanese securities industry had a banner year in 1986. Low interest rates and large surpluses of funds permitted significant expansion of operations. The fiscal quarter ending in September 1986, for example, witnessed an 80% growth in the operating profits of the securities industry as a whole, making it the most favorable closing of accounts in history. Nomura Securities showed a record profit of ¥390 billion, placing it in the top position in Japan's finance industry and in the highest ranks of the world's finance companies. The other major securities companies, such as Daiwa, Nikko, and Yamaichi, also experienced their biggest years in history.

Fueling this securities boom are huge capital surpluses provided by both individuals and corporations, and a rapid drop in interest rates. Individuals' financing assets have been increasing each year, and enterprises are also working harder to increase investment earnings. Because of low interest rates, investment diversification is being encouraged, and stocks, bonds, and investment trusts are forming a larger part of investment portfolios. Such large investors as trust banks have shifted investment away from loans and into securities, accelerating the expansion of the stock and bond markets.

In the midst of intensifying investment competition, securities companies are putting great effort into expansion of investment trust consignment and investment consultant companies. The investment consultant industry law that went into effect in November 1986 will allow investment consultant companies to expand their operations significantly in the future, and it appears that there will be stiff competition between these companies and bank-related investment consultants.

International developments are also changing the face of the Japanese industry. Tokyo has developed into a financial center on equal footing with New York and London. Foreign securities companies with operations in Japan now number over forty, and Japanese securities companies are also playing a role in expanding overseas markets. Nomura Securities and Daiwa Securities recently achieved recognition as primary dealers by the New York Federal Reserve Bank and both firms have received bank-operation permission in London. These developments are important steps toward the realization of a truly global, 24-hour securities market, and have propelled the Japanese securities industry into full-fledged international competition.

Insurance

The life- and non-life-insurance companies of Japan are undergoing a period of thoroughgoing innovations. The amount of life insurance taken out by the Japanese people at the end of fiscal 1985 was approximately ¥6.7 million per capita. This means that Japan has surpassed the U.S. and now occupies the No. 1 place in the world in terms of insurance coverage per person. It can thus be said that Japan has the greatest life-insurance diffusion rate in the world. In order to accommodate the individuality of their clients, Japan's various insurance companies are beginning to diversify their offerings.

In answer to the sudden rise in public awareness concerning interest-rate selection and tax deductions, rapid progress is being made in transforming life insurance into a financial commodity. Variable-rate insurance plans, which appeared in response to the strong demand for savings-oriented insurance, are being offered as a new commodity that places emphasis upon high returns. Sales of these plans began in October 1986. The rate of insurance taken out by the contractee varies in accordance with the actual assets and operational achievements of the insurance company. Since operational proficiency is directly reflected in the insurance rate, high interest rates can be expected when the company enjoys a period of operational proficiency; similarly, operational failure can be

expected to lead to interest rates dropping as far as zero. This is a type of insurance with strong "high risk, high returns" investment qualities that has never before existed among the commodities offered by life-insurance companies.

Variable-rate life insurance was placed on the market by America's No. 3 life-insurance company, Equitable, in 1976, and it immediately became that company's most popular offering. Thus, the wave of innovation that welled up in the U.S. in the mid-1970s has taken a full ten years to reach Japan. Universal insurance, which is considered the definitive commodity in its field (and includes both provisions for abandoning the installment-payment contract halfway through the term, and savings aspects), is expected to appear in Japan in 1988.

However, in both life and non-life insurance, commodities in which the guarantee functions of the past are strengthened are also being put on sale. For example, there is a type of coverage being offered for medical treatment whose purpose is to lessen the individual's medical-treatment expense burden—which becomes heavier each year. Life-insurance coverage with medical-treatment payment guarantees, as well as non-life-insurance packages that also cover the expenses of medical treatment, were made commercially available in April 1986. In contrast to the method employed by most types of life insurance, in which the contracted amount is paid automatically at the time of payment, non-life-insurance plans pay the actual expenses as insurance benefits. While this difference between the two types of insurance does exist, the fact that treatment and hospitalization expenses are paid when one becomes hospitalized because of illness or injury remains the same.

Entertainment

In 1986, the number of Japanese traveling abroad reached 5.5 million, an 11% increase over the previous year, and the first time the figure rose above 5 million. Not only has the stronger yen made travel more affordable, but increased competition among airlines, due to such factors as the expansion of United Airlines' service over the Pacific and All Nippon Airways' international service, has boosted interest in travel.

This has forced travel agencies to work harder to develop new sales packages and services, resulting in the growth of their branch offices. The Japan Travel Bureau and Nippon Travel Agency have recently opened special agencies for package tours.

City hotel business is also becoming active. The ANA Hotel Tokyo, which opened in June 1986, and foreign-owned hotels such as the Hilton and the Century Hyatt, are now challenging the older established hotels in the heart of Tokyo, such as the Imperial and Okura. This challenge from the newcomers has prompted such veterans as the New Otani to expand to Osaka, and the Okura to plan a new facility in Kobe for 1989.

Japan's credit business is also expanding. Credit cards in Japan have been steadily gaining in popularity, and the Japanese credit market reached ¥31.6 trillion in 1984, three times its level of ten years ago. The public now uses credit cards for 18% of its purchases. A leveling-off of the market, however, has intensified competition among suppliers such as credit companies, banks, and consumer loan companies.

With the recent deregulation of financial markets, overseas credit-card companies are developing strategies to enter Japan. Tie-ups between Japanese credit-card companies and overseas enterprises are evidence of this. For example, JCB, Japan's top bank-backed credit-card company, has obtained access to the automated teller machine network of Plus System of Denver, Colorado, America's largest network of such machines. This has enabled JCB to expand its overseas operations to shopping and cashing services for its customers. Citicorp, the largest bank-holding company in the U.S., also began credit-card business in Japan in 1987. With 100 million cards in use, the Japanese market is right behind that of the U.S.

The well-known success of imported fast-food restaurant businesses, such as McDonald's (see p. 204) and Kentucky Fried Chicken, is proof that American-born service companies can flourish in Japan. New joint ventures relying on American expertise are changing the face of Japan's service industry. AIM Services, a meals-provision company formed by Mitsui & Co. and ARA Service of the U.S., and Tokyo Disneyland (see p. 241), an amusement park based on the American original, are typical examples. Other ideas in the service sector recently imported from the U.S. are temporary-employment dispatch services and marriage information services.

Future areas for high growth in both Japan and America are the information industry and health care, both of whose services are based on a combination of high technology and individual attention. The information industry in Japan at present has an inadequate supply of manpower for data processing, software development, programming, and systems analysis. The field of legal services is also considered promising, and American interests are eager to expand this market into Japan.

Bull and Bear Bonds: Treasury-Indexed Variable-Redemption Notes
Nomura Securities

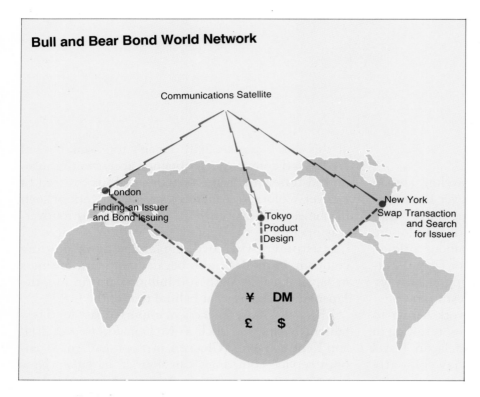

Bull and Bear Bond World Network

Communications Satellite

London
Finding an Issuer
and Bond Issuing

Tokyo
Product
Design

New York
Swap Transaction
and Search
for Issuer

¥   DM

£ $

Bull and Bear Bonds are a high-risk, high-return securities product developed by Nomura Securities. The bonds provide investors with a chance for substantial capital gains by taking a view on interest rate movements, as the redemption payment on the maturity date of the issue is linked to the price of the U.S. Government long bond, specifically, the 9¹/₄% U.S. Treasury bond due 2016. The Bull Bonds' investors will receive a premium redemption if the price of the Treasury bond has risen, and, vice versa, the Bear Bonds' investors can gain a premium redemption when the price of the Treasury bond falls. This structure was created by linking together a number of swap transactions. In all, twenty-three issues of this type of bond were made on the Euromarket in 1986, nine of them, including the first one (that issued by Mitsui & Co. [USA] in May 1986), arranged by Nomura.

In January 1986, the Swaps and New Products Department of Nomura Securities got a favorable response within the financial world to its Heaven and Hell Bonds. These are bonds whose redemption amount varies depending on the foreign exchange market at maturity (specifically the yen/dollar spot rate). The bonds were issued on the Euromarket the previous December by IBM.

This department, which consists of a Swap and New Products group and a Syndicate group, with a total staff of thirty-four (average age around twenty-seven), then began to consider new products to follow up on the success of its Heaven and Hell Bonds. During the discussions, a couple of factors were pinpointed. Global markets were entering a low-interest-rate period and the possibility for further substantial capital gains on straight bonds was thus declining. Furthermore, investors were becoming more comfortable in taking "views" on interest rates and would appreciate a security that enabled them to take such positions. The department thus began to design bonds with variable redemptions indexed to interest rates.

The Nomura staff also kept abreast of both the current market trends and the needs of the bonds' potential issuing entities. They began to consider which interest rate to take as an index

The London Stock Exchange

for the redemption, and how long the maturity of the bond should be. Almost all of the department members contributed to making the issue, discussing such factors as market conditions, structures, and tax issues. At the end of February, the global swap groups of Nomura (that is, the New York, London, and Tokyo teams) gathered in Tokyo to discuss the feasibility of issuing a Bull Bond.

In that meeting the idea of arranging a Bull Bond with a 3-year maturity and redemption linked to the 30-year U.S. Treasury bond (the "long bond") was proposed. Since the duration of the 30-year bond is relatively long, the price movements of it, for a given interest rate change, are considerably larger than that of a 3-year note; thus the purchaser of a Bull Bond can expect a large premium at redemption, if rates move his way. It is of course possible for bullish investors who predict the interest rate will decline at the end of three years to buy 30-year bonds now, but by including swaps and some arbitrage transactions, the Bull Bond could offer better gains to the investor than buying a 30-year bond.

After the basic study was finished, four or five staff members took over the task of designing a structure for the bonds.

Since an idea for a new product may be copied by other companies, the overall structure of the bond was not explained to all the entities engaged in the creation of the first issues. In mid-March, when the preliminary study was finished, Nomura began to search for an issuer. By April, Mitsui & Co. (U.S.A.) was prepared to issue US$50 million of Bull Bonds with a coupon of 10% and a maturity of three years. Under these provisions, if the yield of the long bond declined, the redemption amount increases and vice versa. Nomura negotiated with four or five counterparties to lay off the risk through swaps enabling Mitsui to achieve a low cost of funds and protecting them from the variability of the bond cash flow. The resulting swap structure provided Mitsui with traditional funding while providing the innovative securities demanded by investors.

With the structure settled, only the final preparations for the actual day of issuance remained. As the situation in the financial markets varies every minute, Nomura carefully tracked the market to obtain optimum timing.

Nomura's success in developing these bonds was due to its knowledge of financial markets as well as to its ability to design and structure a new product to suit both investors and borrowers' requirements. It was also due to the lack of rigid organization at Nomura, so that developers did not have to obtain the approval of superiors at each step, especially during actual swap-pricing negotiations, where decisions must be taken very quickly.

Since the first issue, there have been frequent issuances of Bull Bonds on the Eurobond market. The majority of them are far simpler in structure than the Nomura instruments. There are still only two or three companies in the world that have succeeded in recreating the design developed by Nomura.

1986 High Award for Excellence

Bull and Bear Bond Structure and Unique Characteristics

Investors

Bear Bond Investor

Bull Bond Investor

Nomura Securities

Interest Rate at Time of Redemption

BULL BOND

Rise

Drop

BEAR BOND

Rise

Drop

Unique Features of the Bull Bond
1. Redemption payment increases or decreases depending on the level of interest rates at maturity.
2. Redemption payment is indexed to the U.S. 30-year Treasury-bond yield, and investors who predict that the 30-year Treasury bond will provide above-par redemption will purchase in order to gain an increase in principal at the time of redemption.
3. This is a new "high-risk, high-return" product that is aimed at investors who go after capital gains in the midst of worldwide low yield.
4. The issuer can work in a no-risk situation and keep costs low by combining a number of swap transactions.

Unique Features of the Bear Bond
1. Conversely to purchasers of Bull Bonds, investors who predict that the U.S. 30-year Treasury bond will provide below-par redemption will purchase in order to gain an increase in principal at time of redemption.
2. The Bear Bond also effects a no-risk situation and keeps security issuance costs low through a combination of swap transactions on the part of the issuer.

Dream 21: Annuity Fund
Daiwa Securities

Daiwa Securities has become the first Japanese securities company to offer an investment trust in the individual annuity field. Dream 21 has the longest term of any spot investment trust available, with a duration of twenty years. Its investment composition is 70% stocks and 30% bonds for the first fifteen years, and the investment pool is ¥5.2 billion. In Japan, investment trust funds have most often had a duration of four or five years. Dream 21, with its longer maturity, is a sign of the great interest existing in financial service of the annuity type.

The Dream 21 annuity fund differs from most investment trusts in having a twenty-year duration, as opposed to the more usual operating period of four or five years. Development of the fund began in earnest in June 1985, based on two observations. One was that interest in improving life after retirement is high, as evinced by the fact that more than 90% of those sixty-five and older receive public pension funding; the aging of Japanese society further ensures that this market will expand. A second point was that, as in zero-coupon bonds, the longer the period, the higher the interest.

To develop a fund radically different from those already available, Daiwa wished to establish a fund with as long a duration as possible. Initially it considered a thirty-year maturity, but abandoned this when it realized that many people find it hard to think thirty years in advance. Thus, Daiwa settled for a shorter period of twenty years. That in itself was enough to surpass the fifteen-year fund of Nomura Securities and make the Daiwa Dream 21 the fund with the longest duration.

Given its extralong duration, the structure and composition of the fund were run through repeated computer simulations, far more often than for ordinary funds. The results led Daiwa to set the stock composition of the fund at a maximum of 70% for the first fifteen years. The high proportion of stocks in that period is aimed at achieving high yield, with annual dividends wholly reinvested. In the remaining five years, the fund consists of bonds, for stability of yield. From the sixteenth year on, the principal is liquidated in an orderly fashion and combined with dividends to provide a set annuity payment as an annual benefit. This planning stage occupied about a year.

Finding the best name for the fund was another important step. Among

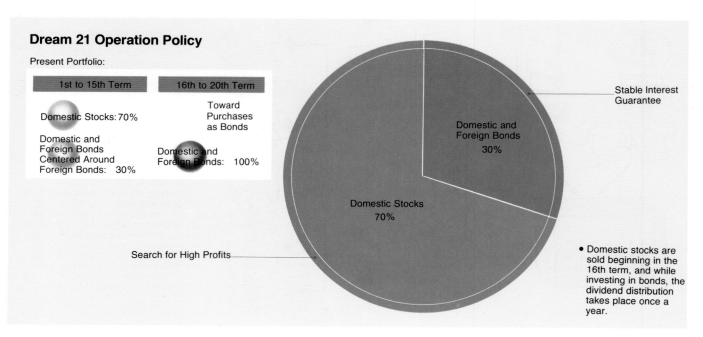

Dream 21 Operation Policy

Present Portfolio:

1st to 15th Term	16th to 20th Term
Domestic Stocks: 70%	Toward Purchases as Bonds
Domestic and Foreign Bonds Centered Around Foreign Bonds: 30%	Domestic and Foreign Bonds: 100%

Stable Interest Guarantee

Domestic and Foreign Bonds
30%

Domestic Stocks
70%

Search for High Profits

- Domestic stocks are sold beginning in the 16th term, and while investing in bonds, the dividend distribution takes place once a year.

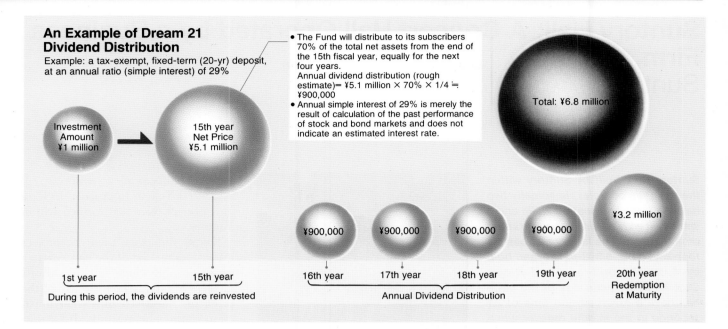

An Example of Dream 21 Dividend Distribution

Example: a tax-exempt, fixed-term (20-yr) deposit, at an annual ratio (simple interest) of 29%

Investment Amount ¥1 million

15th year Net Price ¥5.1 million

- The Fund will distribute to its subscribers 70% of the total net assets from the end of the 15th fiscal year, equally for the next four years.
  Annual dividend distribution (rough estimate)= ¥5.1 million × 70% × 1/4 ≒ ¥900,000
- Annual simple interest of 29% is merely the result of calculation of the past performance of stock and bond markets and does not indicate an estimated interest rate.

Total: ¥6.8 million

¥900,000 ¥900,000 ¥900,000 ¥900,000 ¥3.2 million

1st year | 15th year | 16th year | 17th year | 18th year | 19th year | 20th year Redemption at Maturity

During this period, the dividends are reinvested | Annual Dividend Distribution

suggestions from within the company, "Fund 20" was a powerful contender among the finalists, but some felt that it projected a rather formal image. Instead, the choice fell on "Dream 21," with its implications of buying a dream for the future. Special cases were also prepared so that the securities company warrants could be preserved for the twenty-year period.

Having readied the new fund for the market, the staff of the Investment Trust Department ran up against the objection of the salesmen that a fund with such a long time to maturity would never sell. The sales division plans its selling strategy in terms of funds with a four- or five-year duration. The usual approach is to let customers withdraw from one fund two years after its closed period ends, whereupon they are urged to buy into a new fund. Thus, the twenty-year duration was just too long to handle in terms of the usual sales approach. Marketing was held up until an appropriate strategy could be devised.

The difficulty of selling such a fund resulted in Dream 21 being relegated to a secondary position in the priorities of the sales force. The public offering was made on May 22, 1986, and despite slow initial sales the overall response was unexpectedly good, with the fund being fully subscribed at ¥5.2 billion. That sum, however, is quite

small in the investment trust field. Since the elimination of limits on spot investment trusts in July 1986, securities companies have all been establishing huge investment trusts. With a total subscription of ¥100 billion quite ordinary, the ¥5 billion total subscription for Dream 21 is small. Dream 21, however, was sold in a market totally different from that for ordinary investment funds and without the help of preoffering marketing efforts.

A month after the offering, Dream 21 was unexpectedly featured on television as the first annuity-type investment trust. The television introduction generated a flood of inquiries from investors. The development team saw that response as reaffirming its belief in

The Tokyo Stock Exchange

the great potential of investment programs that would provide for life after retirement. The better-than-expected response has encouraged Daiwa to continue setting up funds with long maturities, differentiating them by varying the maturity period. In developing a series of such funds, Daiwa has adopted a special sales policy that employs direct mail and other techniques distinct from the usual sales approach. Annuity-type investment funds are clearly a coming product as Japan's population ages.

A survey of the customers who bought into Dream 21 revealed that more than half were over forty, in the age bracket to be thinking about retirement in twenty years. Naturally, the largest groups of investors were salaried workers and housewives, with the most common reason for investing in the fund being given as "saving for retirement."

1986 Award for Excellence

Suntory Hall: A Concert Hall Operated by a Business Firm
Suntory

Suntory Hall, built by Suntory within the Ark Hills complex, is actually two halls—a large hall seating 2,006 and a small hall with seating for a maximum of 460 guests. The large hall boasts a four-keyboard, 5,898-pipe organ built by Austria's world-renowned Rieger Orgelbau. The acoustics of the large hall have a reverberation time of 2.1 seconds in the middle register when the hall is full—rendering it world-class acoustically. For the first six months after the opening of the hall in October 1986, the world's finest musicians were invited to perform in the opening season concert series.

The concept behind Suntory Hall dates back eight years, when the Suntory Music Foundation, of which Suntory President Keizō Saji was chairman of the board of trustees, was nearing its tenth anniversary. Suntory is Japan's largest whiskey distiller and produces spirits, beer, wine, and soft drinks. The composer Yasushi Akuta-gawa, a senior director of the foundation, and other directors commented that Japan's lack of a concert hall for classical music was embarrassing. They dreamed of a hall they could be proud of in Tokyo, but assumed that no one could build one. It was just a fantasy.

Fantasy became reality when a proposal was made to Suntory for building a cultural facility as part of Mori Build-ing's Ark Hills complex (see pp. 72–73) in central Tokyo. In August 1982, a new project team was formed within Suntory.

Kazuo Yamazaki, then the project leader for creation of the hall, was in a quandary. He knew nothing about music. One day, when discussing the problem, Saji asked him what musicians' names he actually did know. Yamazaki admitted to having heard of von Karajan, whereupon Saji bluntly told him, "Well, then, go talk to von Karajan!" In September 1982, Yamazaki, still quite ignorant of music, set off to visit concert halls in Europe and the United States. Fortunately in Berlin he was able to arrange a meeting with Herbert von Karajan. The conductor's comment, "Tokyo has no hall with good acoustics," inspired Yamazaki to persevere.

In January 1983, Yamazaki accompanied Saji and others to once again visit von Karajan in Berlin. Von Kara-jan, who had been deeply involved in

The large hall, with 2,006 seats; pine is used for the flooring material and white oak for the walls, creating good acoustics

the design of the Berlin Philharmonic's own concert hall, advised, "Music is created by a union of the performers and the audience. The Vineyard form, in which the audience surrounds the stage, satisfies that condition. Since Suntory is a wine maker, that's the form for you. Suntory Hall is sure to produce good wine."

The group visited the world's finest concert halls—Vienna's Musik Verein, Amsterdam's Concertgebouw, London's Barbican Centre, New York's Carnegie Hall. Several days after they returned to Tokyo, the decision was made: the new concert hall would be on the Vineyard model.

Yasui Architects designed the building and Minoru Nagata Acoustic Engineer & Associates was responsible for the acoustics. In the early summer of 1983, a 1:10 scale model of the hall was completed. The model was filled with nitrogen gas and laser beams were used to simulate sound waves and show how sound would be reflected, spread, and otherwise behave in the hall. In Japan at the end of that year, von Karajan examined the model.

Since the acoustics of a hall are affected by the materials used in its interior finishing, a variety of woods were considered. Pine for the flooring and white oak for the walls were selected. White oak, by chance, is also the material used to make the barrels in which whiskey, Suntory's leading product, is aged.

The building was completed on April 1, 1986. The final delicate adjustments of the acoustics in the actual hall then began while the pipe organ was installed and tuned.

The hall lived up to expectations following the plans and duplicating the results of the test model. A distortion in the acoustics would have necessitated major changes, but Suntory Hall fortunately did not need drastic alteration.

While the hall was under construction, preparations were being made to engage the appropriate performers. The world's leading musicians plan their schedules years in advance, and Suntory wanted to ensure that their Tokyo performances were at Suntory

Suntory Hall opened on October 12, 1986, with a performance of Beethoven's Ninth Symphony

Hall. Starting in 1984, Yamazaki and his group began checking musicians' schedules to assure a successful opening season at the new hall. The new hall was launched by an NHK Symphony concert under the baton of Wolfgang Sawallisch. The opening program, which began on October 12, also included performances by von Karajan and the Berlin Philharmonic on October 28–30.

Unfortunately, von Karajan fell ill just before he was scheduled to come to Japan. The October 28 performance was to have been a major event costing ¥75,000 per person, with a party for von Karajan and the audience. The

opening party was canceled and ¥39,000 returned to the guests. Fortunately, Seiji Ozawa was able to step in and save the evening.

The reputation of Suntory Hall is spreading among musicians in the United States and Europe, who regard it as one of the great concert halls of the world. At last, Tokyo has a concert hall of which it can be proud.

1986 Award for Excellence

Hondex LCD Depth Sounders M-410, M-430: Portable Fish Shoal Locators
Honda Electronics

Even under direct sunlight, this LCD Depth Sounder clearly indicates the position of schools of fish

M-410 and M-430 are transistor LCD depth sounders. Until this product was developed, fish shoal locators were large, bulky items installed in boats. Now amateur fishermen have a handy, compact means of locating fish shoals. In addition to being convenient, this product is inexpensive, a mere ¥39,800, a figure that is approximately one-tenth the price of any other depth sounders. The LCD is visible even in strong sunlight. The product was placed on the market in November 1985, and over 30,000 units had been sold as of January 1987. Eighty percent of these were sold in the U.S.

Although liquid-crystal display has been used in televisions and calculators, depth sounders for locating fish shoals used CRTs until the development of these models. With this new product, depth sounders were revolutionized.

The original notion of using an LCD for a depth sounder was conceived by the president of Honda Electronics, Keisuke Honda, and chief of development, Hisao Kurata, in mid-1984. They felt available depth sounders, including their own models, were antiquated, and that it was time to develop a depth sounder that used an LCD. Previous depth sounders were bulky items installed in boats. Expensive and complicated to use, in general they were regarded as items for professional use. It was Honda Electronics' goal to develop a product that was portable and easy to use, something as small as a portable LCD television, and one that would have mass-consumer appeal. Kurata, himself an amateur fisherman, was personally frustrated by the fact that in order to use a depth sounder one had to own a boat.

Honda Electronics was at first concerned with the pricing of the new product. In general, miniaturization of a product's parts necessitates a rise in cost, but since many other miniature products such as audio and office equipment were being manufactured, it was possible to use known technology. Because a large volume of units,

20,000, was to be produced annually, the parts actually were less expensive than those of standard depth sounders. A mass-production assembly line allowed the use of robots, which further cut costs.

Another problem the company faced was that existing LCD technology was not suitable for a depth sounder. Liquid crystals melt into liquid at high temperatures and turn black. A portable depth sounder that could not withstand direct sunlight would be useless, and so Honda Electronics turned to many liquid-crystal manufacturers to seek their help. Unfortunately, no one had any answers, and the project was shelved for two months.

Kurata and his project team did not, however, give up entirely, and with the

Models M-410 (left) and M-430

help of the Toyohashi University of Technology, eventually found solutions to their problems. Such cooperation between an academic institution and a commercial enterprise is unusual in Japan, where academics in general do not necessarily appreciate commercial applications of their research. Toyohashi is a relatively new institution, only ten years old, and is more open-minded than many other academic institutions. The university has even gone so far as establishing a development center whose purpose is to answer inquiries from local enterprises.

Keisuke Honda is one of the founding fathers of this university. A native of Toyohashi, he took considerable personal interest in the school. The ties between this university and Honda Electronics are therefore quite strong, and it was the university that helped

continued research on the development of the depth sounder.

Five months after initial research began, the tenth liquid-crystal manufacturer approached finally agreed to try and develop a liquid crystal that could function in high temperatures, and within six months a product was perfected, thereby revolutionizing depth sounders.

Before the product's debut Kurata had some last-moment misgivings. Previous depth sounders cost ¥100,000–200,000, and perhaps customers would not take a ¥40,000 product seriously. His fears were unfounded and by the close of 1985, Honda Electronics could not keep up with demand. It began to take orders as far as six months in advance. The bulk of the business is with America, where many units have been sold. As Honda Electronics' first mass-consumer product, the depth sounders are important to this company.

1986 Award for Excellence

Frequency: 200 kHz
Image range: To water depth of 0–50 m in six
  stages
Shift: Sequential shift in 5-m increments
Maximum depth: 95 m
Power output: 20 W
Display: LCD
Function: Sensitivity adjustment, LCD contrast
  adjustment, and freeze
Voltage: DC 12V
Outer dimensions: 140 (H) × 113 (W) × 30
  (D) mm; wt: about 320 g

Overnight Word Processor Plan
Hotel Nikko Osaka

The program was popular among businessmen with hectic schedules

In February 1986, Hotel Nikko Osaka initiated an Overnight Word Processor Plan, which it offered eighteen times during the year. Tapping today's interest in word processors, this well-timed idea attracted 800 participants, including many businessmen. Customers spend a night at a city hotel, learn personal word processor operation, and take their practice machine home with them. The price, including room, breakfast, lessons, and word processor, is ¥39,800, lower than the standard retail price of the word processor alone. The idea also caught on at other hotels, and has since spread throughout Japan.

The problem of off-season vacancies is a major one for any hotel. In Osaka, competition between hotels is keen, and the oversupply of rooms prompted Hotel Nikko Osaka to search for new ideas to bring in business.

Hotel bookings that include leisure services are now commonplace, and Hotel Nikko Osaka wanted something truly innovative. "Why not a hotel-study program?" thought Yasuo Sugiura, manager of the sales planning division of the hotel's service administration. In 1984, with the popularity of personal computers, this seemed to be a perfect idea.

The hotel began with a Personal Computer Instruction package lasting for three days in January 1985. Anticipating a group of about twenty, the hotel received 400 applications. It was clear from this response that people were receptive to the hotel-study idea and that it had a large market potential.

Since personal computers had proved so popular, word processor study was a logical extension. In March 1985, the hotel held an overnight word processor course. Customers complained, however, that they would quickly forget what they learned in that one night, because they had no word processor at home.

Addressing this need, the completed package concept was devised. It was made more affordable by a drop in word processor prices in 1986. The itinerary began with check-in at the hotel by 1 PM on the first day. This was followed by instruction on making documents and editing until 8:30 PM, with dinner served between the separate sessions. On day two, following breakfast, instruction on print out and creating additional characters was given from 10 AM until noon.

From February 24 to May 1, the hotel held the course eleven times, with 545 participants, and between July 19 and 25, seven additional sessions drew 252 more attendants. All classes were filled the day they were announced.

The popularity of this plan derives from the appeal of learning how to use a word processor in only two days, and the very low price. The cost of the entire package, including room, breakfast, instruction, and word processor, was only ¥39,800, ¥10,000 less than the cost of the word processor itself. The low price was made possible by the hotel's high-volume purchasing ability. Naturally the profit margin attained was low, yet this was acceptable since the hotel's aim was to counter high-vacancy periods during holidays and the off-season when businessmen are difficult to attract.

Other hotels, facing similar problems, followed suit quickly. Less than one month after the start of Hotel Nikko Osaka's courses, others appeared, and within three months, city hotels from Hokkaido to Okinawa were offering similar study programs.

The hotel presently has concluded operation of the plan. Consumers have become more sophisticated and are less inclined to be attracted by the low price of the machine necessarily featured in a package like this. Their preferences tend toward more expensive models featuring a wide range of high-power functions. Yet the price of such models is too high to permit a marketable hotel package like the one offered by Hotel Nikko Osaka. However, the plan served as an important experiment in innovative marketing.

As city hotels seek to expand their variety of customers in the future, this plan indicates the importance of being attentive to society and imaginatively responding in kind.

1986 High Award for Excellence

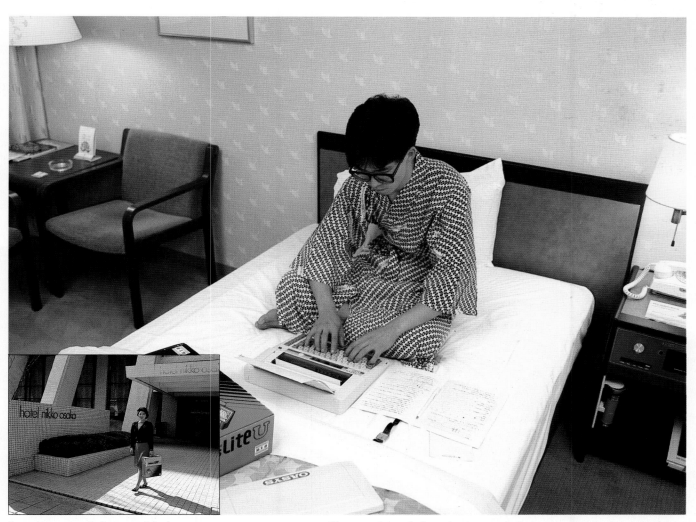

A word processor that you can take home

Many people use their word processors in their rooms after the first day's classes

FREEROAD: A Rent-A-Car Showroom
Nippon Rent-A-Car Service

In October 1985, an automobile showroom opened at the Nippon Rent-A-Car headquarters in Shibuya Ward, Tokyo. The new auto showroom received much acclaim as the first in Japan to cross manufacturers' lines; it displays a total of fourteen models, two each from seven leading domestic manufacturers. Drivers may rent the same models as those on display. With the added attractions of a satellite radio studio and a coffee *shop, the showroom has attracted an average of 500 visitors a day.*

Nippon Rent-A-Car wanted to build a new headquarters as the final step in its fifteenth anniversary celebration. The company wanted not just a plain office building but a place where young people would gather.

Nippon Rent-A-Car Service had housed its headquarters in a rented building in the Shibuya district of Tokyo, but the offices had become cramped as the company's scale of operations grew. The then president Kōzō Ishikawa (now vice-chairman) decided to construct a new headquarters building about a year before the fifteenth anniversary of the company's foundation in March 1984. In order to initiate these plans, the company bought a new lot near its original headquarters.

Nippon Rent-A-Car wanted to

14 cars, including new models from seven makers, are on display; rent-a-car service is also available

The satellite radio studio is particularly popular among young people

incorporate in its building something that would not only serve as promotion for the company, but also express its gratitude to its many young customers. This concept of consolidating many functions in one building was the basis of a number of proposals for the building, such as incorporating a restaurant or movie theater. None, however, offered any particular advantages. Finally the company had a major advertising agency do some market research and, as a result, decided to establish an automobile showroom as the core of the headquarters building.

President Ishikawa was hard-pressed to decide how to develop the plan until he was given an excellent suggestion by Yukio Sugiura, then an officer of an automobile dealership in Nara prefecture and now a senior vice-president of Nippon Rent-A-Car. Sugiura noted, "Dealers now are too constrained in sticking exclusively to the lineup of a particular manufacturer. If someone broke out of that restriction…" Ishikawa adopted his suggestion and decided in late 1983 to build a showroom that would display cars of many manufacturers under one roof.

In designing the showroom, the plans were considered with care. The company decided to build a coffee shop, set up a satellite radio studio, and open a reservations counter for renting cars overseas as well as making available for rental the same models that

were on display. The new showroom did away with the irritating characteristics of already-existing showrooms. Thus, it was decided that at FREE-ROAD, the staff would not approach the visitors, allowing them to browse freely.

The biggest worry was how much cooperation the company would receive from automakers. The individual car companies thought that a permanent exhibition of automobiles from more than one manufacturer was not a welcome experiment. Not surprisingly, each manufacturer initially said that if Nippon Rent-A-Car would make an exclusive arrangement, it would supply cars and money, or that only if the other companies agreed, would it consider the joint showroom. Convincing the manufacturers was a task that fell to Nippon Rent-A-Car managing director Yoshihiro Morimoto, who had solid connections with them through his experience in purchasing cars for the company rental fleet. The manufacturers finally agreed just a month before construction was to begin. Toyota, Nissan, Mazda, Mitsubishi, Honda, Isuzu, and Fuji Heavy Industries all agreed to supply two models each. They provided models that were either particularly oriented to the youth market or currently popular.

Although FREEROAD grew out of the experience and ideas of all of Nip-

pon Rent-A-Car employees, President Ishikawa's tenacity in pursuing the project played a great role in its success.

As the company had hoped, FREE-ROAD became highly popular among young people. Although it is located at a little distance from the center of Shibuya, it draws more than 15,000 visitors a month. The rent-a-car side is doing well, thanks to the newness and novelty of the models available.

Nippon Rent-A-Car regards FREE-ROAD as a marketing laboratory, a test site for improving its existing business and developing new services. One experiment is a service in which the company will sell a consumer the car he has rented, as is. If a customer drives a rental automobile and likes it, he can call up the pertinent information for buying it on a personal computer: the date of the new car registration, the options it is provided with, and its price. In the U.S., sales of used rental automobiles are commonplace, but they are unusual in Japan. Nippon Rent-A-Car now plans to extend this service to its nationwide network of rental agencies.

Plans call for opening similar showrooms in five other major cities in Japan. FREEROAD, which was started as a means of attracting and acquiring information about young people, is growing to be one of the basic foundations of Nippon Rent-A-Car's operations.

1986 High Award for Excellence

An outside view of FREEROAD

SALES AND DISTRIBUTION SYSTEMS

TRENDS IN THE 1980s

Traditionally a service-oriented society, Japan is turning its sales and distribution networks high-tech.

Japan's distribution industry is in the midst of change. Retailers such as department stores and supermarkets are attempting to increase sales by opening new branches. At the same time, they are reevaluating their shops and products and introducing computer systems for tracking orders from wholesalers and manufacturers. The restaurant industry, which once enjoyed double-digit growth, has been detrimentally affected by rash speculation that resulted in bankruptcies and increased competition. Some restaurants are beginning to join hands with major enterprises to survive.

By contrast, two areas of the distribution system are showing success. Door-to-door-sales and mail-order businesses, despite criticism from a number of consumers, continue to grow by 10% annually. Co-ops—consumer cooperatives that buy in large lots for a group of members—are showing an annual increase in sales of 20%. They are so successful that small- and medium-sized businesses are beginning to demand government regulation of co-ops.

Consumer tastes are changing, too. They are becoming more discerning, demanding quality rather than appearance and quantity. The distribution industry's response has been four-pronged. Its businesses are attempting to carve out a new future based on: development of new ventures; improvement of sales and cultural activities; internationalization; and high-tech communication.

The greatest diversification is in Japan's supermarkets. Jusco, for example, has been expanding its scope into specialty shops selling shoes, men's and women's clothing, and traditional Japanese clothing, and family-style and seafood restaurants. It is also developing shopping centers that include these kinds of retail outlets. The Seibu Saison Group has not stopped with diversification alone. In 1985, it opened Tsukashin (see pp. 250−51), a shopping center in Amagasaki in Hyogo prefecture that includes not only department stores, specialty shops, and restaurants, but also a sports center and an all-purpose hall.

Royal, a major suburban restaurant chain, has joined with Nissan Motors to open restaurants. Supermarket chains such as Daiei have installed counters inside their stores to sell insurance and provide moving services. Convenience stores such as Seven-Eleven·Japan serve as pickup points for parcel delivery services and also sell tickets to movies and concerts. Large department stores such as Seibu, Mitsukoshi, Matsuzakaya, and Tokyu are expanding their culture centers, adult-education facilities attended primarily by women. Restaurants are increasing their home delivery services. Recently, based on the American model, even pizza is delivered to homes.

It appears that competition to provide services will continue to intensify within the distribution industry for some time to come. One after another in 1986, department stores in Tokyo began to stay open until 7 PM, extending their hours by an hour. Twenty-four-hour operation has not yet appeared among Japan's major supermarkets and department stores, but it is expected to do so in the near future. Another example of competition is the growth of specialty services within the distribution industry. Yamato Transport delivers small packages door-to-door (see p. 243). Housecleaning services are also gaining popularity (see p. 244).

Companies such as Jusco and Yaohan Department Store are moving into the international market by opening branches in Southeast Asia. In general, Japanese businesses in the distribution industry are taking advantage of the strong yen to buy raw materials in these countries and also to form joint ventures there to manufacture products for import to Japan. In 1986, Daiei and Tokyu, particularly, attracted the attention of the retail industry with their private-brand products, often imported in whole or in part from other Asian countries.

The industry, especially department stores and supermarkets, is also beginning to use computer systems to increase operating efficiency. Ito Yokado, a supermarket company, was the first to introduce a point-of-sale computer system in its stores. In the suburban restaurants of Skylark, employees take orders on hand-held devices that relay messages to the main computer, which then relays the information to the kitchen. Manufacturers such as Lion, a leading producer of toothpaste and detergents, and Shiseido, Japan's largest cosmetics company, are beginning to set up on-line systems for placing and receiving orders from wholesalers. There is also great activity in joint projects such as value-added networks (see pp. 122−23), and the linking of manufacturers, wholesalers, and retailers through information systems.

Establishing advanced communication systems in order to set up effective sales-promotion measures that eliminate waste in both stocking and sales will be an extremely important trend in the future.

While there are differences in national customs that make international comparisons difficult, Japan's distribution industry appears to be several years behind the U.S. in high-tech information systems and the development of specialized services.

Men's Kan: A Men's Fashion Outlet
Marui

Marui's Men's fashion outlet

In March 1986, in response to a growing interest in fashion among Japanese men, Marui decided to transform its Shinjuku Sports outlet, a sporting-goods specialty store, into an outlet that specializes in fashions for men, with forty-one separate store outlets selling seventy designer brands. Marui, involved in selling designer clothing since 1976, used its years of experience to turn the store into a success. The store's sales area is 3,300 m², and sales for the first fiscal year are expected to be around ¥6 billion. Marui's sales comprise 10% of the total sales of men's designer clothing in Japan.

Marui is a chain of department stores that employs a unique installment-payment and credit-card system. Marui also offers a package plan for driving schools (see p. 237). Marui is particularly popular with students and young adults, and most of its retail outlets are located in the Tokyo metropolitan area. The company's policy is to concentrate on popular shopping areas such as Shinjuku, a district known for its department stores, restaurants, and theaters, where Marui owns five separate shopping buildings. As of 1984, it had fashion, young fashion, interior, electrical goods, and sporting goods stores, all of which together make up Marui's Shinjuku stores.

The Shinjuku stores have been profitable, with sales of ¥52.1 billion in 1985, a figure that represents almost 15% of Marui's total sales. Of the five Shinjuku stores, the sporting goods outlet lagged behind the others in sales. Various proposals for renovation of the Sports outlet were considered, including a store with a unisex theme. The current manager of the Men's outlet, Tsuneo Nakajima, who was involved in this project from its early stages, says that the selection of the men's fashion building proposal was an easy decision. Bolstering its confidence in the future success of the store was many years of experience in the sales of designer clothing.

Most designer fashions in Japan are geared towards women, but recently men have displayed considerable interest in fashion. Within the past several years, many successful men's fashion magazines have appeared on the market, indicating that the time was right for the introduction of a store that specialized in men's designer fashions.

Koshin Satoh's Arrston Volaju boutique

Older Japanese men in the past have displayed little interest in fashion or designer brands, but this is not the case with younger generations. In Nakajima's opinion, "As is the case with women, men have entered an era where self-expression is made through fashion."

In December 1985, the final decision to proceed with the Men's outlet was made, and all that remained was to select which brands should be featured in the store.

The key to the success of any store is its merchandise, a fact that is particularly true in the fashion retail

Young men lining up for a sale

business where competition is fierce. Marui was able to assemble an impressive selection of designer goods in a short period of time, a feat that was only possible because of Marui's previous experience with designer clothing. Among the seventy designers featured in the Men's outlet are Issey Miyake, Yohji Yamamoto, and Rei Kawakubo. In Nakajima's opinion, the relationship between retail stores and designers is one of mutual nurturing, and trust developed over years of working together was very important in the creation of this store. Furthermore, because this was the first department store in Japan that would handle men's designer clothing exclusively, there were high expectations and a sense of anticipation among Marui's many connections in the industry.

All eight floors of the Men's outlet feature designer clothing for men. Brands that appeal to similar tastes are grouped together. This way, customers can go to a specific floor, compare brands and merchandise, and select their purchases. Spacious aisles allow for comfortable shopping.

On March 1, 1986, the store opened. Nakajima was certain that it would succeed, not only because of Marui's successful record in selling men's fashions and various designer accessories, but also as a result of the appropriate location of the new store. As many as 90% of the customers visiting Marui's Shinjuku stores are in the targeted age group—twenty-nine or younger.

Nakajima's confidence was well founded. Sales have surpassed original targets, and the Men's outlet has made a contribution to the popularity of men's designer fashions in Japan. An indication of the enthusiasm of the customers is that before the store opens for its biannual sales, several hundred young men line up from early in the morning before opening hours to get the best selections.

Nakajima is pleased with the results but not yet entirely satisfied. "The more numerous the customers, the more I feel a responsibility to answer the expectations of our young clientele." In order to continue to lead the way in providing fashions for the young, Marui began further renovation of the Men's outlet in March 1987.

1986 Award for Excellence

The Pour Homme Corner of the Yohji Yamamoto boutique

The floor guides to the 3rd and 8th floors

PLANET Data-Exchange System: An Industrywide VAN
Planet

PLANET is a data-exchange service linking manufacturers and wholesalers using a VAN (value-added network) established by Intec. It is designed for the household-products and cosmetics industry, and provides **data on orders, deliveries, sales performance, and billings. Using a VAN requires the installation of a terminal device such as a personal computer. Whereas private VANs connect only one manufacturer with one whole-** **saler, PLANET provides a single terminal link between customers and manufacturers throughout the industry. Since PLANET's introduction in January 1986, similar networks have appeared in other industries.**

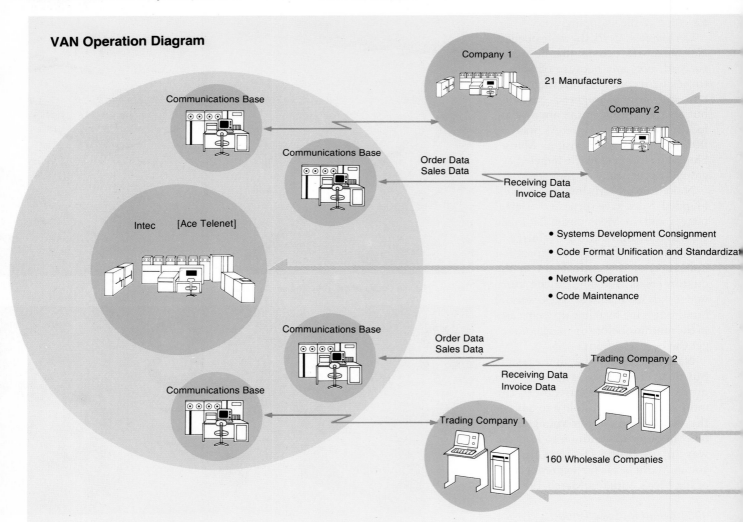

VAN Operation Diagram

Company 1

21 Manufacturers

Communications Base

Company 2

Communications Base

Order Data
Sales Data

Receiving Data
Invoice Data

Intec   [Ace Telenet]

- Systems Development Consignment
- Code Format Unification and Standardizat
- Network Operation
- Code Maintenance

Communications Base

Order Data
Sales Data

Trading Company 2

Receiving Data
Invoice Data

Communications Base

Trading Company 1

160 Wholesale Companies

In establishing PLANET, its originators faced two major obstacles. Private VANs connect a single manufacturer to a single wholesaler, but the PLANET system was to be an industrywide service connected by a single telecommunications network. This necessitated convincing rival manufacturers, locked daily in fierce competition over new products and sales, to provide funds and create an operating company. The second obstacle consisted of signing up wholesalers for the new network. Participants would need to install a terminal device for the VAN, such as an office or personal computer, and would be reluctant to bear the cost. The idea of a joint network also appeared to jeopardize privacy when entrusting critical data on deals between customers to a third party, however briefly.

This did not daunt the originators of the idea, however. The president of Lion, a leading household product manufacturing company, was the driving force behind PLANET. He was convinced of the need for an industrywide network. Lion already had its own large-scale network that comprised terminals installed in 146 wholesale businesses. It was the biggest network in the industry. Despite its secure position, Lion felt that if every company started up its own network, the industry would become a tangle of confusion. A flood of private VANs built to connect individual manufacturers with the wholesalers they deal with would be extremely inefficient, since it would require a wholesaler to establish a separate VAN for each manufacturer from whom it wished to place orders. The cost of using a VAN would thus multiply with the installation of each newly created network. Establishing one VAN for common use in the industry would reduce the system-development costs borne by the company and could contribute to more efficient distribution within the industry.

This argument was reinforced by circumstances in the industry. Kao, a major manufacturer of cosmetics and household goods, had already developed its own large-scale network linking sales companies (its affiliated wholesalers) and retail stores. Kao's rivals, stimulated by its example, saw that there was a common interest in building a joint network for themselves. In trying to obtain the cooperation of wholesalers, however, they initially received a mixed response. Many wholesalers voiced doubts about investment in the system and about security.

Planet, the operating company for PLANET, was founded in August 1985. Meeting with some 100 wholesaler representatives at a gathering in Tokyo in October 1985, the managing director of Planet won their support. He explained first that the manufacturers would bear the cost of the terminals installed at the wholesalers' offices. This was a powerful appeal to the wholesalers, since it meant that they would obtain a free personal computer that they could also use for accounting and other purposes. Addressing the problem of security, the director emphasized that PLANET would be run entirely by the operating company. Since Intec would do all the data processing, neither the manufacturers nor the wholesalers would be able to access the data. This was explained at meetings at eleven sites throughout Japan, and Planet managed to erase the wholesalers' doubts.

The system began a telecommunications service five months later, and within a year it was being used by twenty manufacturers and about 200 wholesalers. Its influence on the distribution industry in Japan has been considerable. In October 1986, seven producing companies and seven wholesalers in the liquor and processed-food industry established a data-exchange service called FINET, similar in concept to PLANET. The eyeglass industry has also witnessed the development of a unified VAN called MEGANET, presently used by six companies. Such industrywide networks are expected to become more prevalent in the next few years, as companies search for new ways to rationalize their accounting and distribution procedures.

1986 Award for Excellence

- User Company Canvassing and Organization
  - Network Utilization Contracting
  - Network Utilization Fee Collection
  - Demand Adjustments

Industrial VAN Operation Company
PLANET

- User Company Canvassing and Organization
- Terminal Offering
- Software Package Sales
- System Consultation
- Demand Adjustments

(as of Jan.'87)

INFORMATION AND COMMUNICATIONS EQUIPMENT

TRENDS IN THE 1980s

The computer market used to be IBM versus the Others. Now the picture has sharpened: it is IBM versus Japan. —— Information Equipment

Privatization of a ¥5 trillion-a-year company broke its monopoly and resulted in an entirely changed telecommunications market for Japan. —— Communications Equipment

Information Equipment

When IBM of the U.S. established its Asia-Pacific Group headquarters in Tokyo, its arrival caused quite a stir. It employed 500 regular staff members, including 300 foreigners, in 1984, and the media went so far as to cry: "IBM's occupation army has landed in Japan!" Given Japan's international position as the second largest computer market in the world, however, there is nothing at all strange about IBM's decision to build a base in Tokyo.

It is not just a matter of the size of the market, either. Japan is the world's largest computer battlefield. While IBM has a 60% share of the computer market worldwide, Japan is the only advanced country where it has less than a 30% share. Moreover, Japan is thronging with powerful manufacturers in such areas as semiconductors, and is fast becoming a supplier of high-tech equipment. It is perfectly natural for IBM to take Japan very seriously—and to make it clear that it is doing so.

The world computer market revolves around IBM. Since the U.S. Justice Department dropped its suit against IBM for violating monopoly laws in 1982, this trend has grown even stronger. In the U.S. there used to be a group of manufacturers of equipment not compatible with IBM's, known as "the Bunch." But with the merger of Sperry and Burroughs and the resulting creation of a new company, Unisys, in 1987, the balance of IBM-versus-the-others has quietly begun to collapse.

In Europe as well, major manufacturers have abandoned the competition to develop hardware. In the midst of this, it is only Japanese industries who have not lost the ability to compete. To put it in somewhat dramatic terms, it is expected that in the latter half of the 1980s the players in the global computer industry will be simply IBM versus Japan.

Japan has worked hard to catch up with U.S. companies, including IBM. It began to work on creating a national flag computer in 1965, and has achieved considerable success. In 1972, the Ministry of International Trade and Industry organized six Japanese companies into three groups: Fujitsu and Hitachi; NEC and Toshiba; and Mitsubishi Electric and Oki Electric Industry. Subsequently, Toshiba withdrew from manufacturing and developing *general-purpose* computers, and Mitsubishi and Oki also disappeared from the market. The three who remained were Fujitsu, Hitachi, and NEC.

Fujitsu and Hitachi followed the IBM-compatible route in their equipment. IBM-compatible refers to architecture in which IBM software-system standards are followed so that IBM software can be used with very little alteration. The two companies had cooperated on joint development of the M Series, designed for IBM software. The one manufacturer that has made a good show of producing equipment not compatible with IBM is NEC, which has a cooperative relationship with Honeywell.

In the domestic market, IBM and Fujitsu have engaged in a fierce battle for top place in the *all-purpose* computer market, with Hitachi just a step behind. IBM and the two manufacturers of IBM-compatible hardware hold a 75% market share, with NEC in pursuit of the three companies.

Of course for *general* computers, with the exception of mainframes, IBM's influence is not that great in Japan. In the field of office computers, Japanese manufacturers such as Fujitsu and NEC are in the lead. Moreover, in the personal computer field, NEC is the top manufacturer, with about 50% of the mar-

ket. IBM is doing well in computers for industrial and business use, but in the field of home computers it is not as successful.

Foreign companies generally have difficulty entering the Japanese market. For example, Apple Computer was slow in dealing with the Japanese language in its equipment, and its strategy for entering the Japanese market has been almost completely unsuccessful. Indeed, many U.S. and European manufacturers have not enjoyed the success they anticipated in Japan. The sole exception is IBM. The major reason is probably that foreign companies cannot respond quickly enough to the special needs of the Japanese market, including the incorporation of the Japanese language into software systems.

In 1986, Japan unilaterally abolished all import duties on computers and peripheral equipment, with the aim of easing trade friction. In computer bodies, there is no imbalance in Japan-U.S. trade. In the area of printers and disk drives, however, the Japanese are growing stronger and this could cause friction.

From now on, we can expect Japanese companies to manufacture locally in the U.S. and to actively promote cooperation with local companies there. For the U.S.-Japan computer industry, competition and cooperation are the key words of the future.

Communications Equipment

The liberalization of telecommunications in April 1985 has greatly changed the telecommunications market in Japan. Following the privatization of AT&T in the U.S. and British Telecom in the U.K., Japan's NTT (Nippon Telegraph and Telephone) also became a private corporation. Four telecommunications operations began in April 1986, quickly followed by many other new enterprises entering the field. A variety of businesses in new media also came to life, including VANs (value-added networks), telecommunications networks for personal computers, and videotex services, and the telecommunications market promises to continue to expand. With such market growth, major U.S. and European manufacturers of telecommunications equipment have strengthened their efforts to enter Japan, leading to fierce competition for sales with Japanese manufacturers.

NTT, which had monopolized all Japanese domestic telecommunications services, was privatized in April 1985. As compensation for relinquishing its monopoly, NTT won the right to invest, and it quickly began setting up subsidiaries. These now number more than seventy, including a VAN company that is a joint venture set up with IBM Japan, and an international-communications consulting company that was set up with general trading companies.

With 300,000 employees and annual sales of ¥5 trillion, NTT is a mammoth corporation, even by Japanese standards. Because of the great volume of equipment it procures and supplies, there has been pressure from overseas to open up the procurement system. Canada's Northern Telecom has supplied switching equipment for telephone exchanges, for example, and NTT is gradually expanding its international procurements. The company has held seminars overseas to explain procurement requirements and has called for bids. Meanwhile, more and more major U.S. and European manufacturers of telecommunications equipment have moved into Japan, with the objective of selling to NTT.

In 1986, three companies started providing telecom services—Japan Telecom, affiliated with the Japan National Railways (now Japan Railway); Teleway Japan, associated with Toyota Motors and the Japan Highway Public Corporation; and Daini Denden, associated with Kyocera—which opened commercial-use, exclusive-line service on the Tokyo-Osaka trunk route. Tokyo Telecommunications, associated with Tokyo Electric, opened the first regional telephone company, offering dedicated line service in the Tokyo metropolitan area. Other regional power companies are planning similar regional phone companies. The four new telecommunications companies plan to offer telephone services from the autumn of 1987, and NTT's share of the market seems likely to be eroded gradually. Companies are also procuring equipment made overseas, with Daini Denden introducing exchange equipment from Digital Switching of the U.S. and optical-fiber cable from Seacore.

There are also movements for new entries into the international telecommunications market. In July 1986, International Telecom Japan (ITJ) was established by Matsushita Electric Industrial. In November 1986, C. Itoh and Cable & Wireless PLC of the U.K., along with Toyota Motors, established International Digital Communications Planning. Both companies, after completing a feasibility study, aim to become operating companies in 1987 and to offer customer services from 1988.

However, the Ministry of Posts and Telecommunications, whose approval is required, has indicated that because of the size of the demand in the international telecommunications market, it will only recognize one new company in the field, and that it will not permit foreign telecommunications companies to take part in management.

With the liberalization of telecommunications,

300 new VAN companies have already appeared, and the market size is approaching ¥400 billion annually. So far, however, the service consists mostly of resale of circuits, with Recruit at the top, so full-scale use of VANs has yet to begin. There is also a growing number of commercial VANs linking retailers with wholesalers and manufacturers.

The CAPTAIN (Character and Pattern Telephone Access Information Network) videotex system, promoted primarily by NTT, finally topped 20,000 participating sets in October 1986. The reasons for slow growth are that terminals are expensive and the information offered is often not well suited to consumers' needs.

Personal-computer networks had 50,000 subscribers at the end of 1986; at present many companies provide free service, and it is expected that real expansion is just beginning.

Urban cable television has also been slow to develop, but 1987 is likely to be the year it will begin.

The use of pagers ("Pocket Bells") was also liberalized in August 1986, and new companies in this business are being created all over the country. Motorola of the U.S. has participated in the Japan Telecom group, which is planning a paging service in metropolitan Tokyo.

In the field of car telephones, liberalized at the same time, Daini Denden and Teleway Japan have shown interest. The Ministry of Posts and Telecommunications estimates that it will be necessary for the two to join forces to resist NTT effectively.

The communications equipment industry is facing hard times overall. Although liberalization has brought about an increased demand for telephones, the sudden increase in the value of the yen as well as friction over trade imbalances has meant a decrease in exports. According to a midterm production forecast put together by the Communication Industries Association of Japan, the production of communications equipment in fiscal 1986 is expected to total ¥1.8 trillion, an increase of only 2.7% over the previous year. This represents a considerable slowing compared to the increase of 8.2% the previous year. The reason is a double-digit decrease in exports, which comprise one-third of the whole.

With total production for 1990 projected at ¥2.2 trillion, the average growth rate will be 5.1% annually over a 5-year period, lower than in the past. Increasing U.S.-Japan friction over communications equipment has caused the large-scale manufacturers to expand their production abroad, and this has contributed to the slowing in domestic production. NTT procurements account for another one-third of demand, but with pressure on NTT to procure more equipment from manufacturers overseas, domestic manufacturers are facing tough times. On the other hand, it is expected that a new demand will be created when NTT opens ISDN (Integrated Services Digital Network), planned for the spring of 1988.

Konica Color 7: A Full-Color Copier
Konishiroku Photo Industry

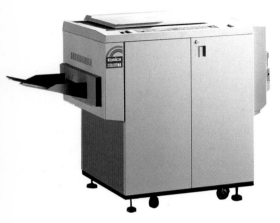

The compact Konica Color 7 copier

Developed for copy shops and businesses such as design firms and fashion houses, the Konica Color 7 combines the technologies of color photography and copy machines in a single unit to provide high-quality color copying. The Konica Color 7 differs from other color copiers first in size; it is smaller, about the size of console-type, plain-paper copiers. It also prints on thin—0.13 mm—paper, back-coated so that it does not curl. It makes three standard-sized copies and reductions and enlargements from 50% to 150%. It turns out ninety copies per hour at a cost of about ¥220 per page. The Konica Color 7 sells for ¥2.48 million.

"As a company, we are involved not only in photosensitive materials, but also in optics, mechatronics, and all types of technology. By combining all our technologies, we have confidence that we can develop products that other companies cannot copy." With those words, Megumi Ide, president of Konishiroku, appealed to his company's technicians in 1984 to begin his "special research system." Under the system, boundaries between specialized technical divisions of the company were removed so all could concentrate on the potential of Konishiroku as a whole.

The first product to emerge from the new system was the Konica Color 7. Its development team was kept small—only five technicians were selected from the fields of copiers and photosensitive materials. The leader of the project, Takao Nimura, explains: "In order to realize development in a short period of time, needless meetings were eliminated, and I insisted on having a small, select team."

An American company—3M—produced the first full-color copier in 1969. Similar products were introduced into Japan ten years ago, but failed to become popular outside specialized copy service shops and the like chiefly because print quality was poor and cost was high.

The goal of the Konica Color 7's development team was to produce high-quality color copiers at less than half the cost of earlier color copiers, which cost some ¥7–10 million. The first area investigated by the development team was instant photography such as that used in the Polaroid Instamatic. If such technology were used, a small copier could be designed. However, instant photography requires special photosensitive material, and the cost would inevitably be high.

In the end, the team worked on a method in which a positive image could be printed directly on paper, bypassing photographic negatives. Fortunately, the technology for this kind of printing had already been perfected. The Sakura Nice Print System (see p. 230), is a minilab that does not

C	±0	+4	−4	−4	+4
M	±0	−4	+4	−4	−4
Y	±0	−4	−4	+4	+4

Simple color adjustment is possible with the Konica Color 7

High-quality color images through color-photography and copy-machine technologies

ment functions and a collection system for waste solutions. The product was put on the market in June 1986, at a cost of ¥2.48 million, far lower than the price projected originally.

Six months after the Konica Color 7 hit the market, 600 machines had been sold. Konishiroku began exporting the product in the spring of 1987, and sales are projected at 30,000 units by mid-1988.

The Konica Color 7, with its high efficiency, is expected to alter the copier market significantly. It was once thought that the market was limited, but the applications of the Konica Color 7 are abundant—from color charts and graphs to prints and photographs. A photofinishing shop, for example, might offer a quick copy service for photographic prints. Even if a customer did not have a color-film negative or positive, extra copies could be made on the spot.

It is predicted that in five to ten years, half of the copy machines used in business will be full-color machines. The Konica Color 7 has also spurred competition. Other companies are beginning to use digital technologies in their development processes. That, in turn, has speeded technological development of color copiers to a breathtaking pace. As a result, both machine and copy prices are expected to drop rapidly in the future. The full-color copier is destined to become a part of everyday life in the near future.

1986 Award for Excellence

require water for development of film and photo paper, thus doing away with the need for plumbing and water-heating facilities. The system is easy to maintain, and although the process is fast and simple, it produces a high-quality print.

The most difficult problem faced in the creation of the Konica Color 7 was shortening the processing time. No matter how superior the print quality, if the process consumes too much time, the machine is not commercially viable. Color paper usually requires

eight minutes per copy. The Konica Color 7 team, employing various devices, reduced the time to four minutes.

The compact size was achieved by adopting a "slit exposure method" that allows for a machine that measures 1,087 mm in width, 650 mm in length, and 1,015 mm in height.

In April 1985, the Konica Color 7 drew large crowds at the Hannover-Messe Trade Fair in West Germany. One year later, new features were added—the reduction and enlarge-

Reprographic process: Color photographic
Copy size: A3 (297 × 420 mm), B4 (257 × 364 mm), A4 (210 × 297 mm)
Reduction/enlargement: Zoom control from 50−150% (1% increments), at 2 preset ratios
Copy paper: Special color paper/special OHP film

Family Copier FC-3: The First Home-Use Copier under ¥100,000
Canon

Copies of handmade cards

Canon's Family Copier FC-3 is the first copy machine to be priced below ¥100,000. At ¥99,800, it is a product for general home use. It can copy any size up to standard. The core of the machine, the photosensitive drum and the expendable toner, has been combined in a small cartridge, doing away with bothersome maintenance. By simply changing this cartridge, single-color copies of blue, red, green, and sepia can be made, along with the standard black. The size of the machine is 381 (W) × 415 (D) × 137 (H) mm, and it weighs 13 kg.

The Family Copier FC-3 is the first home-use copy machine priced below ¥100,000. It was first presented publicly on June 19, 1986, at the Japan Federation of Economic Organizations. At that time Canon Vice President Keizō Yamaji announced that this machine had opened a new era for the household copy machine. Canon President Ryuzaburo Kaku, sitting next to him, suddenly interrupted, saying, "And I think some day there will be one in every home."

In 1982, Canon put the ¥298,000 PC-20 on the market, making a pioneering move toward the personalization of the copy machine. Along with a low-price word processor, this product made up a campaign for miniaturized office automation. Canon placed a considerable distance between itself and competitors, who entered the field later. However, even though the PC series was for personal use, it was still limited to use by small offices and shops.

Hajime Katayama, deputy group executive of the Copier Products Group, looks back on the way he felt when starting, saying, "I thought it would be absolutely impossible." At that time, the lowest price of the new machines in the PC series was ¥248,000. In order to make machines affordable for most households it would be necessary to bring the price down below ¥100,000. It was also necessary to make a home copier portable and easy to store. Product developers only talked of the impossibilities of creating such a machine.

A unique, unified microcartridge has made a small, lightweight portable copier possible

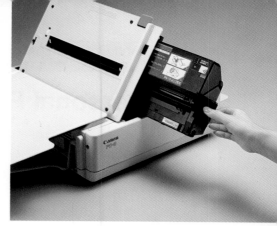
Change the cartridge for 5-tone single-color copying

Katayama discussed the matter with Hiroshi Nitanda, deputy senior general manager of the Copier Products Group, and together they came up with a plan. They established a development team primarily made up of young technicians who had been with the company for only three or four years, an unusual move since less experienced employees are rarely granted such responsibility. The reason for the decision was that people with preconceived notions of copying machines could not develop such an entirely new product.

The most difficult problem was miniaturizing the photosensitive drum, which is the very core of the copy machine. The size of a copy machine is totally dependent upon the size of its photosensitive drum, just as the size of an automobile depends on the dimensions of the engine. Thus it was decided that the diameter of the drum must be reduced to half that of standard machines, down to 3 cm. A diameter of this size means that the portion that comes into contact with

the paper is only a thin line. In order to increase the precision, the whole design underwent a complete overhaul and much thought was put into the shape of the plastic parts. Costs were literally pared away in one-yen increments.

A computer-aided-design system was used, and all parts were miniaturized and internal wiring reduced to the smallest possible proportions. As a result, the entire core portion, including the photosensitive drum, the developing sleeve, and the toner, was packed into a cartridge that is 60% smaller than that of the PC series.

The industrial team presented a number of plans for the body of the machine, but most of them were quite similar to the PC series. In the end, it decided to use the design submitted by a young woman who had only been with the company for one year. Of all the designs proposed, hers was the most innovative.

When a rival manufacturer's president heard the news of the development of the FC-3, he groaned, "That's all well and good, but can you really make a profit at such a low price?" The price of the FC-3 is less than half that of personal copy machines of the past. But Canon had great confidence in the commercial success of its new product. Not only were the number of parts reduced drastically and other design aspects specially devised, but a special unmanned cartridge-production line was created at a Canon factory.

In part due to the reduction of the market price to ¥98,000, within just half a year FC-3 sales went over the 200,000 mark. Foreign production began in the fall of 1986 in France, and

sales have already begun overseas. Katayama smiles wryly as he says, "When President Kaku said one in every home, I thought it would be more like one in every company section." But now he is full of confidence about development of the household market. He seems to have forgotten all about the difficulties over the development of the FC-3, and has even begun to assert: "The day is not far away when we will be able to sell for less than ¥100,000 a machine that is the same size as copy paper and that can print in full color as well."

1986 High Award for Excellence

Copy system: Indirect electrostatic transference system
Copy size: From A4 (210 × 297 mm) down to calling-card size
Copy magnification: 1:1
Copy paper: Conventional paper

A choice of five separate colors—black, red, blue, green, and sepia.

Spot: Personal Facsimile Machine
Toshiba

A tiny giant that offers three functions in one machine

This small, lightweight facsimile machine was developed by Toshiba for use in the places that Japan's love affair with the fax machine has not spread—small shops and offices and at home. Marketed first in August 1986, its retail price is ¥248,000, making it one of the least expensive models available using the GIII international standard. Its compact size—297 (W) × 290 (D) × 100 (H) mm—means that it takes up little space on a desktop. And Spot functions not only as a fax machine but also as a telephone and a copier. Its fashionable design has added to its popularity.

The man who became the leader of Toshiba's Spot research team, Hirohiko Takami, head of engineers in the company's Information Systems Business Department, has developed a philosophy about new products during his long research career. He feels that the proper time to market a new product is when 30% of the technicians are in favor of it and 70% are against it. If half the technicians are in agreement, it is too late for the product—compet-ing manufacturers are already at work; if only 20% of the technicians are in favor of the product, the market is not yet mature enough. In fact, 70% of Toshiba's technicians opposed the development of Spot.

The idea for a low-priced, personal facsimile machine first emerged in the summer of 1985. That year, although the annual production volume of fax machines was growing at a rate of 40%, actual revenue from sales grew only slightly. Consensus in the industry was that the only way to stimulate the market was to develop a demand for personal fax machines. At Toshiba, Takami decided to pull out all the stops and go after the personal fax-machine market.

The selling point of the new product was to be that it combined a telephone, copier, and fax machine all in one simple, inexpensive unit. When the first group of Toshiba technicians was assembled and told about the concept, they were left speechless. The company's technical team had always progressed to increasingly complicated machines, not simpler ones, and members were not excited by this 180° shift in the product concept.

One of the most stringent demands was that the new model be compact enough to fit on a desktop. This requirement dictated a height of less than 100 mm and a width and depth of less than 300 mm. A number of technicians felt the requirement was simply too severe. After a lengthy discussion, Takami submitted a counterproposal. He accepted the argument from one technician that it would be impossible to get all the working parts into one box. Instead he proposed that the parts that could not be placed inside a box of the stated dimensions could be separate from the main unit. The idea was that protruding parts could be placed in a separate case under the desk and the compact main body would sit atop it.

Behind this counterproposal lay Takami's experience gained through countless development projects. If a research team is given too difficult a target, Takami knew, it will rebel. A compromise that sets a more realistic target will be accepted, and the team will soon begin development. In the end, however, an engineer will remain dissatisfied with the easier goal, and will instead forge ahead toward the more difficult target, the one presented first. This was always the way with past development projects, and the result was the same with Spot.

At first, technicians decided to put the power supply outside the main body of the machine. By piling idea on ingenious idea they arrived at a plan for incorporating the power supply in the main unit. Takami will never forget the embarrassed-but-proud face of the engineer who came to his office to tell him of the newest plan. The engineer was the same person who had insisted stubbornly that it could never be done.

After the power supply difficulty was solved, one other problem remained. A fax machine "reads" information using a fluorescent lamp; the reflected light is used to detect portions of the document that are white and portions that are black. The fluo-rescent lamp has connectors on each end from which no light issues. This means that a lamp with a total length of 32 cm is needed to read a document that is 30 cm wide. One way to reduce the lamp length to 30 cm is to change the shape of the bulb and bend the connector section. But such a change would add ¥200 million to the cost of developing the product. Would the team still insist on a finished width of 30 cm? Engineers were caught between the strain of staying at 30 cm and saving ¥200 million.

However, relevant research had already been done into a rare-gas-discharge tube having a diameter of only 7 mm. How about using this tube for the light source rather than a fluorescent one? When this idea emerged one day, Takami and his team immediately jumped at it.

Adding a telephone to the unit was also difficult, but Takami already had some experience with integrating the phone and the fax. This experience helped the team in its efforts to develop the technology to combine both functions in a single LSI circuit.

Ten years ago, a facsimile machine with so many functions would have been the size of a refrigerator and priced at ¥10 million. Spot is about the size of a compact typewriter and costs only ¥248,000. It is one of the fruits of the amazing progress in electronics.

1986 Award for Excellence

Manuscript width: Max. 216 mm
Recording paper size: 210 mm × 30 m roll
 paper
Printer type: Thermal printing (fixed flatbed)
Size: 297 (W) × 290 (D) × 100 (H) mm;
 wt: approx. 4.5 kg

Sending, receiving, and copying; in the office, in the shop, and at home

MELCOM PSI: Artificial-Intelligence Workstation
Mitsubishi Electric

In the kitchen...

The Structure of AI

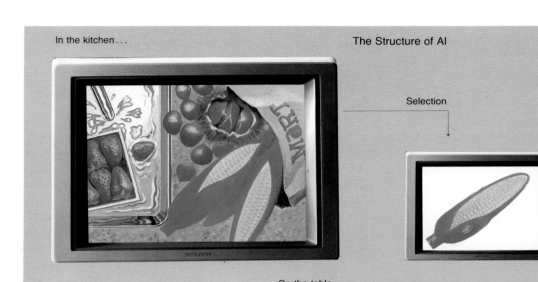

Selection

The beginning of deduction

In the kitchen, there are many kinds of ingredients that can be eaten. Some of them require some sort of processing, and others can be eaten as they are. For the purpose of this example, let's look at corn.

On the table...

From general to specific

On the table, there are many things to eat that have been made from the ingredients in the kitchen. Let's think about popcorn. The non-AI type of computer cannot examine the result, popcorn, and deduce where it came from.

The MELCOM PSI is an artificial-intelligence (AI) computer developed by Mitsubishi Electric through its participation in the Institute for New Generation Computer Technology (ICOT), a joint government–private enterprise project developing a fifth-generation computer. The concept of a fifth-generation computer is to link in a parallel configuration hundreds or thousands of CPUs—central processing units, the brains of a computer—to approximate human thought processes at computer speeds. The MELCOM PSI is not a final but an interim product, designed for functions such as medical diagnosis. It uses sequential processing like current computers, rather than parallel processing. Still, it is attracting attention as the first computer in the world using the AI programming language PROLOG. Over 120 units have been sold.

In 1982, ICOT initiated a project for the development of a fifth-generation computer. At start-up hearings, participating companies proposed numerous themes for developing the fifth-generation computer—reasoning functions, knowledge data bases, AI programming languages, and parallel-processing functions. Each of the companies—general-purpose computer manufacturers such as Fujitsu, Hitachi, and NEC—was put in charge of one of these core elements.

Mitsubishi Electric, a participant in the project, decided to produce a pilot machine quickly with a good chance of realization. Although Oki Electric also took part in the development of the PSI, Mitsubishi Electric was the first to put it on the market,

The world's first commercial PROLOG machine

under the MELCOM trademark.

The road to development was not an easy one. In 1982, the only AI computer was DEC's 2060 minicomputer. Only a handful of frontline researchers in Japan knew PROLOG. Fortunately for Mitsubishi Electric, it had technicians at its Information Electronics Research Institute in Ōfuna, Kanagawa prefecture, who knew PROLOG.

Mitsubishi Electric produced in the MELCOM PSI an intermediate product, not a final one—a machine to support the development of a parallel-processing computer. Still, the company's researchers assigned to the ICOT project decided that if they were to produce a machine, it would be one of high reliability.

High reliability means a minimum of software bugs and virtually no hardware malfunctions. To achieve this goal, the computer must have much in reserve in its hardware structure, input/output structure, and cache memory. If the machine was to be a commercial product, it had to provide a great number of functions that are unnecessary. However, both Mitsubishi Electric and Oki agreed that functions had to come ahead of profit-

ability. Actual development began in May 1983.

Mitsubishi Electric and Oki were the first to use the 256-Kbit DRAM chip, which provided the largest memory capacity available at the time. Mitsubishi Electric developed the basic structure for AI processing by deriving it from tagged architecture. The high-speed processing technology was made possible by writing the system programs in PROLOG, which has built-in unification and guessing functions that are essential for AI.

The first hurdle encountered was the computer's operating system (OS), the intermediary between software, in which human commands are entered, and actual computer processing. A whole range of problems emerged: how to compare and sort data entering the OS; how to control the CPU and the memory; and how to link peripheral equipment such as display units and keyboards.

There were additional problems, too. Chips received from a U.S. semiconductor manufacturer did not meet specifications. Nobody knew methods of debugging or how to predict processing speed.

Mitsubishi Electric threw all of its twenty-five ICOT researchers into the project and conquered the uncharted territory. The pilot machine was deliv-

ered to ICOT on December 24, 1983, just in time to fulfill the company's commitment to produce the computer by the end of the year. Red-eyed from lack of sleep, the researchers came together to cut the tape and celebrate a particularly joyous Christmas Eve.

But development continues. At the moment, work is proceeding on a smaller AI processor using PROLOG. By using a 1-Mbit DRAM, Mitsubishi Electric hopes to produce a machine a quarter of the size and three times the speed of the present model. The final target remains a parallel-processing computer, so the company is trying to link PSIs in parallel. By mid-1988, it plans to develop a multi-PSI linking a maximum of sixty-four units.

Researchers all insist that there is nothing difficult about AI. In the past, people have had to learn to operate computers. With AI computers, people with no knowledge of the machines can still carry out sophisticated knowledge processing.

Interest in the ICOT initiative is not confined to Japan. European and American researchers are also paying careful attention. Since the MELCOM PSI is the first commercial product to come out of ICOT, it has excited much more interest than a new computer ordinarily does. Mitsubishi Electric, which does not manufacture its own general-purpose computer, is pushing the MELCOM PSI aggressively to battle the big manufacturers.

1986 Award for Excellence

Language: Extended self-contained PROLOG
    (ESP)
CPU: Control system: Microprogram system
    (64 bit/word)
    Machine cycle: 200 ns
    Data breadth: 40 bits (data, 32 bits; tag,
    8 bits)
    Cache: 40 bits × 4 kw × 2 sets
Main memory: Capacity—Basic, 20 Mbit;
    Max., 80 Mbit

In the field...

From specific to general

An AI computer, however, is able to examine popcorn and, based upon a knowledge base that tells it that popcorn is made of corn itself, go on to induce that popcorn comes from a cornfield.

SOFTWARE FOR COMMERCIAL USE

TRENDS IN THE 1980s

Due to intense foreign competition on its own turf, the Japanese software industry is growing in both sophistication and size.

With the rapid appreciation of the Japanese yen, major U.S. personal-computer software companies are rushing to enter the Japanese market. MicroSoft, the world's largest producer of operating systems (OS) for personal computers, terminated its long cooperation with Japan's ASCII and established its own wholly owned Japanese firm. Lotus Development, which has shown rapid growth through sales of integrated software, established its own Japanese subsidiary and directly entered the market with the release of the Japanese-language version of its U.S. best-seller, 1-2-3. Following on the heels of Lotus Development, Ashton-Tate has formed a joint venture with Japan Systems Engineering to establish Nippon Ashton-Tate.

Software is one area in which Japan has a negative trade balance. The rush by major American companies to enter the Japanese market is expected to increase this imbalance and should have a favorable though small effect on the U.S.-Japan trade picture. Furthermore, the Japanese software industry will suffer as more and more advanced U.S. software enters Japan. Japanese companies will be eliminated from the picture unless they improve their skills and take the user into account more by making more user-friendly products. The appreciation of the yen will serve as a test for the Japanese software industry to improve its capabilities. The fact that the high yen has made sales in Japan lucrative is not the only reason U.S. companies are rushing into the Japanese market. The main domestic personal-computer manufacturers, which had developed their own lines, are now changing to IBM compatibility, and this has made the Japanese market still more attractive to U.S. manufacturers. MicroSoft, Lotus Development, and Ashton-Tate are all companies that have concentrated on developing software for IBM personal computers. Their market share steadily increased as the oligopoly of IBM and IBM compatibles was established. With the exception of mainframes, the non-IBM-compatibility posture of Japanese manufacturers had caused these companies to hesitate to enter the Japanese market, but the appreciation of the yen and shift to IBM compatibility has spurred them into action.

What changes in the Japanese software industry will result from this entry of American firms? The first thing that comes to mind is the creation of an environment favoring the production of high-quality products. The major U.S. software development firms do not produce software in the same haphazard manner as Japanese companies. On the average, they complete only two or three fully developed products each year for market release. In contrast, Japanese software development companies tend to create ten or more products each year. Although some of these are good products, this is, on the whole, mass production of inferior goods and leaves users dissatisfied.

American software is still affected by the language barrier, but its user-friendliness should set an example for Japanese products. The majority of Japanese companies prefer to develop their own software, and this tendency has limited the improvement of commercial software in Japan. In the U.S., on the other hand, rather than investing the time and money to develop their own software, companies tend to purchase high-quality commercially available software. High-quality commercial software packages appear one after the other due to this great demand.

It is, however, premature to conclude that Japanese companies are suffering from the strong yen. Some have taken advantage of their new purchasing power to establish overseas divisions. Mitsubishi Electric has founded a software development company in the U.S. and others have bought American firms. This avenue cannot be ignored, as the appreciation of the yen has made personnel costs in the U.S. easy to manage. The idea is to purchase a software development company in the U.S., a country with many excellent programmers, and export the completed software to Japan. At this moment, the U.S. software industry is undergoing an unprecedented merger-and-acquisition boom. According to a survey by the American Data Processing and Service Industry Federation, there are over 200 mergers and acquisitions in the U.S. software industry every year. American companies are coming to Japan and Japanese companies are going to the U.S.

It has been less than ten years since the emergence of the Japanese personal-computer industry. Although it is still in its infancy, the appreciation of the yen since last year should help it mature, change the business structure, and lead to a new level of progress.

In comparison with personal-computer software, the amount of package software for mainframe computers is extremely low. As many companies wish to differentiate themselves from their competitors, the tendency is to create their own software. With the exception of software sold by computer manufacturers, there have been almost no "national brand" packages that have been successful.

Many reasons for this can be imagined, but the most persuasive explanation can be found in the nature of the Japanese software industry. The primary business of software development companies, called "software houses," has been to dispatch personnel to computer manufacturers and user firms. In terms of technical expertise, the manufacturers and users are considerably more skilled than the personnel dispatched from the software houses, who serve only as helpers. Their work consists mainly of simple coding, nothing that could be called intellectual work.

This does nothing to improve the skills of the software houses. Many companies also leave the job of educating technicians to the computer manufacturers. These companies could best be called "body shops." In the end, the responsibility for software development lies with the computer manufacturer or the system development section of the user. The software houses lack both the initiative and capabilities.

However, over the last two or three years, signs of a change in this situation have begun to appear. Powerful software companies with considerable technical expertise have emerged. These include companies such as Intec, Toyo Information Systems (a member of the Sanwa Bank group), and Nomura Computer Systems (a subsidiary of Nomura Securities).

The Worker Dispatching Law implemented in 1985 has had a major impact. This law protects the rights of technicians dispatched to manufacturers and users, and places the burden of responsibility for transferred staff on the receiving companies. Although this officially sanctions the dispatch of workers, which up to now had been illegal, the number of dispatched workers has actually decreased since the law was implemented. This is because the users do not want to take the burden of responsibility for the personnel they use and have been more cautious in the use of dispatched technicians. In order to survive, companies that have grown by dispatching personnel have been forced to accept orders for software development on a contract basis, whether they like it or not.

Awareness on the part of the users has also changed in subtle ways. Some EDP (electronic-data-processing) sections of Japanese companies have a backlog of

three years' work in software development. They are no longer able to meet all of their deadlines with custom-made software. Added to this is the problem of the strong yen. For companies engaged in export, reducing expenses is of supreme importance. These companies are increasingly willing to use package software if the cost is low and the functions standard or better.

According to a survey of computer users conducted by the financial newspaper *Nihon Keizai Shimbun*, a total of 463 companies were using 1,288 different types of package software in 1986. The leader is Fujitsu's data-base software AIM, followed by such packages as IBM's CICS, IMS, and DL-1, and Pansophic System's Easy Trieve.

Software that sells in Japan is limited to system software, data-base-management software, and fourth-generation languages. Very little application software sells. Even software that is highly successful abroad has a hard time gaining popularity in Japan due to the differences between the administrative processing system in Japan and that in the U.S. and Europe. Foreign software has to be adjusted to handle the difficult Chinese character (*kanji*) writing system. This has become an impediment to the spread of U.S.-made application software. The tendency to buy system software as a package and add custom-made applications is expected to continue for some time.

Although the relative importance of package software has increased slightly, orders from ordinary companies for the creation of systems still account for most sales. Recently, however, software companies aiming at developing high-value-added business have emerged. These companies act as both system consultants and top-class professional services suppliers. According to one survey, three or four years ago the number of system engineers able to provide this kind of service was 300, but this figure has recently risen to almost 1,000.

There is a great demand for these engineers. The larger the company, the greater the desire for professional services that can find deadwood in the information systems and check whether the efficiency of the equipment has decreased. Industry sources state that such jobs are increasing at an annual rate of 30—40%.

Up to now, the Japanese data-processing industry has been led by computer manufacturers such as Fujitsu, NEC, and Hitachi. On the other hand, the software industry has been created by people leaving the EDP departments of ordinary firms. In this sense, it has been an industry dominated by venture business, but the role of the computer manufacturers has become larger. This is because the various computer makers have begun to establish software subsidiaries nationwide.

For example, as of March 1987, Fujitsu had created a total of fifty-four software companies from Hokkaido in the north to Okinawa in the south. NEC has done much the same. As of March 1986, it had established twenty-one software subsidiaries. Hitachi had twenty-five subsidiaries as of March 1987. They are all engaged in application software development and servicing for users of the parent company's computers, and they also handle part of the development of operating systems for the main company. These companies attract outstanding Japanese students and in ten years are expected to possess considerable development capabilities.

Not only are computer manufacturers getting into the software industry, but companies representing some of the main industries in Japan—steel, shipbuilding, shipping, and electrical power—are estab-lishing many software subsidiaries. The objective is to have these firms participate in the software industry for the parent company. Up to now there have been approximately twenty software companies with annual sales of over ¥10 billion, but these software subsidiaries are aiming at sales in the ¥10 billion range within five or six years after establishment. The Japanese software industry is now entering a period of qualitative changes.

According to MITI, the sales of the software industry total ¥1.6 trillion. This is increasing at an annual rate of nearly 20%, making the industry one of the few growing industries in Japan at present. MITI also has a policy of giving priority to its development. Software is sure to become one of Japan's basic industries after steel, automobiles, and home electrical appliances.

Tontarō: Personal-Computer Software for Hog Raising
Nihon Nosan Kogyo

Tontarō is a personal-computer software package that supports the activities of a hog-raising farm. The scale of management in the Japanese agricultural and livestock industries is small, and thus Japan's use of the computer lags behind that in the advanced livestock nations of Europe and the U.S. Tontarō has received high acclaim as the first full-fledged personal-computer software system that provides the functions needed for effective hog-raising management. When first released in May 1986, sales of 500 sets were predicted for the first two years, but this target was reached in under a year.

Nihon Nosan Kogyo first introduced its NALC (Nosan Analysis of Livestock Control) to the market in 1974. That system used a mainframe computer for user management and administration diagnosis. Nihon Nosan Kogyo had a long record of furnishing computers to the livestock industry. The company is still operating NALC, but the system lacks flexibility due to use of the batch-processing method. The new age demands a personal-computer package that allows users to perform day-to-day jobs such as the creation of daily work schedules and calculations of earnings.

Almost five years were needed for development of this product. In addition to studying European systems, the company repeatedly carried out on-site testing by supplying prototypes to farms purchasing its feed.

The Tontarō package consists of three systems: a production control system for individual hogs and their shipments; an accounting control system for calculation of such cash-flow characteristics as profits and losses; and a management control system, which allows overall management diagnosis. Of these, the production control system has won acclaim for its ability to select and monitor sows with good breeding performance.

The manager spends about thirty minutes each day entering information such as "This sow gave birth." On the basis of this information, the market date for both carcasses and live pigs is immediately calculated separately for boars and sows and becomes important information for mating. The program contains many useful functions, including the calling up of color displays of such information as weekly job schedules and sow-breeding cycles at a single command.

The accounting control system is a special package developed by a group of CPAs and modified for hog raising. It uses the personal computer to automatically calculate and print out revenues and disbursements and a statement of accounts. It is also equipped with an automatic journal function. Another of its features is the use of many "expert systems" elements. Based upon the entered data, the computer decides what operation is to be made next, indicates this to the opera-

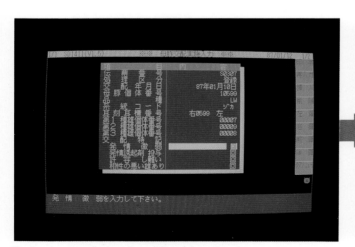

The input screen displays the mother pig's mating data

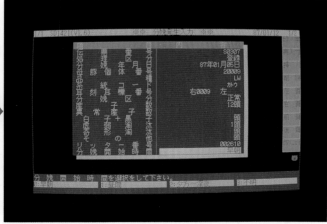

Delivery data such as date of birth and number of piglets in a litter

tor, and draws up a schedule.

Many managers of livestock farms have no experience with computers. Shigeru Tahara, the head of Nihon Nosan Kogyo's Technical Information Section and the person responsible for Tontarō's development, recalls the difficulties in making the operation of the package as accessible as possible to these people. In principle, operation is carried out only with the numeric keys and function keys, to make it as simple as possible. Tontarō also runs on NEC's popular PC-9800 series of personal computers. Nihon Nosan Kogyo received the cooperation of NEC during the development of its software.

The cost of introducing Tontarō into a system depends upon the scale of management desired, but the monthly lease for both software and hardware ranges between ¥35,000 and ¥55,000, with a five-year contract. As an advertising slogan says, Tontarō is "cheaper than hiring another person, and does the work of several!"

For postpurchase servicing, the customer can turn to the branch offices of Nihon Nosan Kogyo; the company itself relies upon the cooperation of NEC service centers. The staff at Nihon Nosan Kogyo feels that this is the ideal situation, as the combination of a feed company inexperienced in the personal-computer field and NEC inspires trust.

In the near future, the company is planning to join the personal-computer communications service run by NEC (PC-VAN) in order to supply users with meat-market and other industry information—currently obtainable only through the company magazine.

A livestock farm is always paying attention to the commodities market and making production plans based on various predictions. In the not-too-distant future, there will be personal computers on almost all major livestock farms, and farmers will create management strategy by working at a terminal.

Nihon Nosan Kogyo has received inquiries from members of the livestock industries in Taiwan, Thailand, and the People's Republic of China, and has started work on the development of an export version of the Tontarō software package. The company is also planning to develop management-software systems for poultry and dairy farming as well, and the president, who named the hog-raising package Tontarō (lit., "Pig-boy"), is playfully pondering the idea of giving them names like Keiko ("Chickie-girl") and Gyūjirō ("Cow-boy"). It is his intention to create an entire "family" of livestock-management software for personal computers.

1986 Award for Excellence

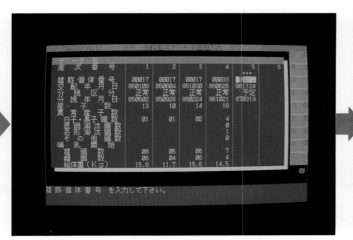

All data, including total weight of litter, can be viewed at once

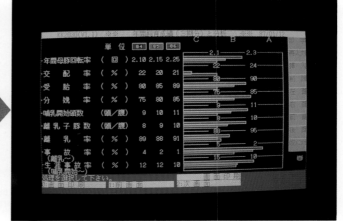

All annual data can be processed and displayed

141

Super-BRAINS: An Expert-System Construction Tool
Toyo Information Systems

This software system allows easy construction of expert systems. Written in LISP, it is equipped with three inference engines—classification-type inference, production-type inference, and frame-type inference—and can be used in a wide range of applications, such as investment consulting, analysis of oil-field test drilling, and diagnosis of malfunctions. In addition, it has won the support of users, as it allows the Japanese language to be used in all stages, from descriptions of the knowledge base to indication of inference results. It is available not only for LISP machines but also for various computer types, from mainframes to minicomputers.

The escape of radiation from the No. 2 reactor of the Three Mile Island nuclear power plant in Goldsburg, Pennsylvania, on March 28, 1979, shocked the entire world. More serious than the fact that a nuclear power plant equipped with the latest technology was not safe was the clear evidence that, despite the existence of numerous instruments to indicate malfunctions, the decisions of the human operators were incorrect—such as shutting down the emergency core-cooling device designed to cool down the reaction chamber in just such situations. No matter how much precision equipment there is, if the operators panic, accidents will occur. As a result, the Japan Nuclear Power Research Center (JNPRC) began to worry about how to ensure the safe generation of nuclear power.

Only a few days after the Three Mile Island accident, the technical staff of Toyo Information Systems (TIS) came up with the idea of applying an accident-diagnosing system to the problem by using artificial intelligence (AI), an area then gaining attention at the academic level. The team immediately drew up an estimate and submitted a proposal to the JNPRC.

From the start, the response from the JNPRC was not very promising. In fact, the JNPRC practically laughed at the idea. However, a few middle-level TIS engineers such as Jiro Okada and Minoru Yamamoto persistently repeated their explanations of the potential of AI. They stressed that this was not a half-baked idea and that the pace of practical applications for AI had increased dramatically. As a result of their efforts, TIS received an order in 1982 from the JNPRC for the development of an accident-diagnosing system.

TIS's involvement in the AI business began at this time. The first expert-system construction tool, BRAINS, was based on the system developed for the JNPRC. This was a framework of the accident-diagnosing system, having no actual knowledge programmed into the knowledge base.

TIS was certainly blessed with good timing. It had planned to use the main AI language, LISP, for expert-system development, but at the time LISP was not a very efficient language, and it

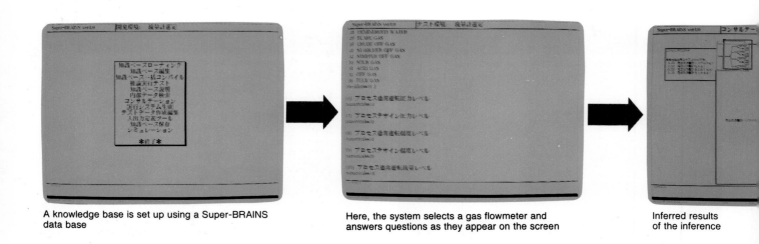

A knowledge base is set up using a Super-BRAINS data base

Here, the system selects a gas flowmeter and answers questions as they appear on the screen

Inferred results of the inference

enjoyed use only at university research facilities. However, just then Professor Wada of the Mathematical Engineering and Information Physics Department of the University of Tokyo's Faculty of Engineering completed his work on UTI LISP. This version of LISP is fast and requires less memory than previous versions. In addition, Wada's work revealed the details of UTI LISP and allowed its business use at no charge.

TIS was also lucky in that the cost of the necessary hardware decreased. A main memory of at least 1 Mbyte was needed to run BRAINS, and the cheaper cost of the memory units made it easy for users to have the required amount of memory.

BRAINS became Japan's first expert-system construction tool. When it was released in 1984, the concept of AI had not yet come into common knowledge and was difficult to comprehend. Difficult to explain without actual examples of what it could do, the system was very hard to market.

However, as AI became more popular, BRAINS began to sell. JGC used it for an instrument-selection system for oil refineries; Idemitsu, for a malfunction-diagnosing system for petrochemical plants; Ohbayashi, as an expert system for retrieval of architectural statutes; and Tokyo Gas, for a malfunction-diagnosing system for an automatic control mechanism for fire engines.

Almost two years were required for the development of Super-BRAINS. The biggest stumbling block was to create a general-purpose system. Super-BRAINS was released in 1986 as a more complete version of BRAINS, which only encompassed classification-type inference, limiting it to tasks such as malfunction diagnosis. Incorporating the requirements of users, TIS added production-type and frame-type inference engines. These allow for the construction of other application systems such as investment counseling. Sanwa Bank's investment-counseling system was made possible by Super-BRAINS.

An expert-system construction tool can be used for various purposes by rewriting the knowledge base. As the way of describing the knowledge base varies from person to person, the tool must be able to handle these differences. TIS imagined various knowledge-base types and stayed in the cycle of testing-debugging-executing for an extended period. This work could not be neglected, for if the system failed to operate properly a major accident might result. BRAINS and Super-BRAINS have been purchased by almost 120 companies in Japan. It is hoped that knowledge engineers with superior skills will emerge to create effective practical systems using these tools.

1986 Award for Excellence

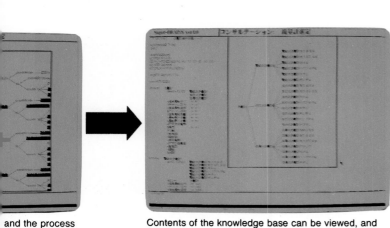

and the process can be displayed

Contents of the knowledge base can be viewed, and the conclusion process can be verified

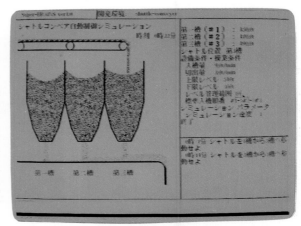

It is also possible to express combinations of as many as 3 types of frame or production inferences; in this manner, inferences can be continued while displaying simulations on the screen

Pharaoh: Multicapability Personal-Computer Software
Val Laboratory

Pharaoh is a comprehensive software package that has a number of capabilities including word processing, data-base management, search, and graph making. While in the process of making up a report, sales data can be calculated, made into a graph, and inserted into the text. Aside from greatly increasing the number of files, the power of the word-processing capability has been strengthened compared to older versions. Development of Pharaoh was initiated in 1985, and in May 1986 it was put on sale. It can be used with NEC's popular PC-9800 series and the IBM Japan Multistation 5550 series. Its retail price is ¥150,000.

Development Department Chief Takashi Okamura, who was responsible for the development of Pharaoh, says: "In its development, we placed the greatest emphasis on ease of use. Users of business software are not always engineers who are well versed in personal computers and other types of computers. In fact, most operators are office workers in charge of daily business operation and other ordinary company functions. Most likely, there are many who use computers only once a week, and maybe even some who use them only once a month. We must make it easier for them, so that they can feel comfortable using our software only occasionally."

One of the aspects devised for Pharaoh was the creation of a method for conversing with the screen. When using most kinds of software, the user has to wrestle with an unintelligible manual. But with Pharaoh all the user has to do is to act in accordance with the instructions on the screen. And user choices based on these instructions—except text—can be input with a mouse. This completely does away with the keyboard allergy that seems deeply rooted in Japanese users.

In addition, the entire range of software capabilities has been made easy for the user to grasp. Pharaoh has a variety of capabilities, including word processing, data-base management, and search. It can also perform a whole string of different types of work without stopping to change disks. However, the user must completely familiarize himself with the various functions it possesses. Okamura says, "Our greatest efforts went into making sure that the functions would be placed where the user expects them to be."

The experience gained in the development of the comprehensive software package Papyrus in 1984 was extremely helpful in the development of Pharaoh. More than 1,000 suggestions from users were received concerning Papyrus. The company divided them

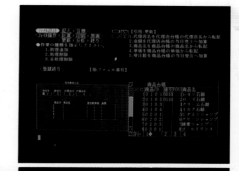

Pharaoh can carry out a broad variety of business processing on a personal computer that had to be done before on more sophisticated office computers; by inputting orders, advancement of any file specified can be carried out

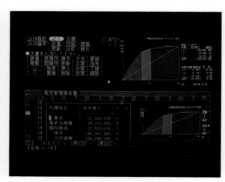

The greatest advantage in the processing of data on a personal computer is the fact that this sort of data can be made into graphs or written up in sentences quickly

Many devices have been provided to assist in the preparation of the user's environment; some of these are ruled lines for the structuring of the readout screen, and selection of the color that is easiest for the individual to read

into 300 categories that were then used as guidelines in the development of Pharaoh. Demands of the users concerning such details as the conversion of *hiragana* syllabary to *kanji* and the display of graphics were incorporated into Pharaoh.

Even those unfamiliar with personal computers can use Pharaoh with ease. This is the major attraction of Pharaoh, whose features have been improved in Pharaoh V, developed in the fall of 1986. This latter software is made in such a way that a personal computer fitted with it can be used as a minicomputer on-line terminal. This permits the average user to operate a DEC VAX minicomputer, previously accessible only to a technician with a great deal of knowledge of computers.

The development of telecommunications networks within Japanese enterprises is proceeding at a fast pace. This is highly significant, since a company can then quickly collect sales data that is scattered throughout the nation, analyze that data, and speedily communicate the results back to all parts of the nation.

For example, a large computer installed in a main office is linked by means of telecommunications circuits to minicomputers in branch offices and personal computers installed in local sales offices operated by those branch offices. In some cases, the local sales offices may have to process the data, operating the minicomputers through personal computers. It is costly and is illogical for the branch office engineers to listen to each and every demand from the individual local sales offices and process that data by themselves.

Pharaoh V can be very useful in operating minicomputers by using both a mouse and a conversation-with-the-screen format. Val Laboratory is convinced that this mode of operation will become increasingly popular in the near future.

Since Pharaoh was put on the market, it has sold 5,000 units, and appears likely to even outstrip Papyrus. High sales expectations derive from the fact that there is a large changeover demand from users of Papyrus. But Pharaoh is not entirely problem-free. Considered in light of the fact that the present memory capacity of a floppy disk is only 1.2 Mbytes, it is clear that this was inevitable.

Since its inception in 1976, the company's goal has been to create a sophisticated computer language that would be easy to use. At first, it concentrated mainly on consignment development of normal large-computer software. However, since the 1980s it has entered the field of personal-computer software. The main purpose behind developments up to and including Papyrus and Pharaoh has again been simplicity of use.

The president of the company calls their work "end-user computering." Key to this is limiting the number of engineers involved in software development, and designing the program so that the users can do as much of the work as possible. The age when the computer is no longer the property of a few engineers is at hand.

1986 Award for Excellence

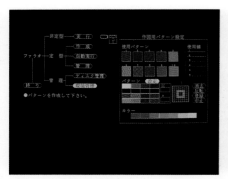

Not only the color of the diagram, but also the pattern of the diagram can be changed according to the user's wishes

With the internal clock, the user can find out how much time it has taken him to do his work; here we see that a certain type of work took 1 minute and 2 seconds to complete; even such detailed calculations as how much time it takes to process 100 bills can be computed

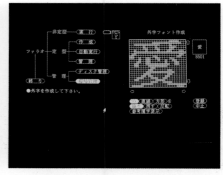

Ordinarily used Chinese characters number around 7,000, but there are more than 50,000 in existence; it is also possible to create characters that are not in the data banks for names of people and places

1-2-3 Release 2J: Financial Software for Personal Computers
Lotus Development Japan

1-2-3 Release 2J (abbreviated as 1-2-3 2J) is the Japanese version of Lotus 1-2-3, a financial software package whose sales have exceeded 2 million units in the United States and Europe.

Up to now, most of the Japanese-language software produced in the U.S. has remained simply a translation of the English-language version. However, this product was redeveloped from the English version in order to afford easy operation for the Japanese user and to stand out among already-established competitive products. It retails for ¥98,000.

1-2-3 2J was a long-awaited product. The English version has been available in Japan since January 1983, and the development of the Japanese version (Release 2J) started in the early summer of 1985. After a one-year development period, the product went on sale in September 1986.

Spreadsheet software is often explained as a collection of forms spread out in the personal computer. The original features are not only the convenience of crosswise calculation, but also the ability to recalculate automatically after data has been changed. Furthermore, the screen can rapidly display changes such as sorting, moving, duplicating, adding new columns and lines, and so forth, which would otherwise have to be done by hand.

Before 1-2-3 was available, there were several types of financial software on the market with these functions. They had all become big hits. The powerful 1-2-3 software was developed from a review of the software already available on the market. It is a synthetic software with not only a spreadsheet function, but data-base and graphics functions as well.

In the U.S., financial software packages are used mainly by executives in making decisions regarding data compilation and simulation. Eventually, their use became widespread among businessmen aspiring to become executives. In Japan, many young businessmen in the fields of research and development, financing, and manufacturing are using this software. In order to compensate for the difference in the two markets and to overcome the competition, since it was late in entering the market, 1-2-3 2J was developed with emphasis on making it appear as if a Japanese firm had produced it, and on making it in essence as Japanese as possible; it became, ultimately, a very Japanese software package.

The following three points were important in producing the Japanese version of 1-2-3.

First, it is in Japanese. 1-2-3 2J was developed after inspecting more than ten existing financial software packages on the Japanese market, and suitable translations of terms were selected.

Second, it is easy to operate. The most difficult aspect of producing the

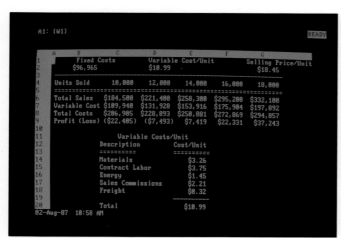

The 1-2-3 English readout—a 12-in color display

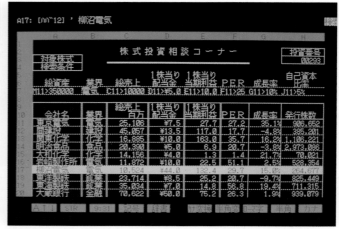

The 1-2-3 Release 2J screen—ruled lines is one of its unique characteristics; it has a 14-in color display

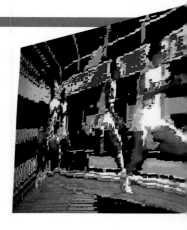

Japanese version was simplifying a software system that could make every aspect of using *kanji* (Chinese characters) easier. One of the reasons that the Japanese have had an aversion to using personal computers is that *kanji* have been very difficult to input from the keyboard. It is also very difficult to read a screen that does not use *kanji*. However, it would be useless to use the system if the process of inputting and displaying *kanji* were too difficult. Therefore, many hours were spent in solving this dilemma.

Finally, it is aesthetically very pleasing. This is one of the most important aspects of 1-2-3 2J. Japanese personal-computer displays are predominantly color displays. Japanese feel that for the same price they would like to see a beautiful screen, although this sometimes conflicts with functionality. Consequently, even business software must have this feature. Also, it has been pointed out that there are completely different sensibilities between Japan

and the West concerning documentation charts. Japanese tend to prefer charts with lines.

One of the main issues in producing the Japanese version of 1-2-3 was how to create software that could accommodate cultural differences as well as afford easy viewing. These points were selected as a result of extensive research conducted throughout its development. The product was continuously tested by many people, including those familiar with personal computers and others who knew nothing at all about them; also, prospective users were asked to evaluate the software. Consequently, the success of 1-2-3 2J lies in allowing consumers to test the product, which is unlike most manufacturers' policies of keeping products strictly confidential. The result is a software system designed with the users' specific needs in mind.

The Japanese version of 1-2-3 has many functions not found in the original U.S. version. For that reason, 1-2-3

2J was translated back into English and is now being exported to the rest of the Far East.

The success of 1-2-3 2J presents a new solution to the transplantation of software, and this is a new discovery in the field of personal computers. The success of 1-2-3 2J will be thought of as a turning point for personal computers used in business in Japan, and the market will probably expand greatly because of it.

*1986 Special Award
(International Division)*

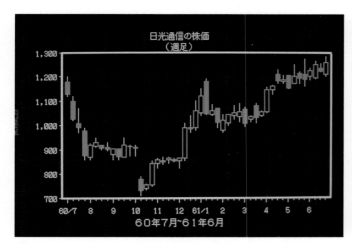

It is easy to create even such complicated graphs as this one, which expresses changes in stock prices

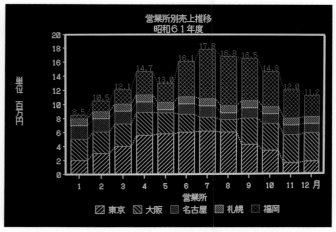

Display colors of bar graphs and width of scales can be changed freely

ELECTRONIC AND MEDICAL ELECTRONIC DEVICES

TRENDS IN THE 1980s

Japan rules the world of general electronics products. It is now making a bid to dominate the semiconductor market. —— Electronic Devices

The world of ME equipment was once the domain of the U.S. and Europe. Japan aims to change all that. —— Medical Electronic Devices

Electronic Devices

Because integrated circuits were first developed in the U.S., participants in the ISSCC (International Solid State Circuits Conference), including companies and research institutes, have until recently been exclusively American. In the past few years, however, the number of Japanese reports filed at that conference has increased dramatically, and in 1985 actually surpassed the American total. Since all reports are evaluated and approved beforehand by experts in the field, the merit of these presentations is unquestionable.

In 1986, NEC and Toshiba gave papers on the 4-Mbit DRAM, the latest breakthrough in VLSI technology. Only one American company, Texas Instruments, has made a contribution in this field. All three companies have succeeded in placing some 9 million transistors and other elements on a 1-cm^2 silicon substrate. The width of a single circuit is between 0.8 and 1.0 μm. Just one of these VLSIs, which are at present the most advanced commercialized technology available, can do the work of four 1-Mbit DRAM chips. It can hold approximately 260,000 Chinese characters in its memory, or about sixteen newspaper pages. In actual use, all the information contained on one or two floppy disks could be entered into a single 4-Mbit DRAM chip for faster data processing. Such a chip also has important applications in improving the pause and slow-motion functions in VCRs, which presently employ magnetic heads.

The 256-Kbit DRAM chips that now form the bulk of ISSCC presentations made their appearance in 1980. Four years later the 1-Mbit DRAM made its debut. It took only two more years for the 4-Mbit DRAM to appear, and there is no predicting how far miniaturization will go. The semiconductor industry is fiercely competitive, and only those companies that can sustain continuous technological innovation will survive. In Japan, companies such as Hitachi, Fujitsu, Mitsubishi Electric, and Matsushita Electric Industrial are all aiming to commercialize 4-Mbit DRAM technology.

In contrast, no likely manufacturers of 4-Mbit DRAM chips other than Texas Instruments can be found in the U.S., although IBM and AT&T both have active development programs keyed to in-company applications. Texas Instruments itself has announced that mass production of its new chips will be the responsibility of Japanese factories, and it seems likely that Japan will continue to lead in the production of VLSI memory cells as well. While South Korean manufacturers have recently entered the semiconductor field, they have as of 1987 only reached the stage of commercializing the 1-Mbit DRAM, and do not yet pose a challenge to Japanese manufacturers. The strength of South Korean companies lies in their ability to supply more generalized products at lower prices, rather than in competition at the highest level.

Another field where Japan has an edge is in the commercialization of HEMTs (high-electron-mobility transistors), which are semiconductor elements that employ chemical compounds different from those presently in use. Such manufacturers as Fujitsu, Sony, Toshiba, and Mitsubishi Electric have begun production of HEMT microwave-amplification elements for use in satellite communications and other fields.

Yet Japan's lead in electronics is even more apparent in IC-production technology, where Japanese developments in total quality control and other techniques have had a significant impact on productivity. An 80% share of the world DRAM market amply demonstrates the success of Japanese methods.

According to industry figures, in 1970, 20–30% of all semiconductors were made in Japan. In 1982 this share reached 30–40%, and in 1985 Japan's NEC attained first position in sales value in the world.

Japan's reputation for high-quality production has brought many competitors to Japan. Texas Instruments currently has three VLSI chip manufacturing plants in Japan that produce memory elements and the logic elements that are used to perform a wide variety of operations. All three are famous for their high level of productivity. In addition to producing 256-Kbit DRAM, 1-Mbit DRAM, and TTL (transistor-transistor logic) chips, these plants have begun to manufacture value-added chips for use in DSP (digital-signal-processor) and GSP (graphic-signal-processor) systems and in AI (artificial-intelligence) computers and other systems. In 1989, Texas Instruments plans to establish a research-and-development center in Japan, to undertake work on the next generation of VLSI chips. Similarly, Motorola established a new company in Japan in May 1987 in cooperation with Toshiba for production of VLSI chips, with which it hopes to reestablish itself in the DRAM market. Many other U.S. companies have consigned production to Japanese companies, increasing Japan's share of world IC manufacturing.

But Japan is not only the world's largest producer of ICs, it is also the world's largest market. According to industry statistics, Japan's market stood at approximately US$10.5 billion in 1986, whereas the figure for the United States was about $8.7 billion.

It is generally felt that factors such as investment capital, wide-ranging development capacity, and human resources will play an increasingly important role in the semiconductor industry. In this respect, Japan's comprehensive electronics manufacturers will have an edge over the specialized semiconductor makers in the United States. Japan has come to dominate the world market for condensers, resistors, and other miniaturized components that are used by general electronics manufacturers. It now appears that Japan is also on the way to dominating the semiconductor market, which represents the cutting edge of technology.

The same can be said for the materials and manufacturing equipment that support IC technology. In the past, as much as 80% of the equipment used to produce semiconductors in Japanese factories was made in the United States. However, in the last four or five years, this ratio has been reversed, and now 80–90% of all new semiconductor facilities installed in Japan are domestically manufactured.

Nippon Kogaku has made great progress in the wafer-stepper technology used to trace electronic circuits onto a silicon base material, and now stands shoulder to shoulder with the world's largest manufacturer, GCA of the United States. Another example of Japanese innovation is the development of synchrotron radiation equipment, which is expected to open the door to the next generation of chips. Research in this field was initiated with financing provided by a consortium of thirteen Japanese companies. As for the silicon base material, several Japanese companies bought out their American competitors, and thus much of America's silicon production takes place within an overall Japanese framework. From these and other measures, it is safe to say that the Japanese electronics industry can look forward to strong growth in the future.

Medical Electronic Devices

The competition to develop new products in the field of medical electronics (ME) equipment is growing fiercer among manufacturers in the U.S., Europe, and Japan. Although U.S. and European makers originally dominated in developing and manufacturing equipment in this field, Japanese companies—as skillful as ever at importing basic concepts and adding improvements to make more competitive products—have been successful in the U.S. and European markets in the past year or two.

One of the most important developments in this field is magnetic resonance imaging (MRI) technology. This technology makes use of the nuclear magnetic resonance phenomenon that occurs in a strong magnetic field to describe the distribution of proton density and indicate the presence of tumorous tissue within the human body. This means that, unlike earlier ME equipment, it makes a direct connection to the scientific makeup of the human body to supply information about the living organism. This new entry in the ME field is expected to become the authoritative diagnostic tool for cancers deep in the body, such as brain tumors, which have been difficult to locate with existing equipment.

The most active developers of MRI technology have been General Electric in the U.S. and Siemens in West Germany. The first Japanese model was developed in 1983 by Toshiba, top in the ME field in Japan. Many other local companies, including Hitachi, Shimazu, Mitsubishi Electric, and Sanyo Electric, have since come out with similar equipment. Development of MRI systems requires expertise in a wide variety of areas, such as computers, electronic engineering, and superconducting magnets, putting large electrical manufacturers that already possess such technology at an advantage.

With MRI, the stronger the magnet, the better the diagnostic power. Following GE and Siemens with their resistive MRIs of 1.5 tesla class, Toshiba and Mitsubishi Electric plan to bring out models of their own within the year. In their strategies for challenging GE and Siemens, both companies appear confident that in addition to the basic functions of their equipment, its durability, reliability, and superior image-reproduction technology will make it competitive.

The current exchange rate, however, makes imported ME equipment price-competitive in the Japanese market. ME equipment is one of the three main product fields Siemens is targeting in Japan, and the company is busy making sales to such places as university hospitals. At the same time, GE is taking the offensive in Japan through a company called YMS (Yokogawa Medical Systems). Strong-magnetic-field equipment costs from ¥5 million to ¥1 billion per unit, making it by far the most expensive instrument in the ME field. Competition in the Japanese market among U.S., European, and Japanese manufacturers is expected to be fierce.

Japanese manufacturers dominate in another important product in the ME field, the computerized-tomography scanner. This equipment was the first to make possible accurate diagnosis in cases such as cerebral hemorrhage. YMS is now supplying X-ray-CT equipment to GE on an original-equipment-manufacturing (OEM) basis, and GE is cutting back its production of all but certain types of sophisticated equipment: GE decided that YMS products were superior in both quality and cost. YMS continues its battle for a share of the Japanese market with Toshiba, the top local manufacturer of X-ray CTs. Since the

initial demand by hospitals for such equipment has already been filled, future business will consist mostly of filling the demand for replacement equipment.

Equally important in the field of medical electronics manufacturing is ultrasound equipment. At the moment, industry attention is focused on the entry of Fujitsu, a computer maker, into the market. The selling point of the Fujitsu ultrasound equipment is its very sophisticated diagnostic capability, such as the color Doppler function, which can show on a color video monitor the flow of blood within the heart, something heretofore considered technically very difficult. Fujitsu is doing OEM for ATL (Advanced Technology Laboratories), a large U.S. manufacturer of electronic medical equipment, but is also now considering sales within Japan under its own brand name. Everyone is watching with interest to see how Fujitsu will battle it out with the power players in the field—Aloka, Toshiba, and GE-YMS.

The manufacture of ME equipment requires the latest and most sophisticated electronics technology, so even with the soaring yen, Japanese manufacturers do not expect the NICs (newly industrializing countries) to pose a threat right away. Electronics makers in those countries are expected to move into the field with technologically simpler equipment, however, such as electrocardiographs and electroencephalographs.

Although expansion of the field was temporarily slowed by government policies to bring down medical costs, it is now enjoying growth, and the long-term prospects seem bright. Japan's annual ME production is soon expected to reach sales of about ¥350 billion.

FHR01FH: Microwave Ultralow-Noise HEMT
Fujitsu

The FHR01FH amplifies minute signals sent from such sources as communications satellites. It amplifies signals about ten times under normal conditions of temperature. It is a compound semiconductor device that utilizes the characteristics of the swiftly moving electrons that are generated between two different semiconductor layers. This new device was announced by Fujitsu in 1980, and the scientific world has waited eagerly for it to be made into a viable product and put on the market. Sample prices range from ¥150,000 to ¥200,000; at present, 1,000 units are being produced per month.

The nature of the matter between the stars is thought to hold important keys to the solving of such riddles as the creation and birth of living beings throughout the universe, and scholars the world over are searching for answers. To this end, they are trying to analyze the faint signals emanated by interstellar matter. Since the signals are very weak, it is extremely difficult to process them without amplification. The following experiment was made using an HEMT (high-electron-mobility transistor) device to amplify such signals at Tokyo Astronomical Observatory's Nobeyama Radio Observatory.

The amplifier is made up of two HEMT chips (about 0.16 mm² each) placed on top of a ceramic base plate, with wiring connecting the various elements. By cooling this device to about −250° C with a circulating-helium refrigerator, the faint interstellar signals can be amplified about forty times. This device can also suppress the generation of static noise during amplification.

The results of its experimental use at the Nobeyama Radio Observatory were very favorable. It succeeded in receiving radio waves of 22−24 GHz from a number of areas in the galactic system, and it also succeeded in observing such things as the spectral lines of ammonia and hydrogen.

As soon as the results of experiments conducted with the FHR01FH were published in academic and astronomical magazines, requests began pouring

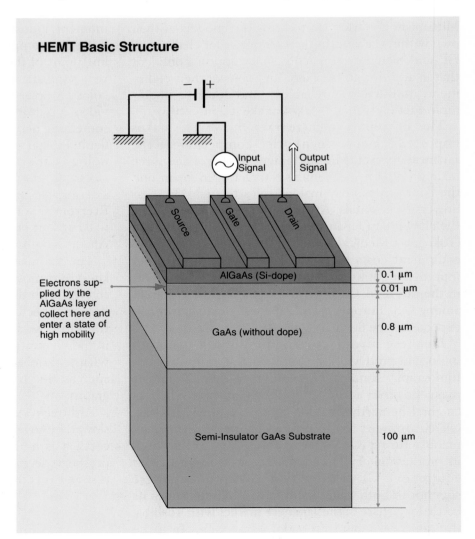

HEMT Basic Structure

Input Signal
Output Signal
Source
Gate
Drain
Electrons supplied by the AlGaAs layer collect here and enter a state of high mobility
AlGaAs (Si-dope) — 0.1 μm
0.01 μm
GaAs (without dope) — 0.8 μm
Semi-Insulator GaAs Substrate — 100 μm

in from radio observatories all over the world for samples, beginning in the summer of 1986.

The HEMT amplifier is known as a high-speed device. If the speed of the electron flow in the present main-stream silicon device is taken as one, a gallium-arsenide device is three times faster, and the HEMT device is a full five times faster. Furthermore, if the HEMT element is cooled to less than −200° C, its electron flow rises even higher, to around nine times faster. Thus, it is clear that this is the next-generation favorite as a compound semiconductor device.

The idea for an HEMT amplifier was hit upon by Fujitsu in 1979, and was announced a year later by Takashi Mimura of its Fukuta Research Lab. The fact that the electrons in the contact face between the gallium arsenide and gallium aluminum would theoretically move at high speeds when the two faces were placed against each other was announced by Dr. R. Dingle of AT&T's Bell Laboratories in 1978. But no company made the attempt to make a product based upon Dingle's discovery. Mimura set about to bring this theory to reality by using only a single layer each of gallium arsenide and gallium-aluminum arsenide, and he succeeded to the extent of actually making a prototype.

The development of an HEMT was made known to the public in June 1980. At that time, there was a strong response not only from domestic semi-conductor-related research organizations but from those of Western nations as well. It was comparatively

A land station for satellite communications; the FHR01FH is used in such communications

simple to make a single prototype for research-and-development purposes, but a number of supplementary techniques were necessary in order to permit it to be mass-produced. It would be imperative to ensure uniform functionality of the special characteristics for each and every device, to confirm dependability through long periods of use, and to supply it at a price that would be sufficiently low to compete with the other products on the market.

Fujitsu's Compound Semiconductor Lab Chief Yasutake Hirachi and Microwave Semiconductor Engineering Department Chief Kiyofumi Ohta and his staff set out to bring these expectations to reality. The aspect of the research that gave them the most trouble was the most appropriate shape for the gallium-aluminum-arsenide layer to be placed atop the gallium-arsenide layer. Achieving a uniform crystallization leads to the high-speed capabilities necessary, but since the thickness that could be used was in units of several hundredths of a micron, the work seemed "to demand the type of precision that would be needed to line up molecules one by one with an ordinary pair of tweezers." Hirachi and his staff utilized the molecular-beam epitaxial equipment at the Fujitsu Research Lab, and succeeded in the difficult task of shaping this thin membrane. In 1986, an HEMT production line was set up and production was initiated at the Kawasaki factory.

Around the time that the Kawasaki plant began producing the HEMT devices, such other major manufacturers as Sony, Toshiba, NEC, and Mitsubishi Electric also began to make them. This is because they all believed that along with use in such devices as communications satellites, a huge market would open up in the future for the HEMT. Sales competition among Japanese manufacturers centered around the HEMT is just about to get into full swing.

1986 High Award for Excellence

Ultralow static index: 1.8 dB (f=20 GHz)
High concomitant gain: 8 dB (f=20 GHz)
Newly developed metal wall hermetic package:
 FH type

HEMT Design Diagram

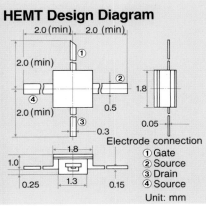

Unit: mm

Electrode connection
① Gate
② Source
③ Drain
④ Source

SLD103U and LT022MS: Standardized Laser Diodes for Ultracompact CD Players
Sony / Sharp

Today's laser diodes are now only about one-fifth the size and one-quarter the weight of those of the past. This development has contributed greatly to the standardization of the making of laser diodes. A laser diode is the single most important part of a CD (compact disk) player. Sharp, the leading manufacturer of laser diodes, and Sony, the top manufacturer of CD players, have joined hands in the development of these products. At the beginning of 1987, Sony was producing 300,000 SLD103U and Sharp 200,000 LT022MS laser diodes per month, priced at ¥2,500 each. They now are planning to increase production.

Around 1983 electronics manufacturers were looking for ways to make CD players even smaller, so that portable CD systems and car CD systems could be developed. To this end, in 1983, Sharp's Display Division of its Electronic Components Group began work on the miniaturization of the laser diode. At that time, researchers were working on the reduction of the oscillator reference plane's diameter from 9 mm to 7 mm, but little effort was being made toward developing an actual consumer product. This was because of the intense price war between rival manufacturers at the time.

At that point, Sharp heard that Sony had also begun its own independent research on miniaturization of the laser diode. At the end of 1985, Sharp and Sony began discussions on the subject. As they were both concerned with the same problem, they found it easy to approach each other on the subject; but when it came to the unification of standards, there were sharp differences of opinion. Sony proposed that the space between the terminals be left at 2.54 mm in order to be able to continue using its old test equipment. But Sharp insisted upon trying to reduce the space to 2 mm and refused to give in.

The problem was eventually solved when Sharp pointed out that from the standpoint of the future development

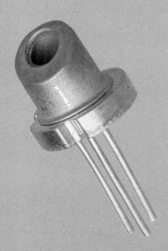  

A terminal interval of 2 mm has become the standard for ultrasmall semiconductor lasers; on the right is the Sharp LT022MS, and on the left is the Sony SLD103U; in the center is the part used by both companies

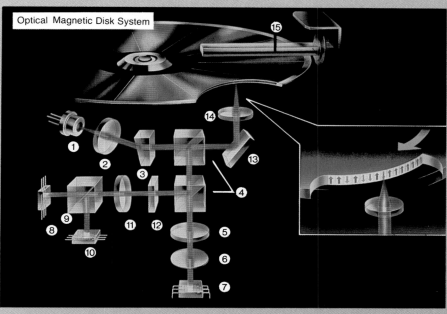

Optical Magnetic Disk System

① Semiconductor laser   ⑥ Cylindrical lens   ⑪ Lens
② Collimating lens   ⑦ 4-quadrant photodiode   ⑫ $\frac{1}{2}$-wavelength plate
③ Bending prism   ⑧ Photodiode   ⑬ Mirror
④ Beam splitter   ⑨ Polarizing beam splitter   ⑭ Objective lens
⑤ Lens   ⑩ Photodiode   ⑮ Electric magnet

of CD players, it was most desirable to make the laser diodes as small as possible. Sony agreed with that and gave in to Sharp's proposal. A 2-mm space is the smallest width that can be obtained with present-day technology and that still allows laser reliability to be maintained. At the end of February 1986, a formal agreement was signed by Sony's Diode Business Headquarters' Assistant Chief Department Head Masahiro Takahashi and by Sharp's Electronic Components Group's Deputy General Manager Akira Fujimori.

Work proceeded at a fast pace, with the renovation of manufacturing equipment in March, and the beginning of actual production in May. Quick progress was made by both companies, resulting in a monthly production rate of 300,000 diodes for Sony and 200,000 for Sharp by the beginning of 1987.

The technology involved was originally developed in the Research and Development Section of AT&T (Bell Laboratories), where the first successful continuous operation of laser diodes at room temperature was achieved in 1970. Early laser diodes had lifespans of only a few minutes, and there was no specific, practical use to which they

could be put at that time. In addition, there were virtually no manufacturers interested in merchandising them.

At this time, such Japanese manufacturers as Sharp and Mitsubishi Electric doggedly continued research on the diodes. The production increase in Japan was so great that Japanese manufacturers now enjoy a 99% share of the world's laser diode market. At present, products with lifetimes of 20,000 hours at room temperature are the norm, and their price has dropped to as low as ¥1,000.

Since the propagation of the laser beam is very narrow and critical, it is extremely difficult to mount the smaller-than-a-rice-grain laser diode in a package. However, Japanese manufacturers have automated even such delicate production processes as this, bringing their costs down far enough to be able to implant the laser diode in many products for daily use. Japanese manufacturers are often accused of making products in direct imitation of those developed in the U.S., but here the production technology of Japanese enterprises is formidable indeed.

In April 1986, Sharp and Sony made a joint press announcement of their accomplishments, and at the same

time they took the designs of their new laser diodes to other diode manufacturers and to CD-player manufacturers. For electronics manufacturers, the standardization of the laser diode meant great simplification of CD-player designs and the rationalization of assembly processes.

The diode manufacturers also welcomed this development and took a forward-looking stance in terms of practical applications. Recognition has been obtained from the Electronic Industries Association of Japan concerning the standardization of the laser diode's outer shape, and application has been made to the IEC, the European electronics parts standards organization. It appears that the day is fast approaching in which Sharp and Sony laser diodes will be the world standard.

1986 Award for Excellence

Oscillator wavelength: 780 nm
Package diameter: 5.6 mm
Lead pin pitch: 2.0 mm
Lead diameter: 0.5 mm
Laser diode chip distance from reference plane: 1.35 mm
Operating temperature: −10°C to +60°C
Storage temperature: −40°C to +85°C

V60 (μPD70616R): A 32-Bit Microprocessor
NEC

NEC, the first Japanese company to develop a 32-bit microprocessor, marketed its V60 in May 1986. This 32-bit chip is the best MPU now available for office computers. It is NEC's strategic entry in the race for first place against two American products: Intel's 80386 and Motorola's 68020 chips, which are ahead at the moment. NEC's product is equal to the American chips in terms of its demand-processing speed of 3.5 million demands per second, and its size. It is a 375,000-transistor LSI utilizing a delicate electronic technology that makes it possible to attach 1.5-μm-wide wires to a 196-mm² base.

In February 1986 in Anaheim, California, NEC Microcomputer and Memory Engineering Department Technology Chief Researcher Yoichi Yano presented Japan's first 32-bit MPU to the International Solid-State Circuitry Committee. After Yano's presentation, many people began asking questions immediately. The most persistent questions were from America's Motorola, an advanced rival manufacturer. At the same time, the chip was introduced in Tokyo and Munich, making it the first Japanese IC product ever to be presented in West Germany.

In the field of the one-chip microcomputer and its peripheral LSI, NEC—who had received an MPU manufacturing and sales rights grant from Intel—had already been confident of its superior position among the world's semiconductor manufacturers since the 1970s. But NEC thought that it should create its own MPU technology, and this ambition served as the genesis of the V60.

By the end of the 1970s, Intel prod-

ucts of 8 and 16 bits had already appeared. Thus, it was necessary to follow Intel's operation demand-processing system. But there was absolutely no need for the development of a 32-bit chip to be held down by the fetters of the past, so NEC created a new architecture and judged that it was the new developments of the 32-bit V60 and its successors that would bring the architecture to full life. Thus, in 1979, NEC initiated the V-series project

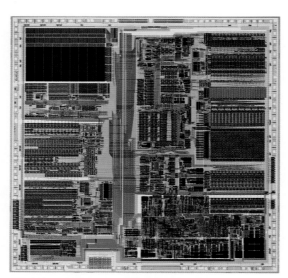

375,000 transistors are on this 14 × 14-mm chip

upon the two pillars of conformity with Intel's demand-processing system and its own MPU architecture.

Work on the design for the V60 was initiated in 1982, and the basic design was completed in the following year. By 1985, the chip layout design and related matters were also completed. Through the cooperation of the Microcomputer Software Development Department, the software for the chip was also prepared, and an LSI with the largest scale of integration ever was

perfected as a logical IC. In the spring of 1986, samples were shipped out. In the interim, the research group had grown to as many as 100 members during peak periods.

Its most immediate applications after it was put on the market were in such communications control devices as modems and switchboards, and in such factory-automation machines as robots and NC (numerical-control) machine tools. One of the unique fea-

tures of the V60 is that when two are combined, one can observe the working conditions of the other and effect an automatic changeover in case of a malfunction. Also, when three are used together, the system has an added majority-rule function through which it will choose the answer on which two chips agree. These special features raise the reliability of communications control devices. Another reason for the increased interest in the V60 is its floating-point operation function, which is useful in the diagrammatic calculations necessary in providing position information for the motion of such machines as robots. At the end of 1986, about fifty companies had recognized its potential and had already begun using it in their communications control devices.

At the same time, however, in the fields of personal computers and workstations—which were the original sales targets—IBM, the largest producer, has not yet made a clear decision on production of a 32-bit personal computer, and in its workstation MPUs is already using Motorola products. As a result, NEC finds sales in these areas a bit slower than had been expected. Thus, it appears that there are still a number of problems to be solved before the V60 gains broad popularity and utilization. One problem is that NEC's second sourcers do not increase; this is because of the reluctance of other semiconductor manufacturers to get involved in patent and copyright disputes with Intel.

At present, such a dispute is raging in U.S. courts concerning whether or not NEC has violated Intel's MPU microcode copyrights. However, this dispute was over 16-bit MPUs, and does not affect the V60. It will be of interest in the future to see whether or not a second sourcer will appear.

The V60 has an output power of 16 bits, and its internal operation is effected by a 32-bit architecture. In order to further facilitate the possibility of high-speed processing, the V70, which has a complete 32-bit system that provides 32-bit output power as well, has recently been put on the market. NEC intends to continue to develop high-performance 32-bit MPUs, such as a V75, one after another, basing the new products upon the V60 and creating a 32-bit-chip market resting firmly upon NEC architecture.

1986 Award for Excellence

On-chip demand paged-memory
   management unit
32-, 64-bit floating point support
Architecture optimized for high-level languages
3.5 MIPS (at 16 MHz operation)
V20/30 emulation mode
Functional Redundancy Monitor (FRM)

The first 32-bit microprocessor developed in Japan

NEC's answer to U.S. products

Heartner: A Miniature Electrocardiograph
Medec International

The Heartner can record an electrocardiogram (EKG) in a mere forty seconds. Small enough to fit in the palm of the hand, it can be connected to a device at the hospital to print out a copy of the heartbeat pattern. With this device, cardiac patients can take their own EKGs whenever they feel that something is wrong with their hearts, instead of having their EKGs recorded at a hospital or wearing a 24-hour monitoring device. Through Fukuda Electronics, Medec International sold more than 2,000 units, priced at ¥95,000 each, from April 1986 through February 1987.

The heart emits an extremely low-voltage electrical impulse, which an electrocardiograph picks up and presents in a graph. That graph, an EKG, can be studied to determine whether or not the heart is functioning normally.

In hospitals, the usual method of taking an EKG employs a large-scale electrocardiograph that prints out a graph representing the heartbeat pattern immediately. The patient is at rest with electrodes attached to his chest, arms, and legs. Many heart conditions, however, only reveal themselves by occasional abnormalities in the heartbeat that occur suddenly and unpredictably, perhaps once a week or once a day. For such conditions, a halter-style EKG recorder has recently become popular; however, it has a 24-hour maximum recording time, so that it cannot cope with conditions that show up only once a week, for example. It is, moreover, both uncomfortable to wear and quite expensive.

Since some abnormalities show up on an EKG only during the course of a patient's problem, the best solution is to let the patient take his own EKG whenever he feels the need. This concept came to Toshiharu Katahira, president of Medec International, a company that imports and sells medi-cal equipment and has also ventured into developing its own products. Every spring and fall, Katahira's wife has episodes of severe heart pain. When she goes to the hospital to have her EKG taken, however, the results are always normal.

Watching his wife press her right hand to her chest gave Katahira the idea of developing a simple, hand-held, heart-monitoring device that could record the EKG pattern if pressed near the heart. Katahira talked his idea over with a cardiologist he knew and learned that if a device could record the pattern of forty seconds of heart action, the resulting EKG would be sufficient for analysis.

Katahira then went to Akio Nagano, who singlehandedly directs Medec International's new-product development, with a detailed request for a new product: it was to be a commercially viable EKG recorder small enough to fit in the palm of the hand, able to record about forty seconds of heart pulses in an IC memory, pocket-sized (61 × 71 × 33 mm), and light (about 100 g). The design had to allow for the device to output its data on usual hospital electrocardiograph machines. What worried Nagano was combining miniaturization with the ability to record the EKG signals accurately. The problem, as he saw it, was that too small a device would have inferior performance.

At the end of 1985, it was completed according to his specifications and was ready to market. The device, named the Heartner, has a pin on its side that, when pulled out, causes it to beep intermittently. The user then holds the device in his hand, front facing the palm, and presses the reverse side against his chest, below the left nipple. In a few seconds the beep changes to an

The portable Heartner
(actual size; thickness is 33 mm)

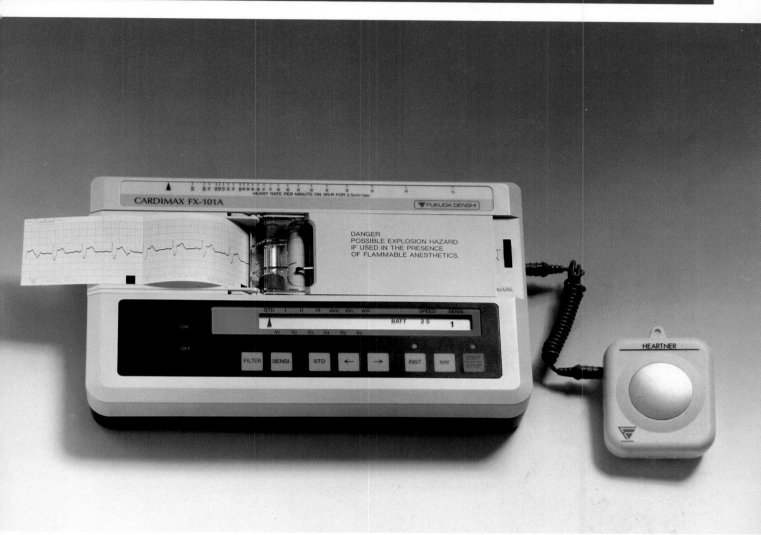

After recording with the Heartner, connecting it to an electronic reader enables one to study one's EKG pattern

intermittent "pip, pip" as the device records the EKG. After forty seconds, the recording is over.

Although Medec International handles medical equipment, its sales capacity for its own innovative product was weak. Thus, Katahira decided to enter into a cooperative agreement with Fukuda Electronics, Japan's largest manufacturer of electro-cardiograph machines, for the marketing of the Heartner. It adopted the strategy of selling the new device to cardiac patients through its hospital and clinic sales network. Given that the halter-style EKG recorder alone retails from ¥800,000 to ¥1,200,000, the Heartner, which sells for ¥95,000, is significantly cheaper.

Those involved thought that it would help popularize the Heartner if

hospitals and clinics stocked the devices and lent them out to patients. Indeed, doctors welcomed the idea of the patients' being able to record EKGs during the course of the subjective symptoms and did buy the devices. Cardiac patients also bought them, too; about 30% of sales have been made to such individuals. Since no such simple EKG-recording device is sold overseas, a serious move toward exporting the Heartner is on the current agenda.

The Heartner is highly effective at sensing what the patients are actually feeling, which assists the physician by helping him to prescribe the appropriate treatment. Moreover, simply having the device with them increases the patients' sense of security and reduces stress on the heart.

In 1987 Medec International plans

to introduce the Tele-Heartner, which can transmit the EKG recorded by the Heartner over a home telephone to a hospital or clinic. The new method allows for immediate printout of the EKG and analysis so that the hospital can order emergency measures for the patient if needed. As the number of cardiac patients rises, the need for such simple diagnostic devices will grow steadily.

1986 Award for Excellence

Electrodes: 2 silver-plated electrodes on both sides of the body
Input signals: 1 unipolar induction channel
Input level: Maximum ±3 mV
Input impedance: Above 3 MΩ
Discrimination ratios: Above 80 dB
Frequency range: 0.16–16 Hz (−3 dB)
Time constant: 1 sec/Filter—hum (54 Hz)
Recording duration: 40±5 sec
Power source: Lithium battery 3V × 2CR-2025

THE 1982–85 NIKKEI AWARDS

CARS,
WATCHES,
HOME
APPLIANCES, AND
CAMERAS

Familia: Full-Time 4WD
Mazda Motors

The Familia full-time 4WD is an innovative automobile designed and manufactured by Mazda Motors. Mazda, the fourth largest automobile manufacturer in Japan, has long been at the forefront of innovation in the automobile industry. In 1967, it introduced the first twin-rotor rotary-engine automobile in the Japanese market. With the Familia full-time 4WD it has continued its pattern of leading the way with new products. The Familia is the first full-time four-wheel-drive compact car in Japan.

Mazda has been producing its Familia series of two-wheel-drive compact family cars since 1964. The decision to manufacture models with four-wheel drive addressed certain changing social needs in Japan. More than ever, the hardworking Japanese are spending both time and money on leisure. Owners of passenger cars, therefore, want cars that are not only appropriate for daily use, but also for trips or excursions where, for example, they might need to drive in snow or on mountain roads. In addition, since full-time four-wheel drive allows for a safer ride under any road conditions and a stabler ride at high speeds, it satisfies a growing consciousness of safety standards in Japan.

The difficulties Mazda faced in developing such a car were obvious. Not only did it need to create a four-wheel-drive mechanism applicable to a compact car, but it also had to keep production costs down so Mazda could offer the automobile at an affordable price. Without the restrictions of adding four-wheel drive to the already existing Familia compact car, with its spacious interior due to its front-engine, front-drive system, Mazda, with all of its technological experience, could have developed a full-time four-wheel-drive car with relative ease.

Audi, the well-known West German automobile manufacturer, had already developed a full-time four-wheel-drive car using the technology applied in conventional four-wheel-drive trucks. Its four-wheel-drive system, however, was appropriate only in large cars, and could not be used in a compact. Mazda also considered developing a part-time four-wheel-drive model, but decided against it since such systems are more likely to produce vibration and noise when turning corners and sometimes cause locking of the wheels during tight cornering unless the four-wheel drive is disengaged.

The biggest challenge Mazda faced was in the center differential, necessary for four-wheel drive. In the past, such differentials have been complicated, bulky, and expensive. But for the Familia, Mazda designed a compact, light center differential, with a compact planetary gear system, located on the same front axle as the front differential, which saves space.

Mazda was also able to install a four-cylinder, 16-valve turbo engine with 140 ps (JIS)—not the 85 ps of a standard family car—in the Familia, since the load on each driving wheel in a four-wheel-drive automobile is roughly one-half of that on a two-wheel-drive vehicle. The Familia 4WD is priced at ¥1.89 million for the top model.

1985 Award for Excellence

3-door hatchback GT-X
3,990 (L) × 1,645 (W) × 1,355 (H) mm
Weight: 1,090 kg / Capacity: 5 persons
Engine: DOHC, in-line 4-cyl, 1,597 cc
Max. power: 140 ps / 6,000 rpm
Max. torque: 19.0 kg-m / 5,000 rpm

An all-weather cruising hatchback

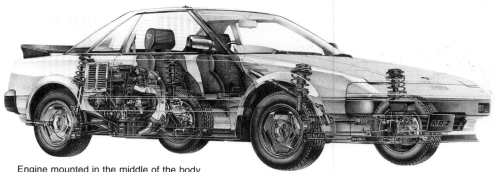

MR2: Sports Coupe
Toyota Motors

Toyota, the world's No. 2 automobile manufacturer behind General Motors, has recently been known as a company that produced mass-market automobiles lacking in individuality. Struggling to shed this dowdy image and design an automobile for an increasingly sophisticated domestic customer, Toyota took a leap into the unknown and developed Japan's first two-seat, mid-engine sports coupe, the MR2, which went on the market in June 1984 after four years of work.

A luxury, two-seater with the engine

Engine mounted in the middle of the body

located midway between the driver's seat and the rear axle, the MR2 handles far better than front-engine, front-wheel-drive automobiles. Vehicle weight is distributed almost evenly between the front and the rear, so the yawing movement coefficient has been

substantially reduced.

In Japan, the MR2 was named the Car of the Year for 1984, and in the United States, it was chosen Import Car of the Year.

1984 Award for Excellence

Charade: A 1,000-cc Diesel-Engine Automobile
Daihatsu Motors

3-cylinder, 1-liter diesel engine

The Charade from Daihatsu Motors features the world's smallest diesel engine—1,000 cc.

Before the Charade appeared in January 1983, there was no diesel smaller than that in the 1,300-cc Fiat. Conventional wisdom in the auto industry held that the minimum amount of displacement possible per cylinder was 400 cc. By examining basic diesel research and the materials in engine parts, Daihatsu managed to break this barrier and create an engine with a displacement of 331 cc per cylinder.

Daihatsu also managed to design a small diesel engine without sacrificing fuel efficiency and durability. When traveling at 60 kph the Charade can go 37.1 km on a liter of fuel.

In 1984, Daihatsu began marketing Charades with turbos, and in 1986, with automatic transmissions. For three consecutive years from 1983 to 1985, Daihatsu led its competitors in automobiles, and the Charade made an important contribution to that success.

1983 Award for Excellence

City Turbo Automobile
Honda Motors

This 1,200-cc automobile is equipped with what was, at the time of design, the world's smallest turbo engine.

Using a new electronically controlled, fuel-injection device and titanium alloys, Honda boosted the car's maximum power to 100 hp. With its compact frame and light weight—690 kg—the vehicle, selling for ¥1.09 million, handles like a sports car.

The idea for the City Turbo arose when a Honda employee suggested installing a turbocharger in a conventional City model for a car that would

be "ridiculously fast." A turbo was put in a 67-hp engine, and the turbo pressure was increased to raise horsepower first by 20%, then by 30%.

Then a Honda executive decided the power should be increased by 50%. While the engineers thought this unreasonable, they experimented with new materials, including titanium, magnesium, and resins. When they reached the goal, they had applied for 180 patents.

1982 High Award for Excellence

Honda's City Turbo

FF-Gemini: Compact Automobile
Isuzu Motors

The FF-Gemini is a no-frills compact car that has become Isuzu's best-selling model in Japan. Sold in the United States by General Motors under the name Chevrolet Spectrum, the Gemini was put on the market in Japan as an alternative to high-priced, high-tech cars. Its five-speed, four-door sedan costs ¥944,000.

The idea for a sparsely equipped, back-to-basics, popular vehicle came from a group of young Isuzu designers who at first encountered a generation gap when they presented their plans to the company executives. Time and again, these young designers met with resistance to their proposal, on the grounds that a car with such a simple design could not sell. Even subjects such as seat design provoked differences of opinion so great that, at one point, some of the older designers considered scrapping the project altogether.

Finally, however, the determination and sincerity with which these young designers advanced their ideas won over the opposition, and the project began to move ahead.

The success of the car had its begin-ning with the familiarity of the design-ers with their market. The target group for the FF-Gemini was people in the same age group as the designers, namely those in their twenties. Thus, the car was designed for a generation of Japanese that places increasing em-phasis on individuality, and the design team was easily able to come up with features that would appeal to them.

The person in charge of the designers used to imagine the little compact as a brilliantly colored bird, with a long beak and short tail, flying with amazing smoothness just above the water. One of the colors they recommended for the hatchback model—to the initial horror of older designers—was what they call seashell blue. These days, 40% of the hatchbacks sold are this color.

The design team strove for comfort in the FF-Gemini. To achieve the goal, the "optional extras" were eliminated, leaving only those features that were necessary for a comfortable drive. The FF-Gemini was to be a true "quality compact." At first glance, it appears to be just "a cute little car," but the inte-rior is as roomy as that of any other car in its class. And although more and more cars were being made with high-performance features such as turbo and electronically controlled, fuel-injection engines, Isuzu surprised the market with its announcement that the FF-Gemini would be equipped with a simple carburetor gasoline engine. To improve the handling of the car in city driving without such sophisticated features, the company improved the FF-Gemini's pick-up by increasing the engine compression ratio. The sales slogan chosen for the new car was "shortstop of the road," a phrase that went over extremely well in baseball-crazy Japan.

With the low-priced car market growing at only a relatively small rate, Isuzu entered a highly competitive market. Despite stiff competition, Isuzu sold 51,000 Geminis in the first sixteen months the car was on the market.

Isuzu's best-selling model in Japan

1985 Award for Excellence

3-door hatchback
  3,960 (L) × 1,615 (W) × 1,370 (H) mm
  Weight: 860 kg / Capacity: 5 persons
  Engine: OHC, in-line 4-cyl, 1,471 cc
  Max. power: 86 ps / 5,800 rpm
  Max. torque: 12.5 kg-m / 3,600 rpm

Civic Ballade: A Series of Automobiles
Honda Motors

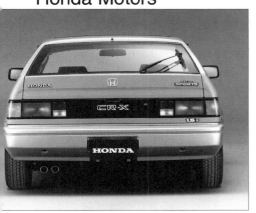

The stylish CR-X

Ordinarily, the differences in a series of automobiles are variations on a theme—that is, on a single model. In the case of Honda's Civic Ballade series, four different models were designed afresh—all the way down to the wheelbase. As a result, the series features four different basic types of automobiles, allowing for a great deal of variety within the group.

The Civic Ballade series, priced from ¥823,000 to about ¥1.7 million, includes two-passenger coupes (CR-X model) and three-, four-, and five-door automobiles, with three types of engines—1,300 cc, 1,500 cc, and 1,600 cc (this last is available in Japan only). These cars have attracted a wide range of drivers, from young people to the middle-aged. Among younger Japanese drivers, the CR-X two-seater, based on an idea from the American Honda and designed to have a "California flavor," has sold exceedingly well. The CR-X's style is much bolder than that of most compacts in Japan, and its success started a new trend in Japanese small-car design.

1983 Award for Excellence

Vista and Camry: Two Small, Deluxe, FWD Automobiles
Toyota Motors

For Toyota, the Vista and the Camry front-wheel-drive automobiles represented a significant refinement of models and markets—cars with both a feeling of luxury and the practicality of small size and fuel economy, and aimed at drivers in their thirties and forties with families.

The idea behind the new models was to create a car with the interior dimensions of the Mark II, a model one class above the Vista and Camry, and an exterior similar to the Corona, one class below.

"The development process was unprecedented inside the company," remembers Shirō Sasaki, a Toyota director. "Everything, aside from the bolts, was redesigned."

The results were two front-wheel-drive models with a formal, unobtrusive appearance that yet convey a feeling of roominess inside, and are equipped with a light, compact engine, mounted sideways, for good gas mileage. The Vista and Camry models were 2S-engine passenger cars.

1982 Award for Excellence

Toyota's low-fuel-consumption car

March: A Small, 1,000-cc Automobile
Nissan Motors

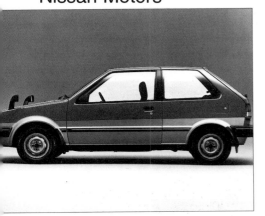

Nissan's 1,000-cc March

The 1,000-cc March is the smallest front-wheel-drive automobile that Nissan had marketed until this time.

Developed for women seeking an easy-to-drive car and families looking for a reasonably priced second car, the March was designed with an interior as roomy as automobiles a class above, although the body is compact-sized. First sold as a 3-door hatchback, a 5-door model was later added to the line.

The first truly lightweight Nissan car, the March has an aluminum cylinder block that is lighter than a conventional cast-iron block, making the March weigh in at 610–655 kg. Marketed abroad as the Micra, the March features a bigger bumper and side-guard molding for increased safety.

The automobile appeared on the market in October 1982 under the slogan "A new car for a new age." Nissan produced it on the most advanced production line in the world at its Murayama assembly plant. At its peak, the plant was completing 20,000 vehicles a month using 216 robots.

1982 Award for Excellence

Digipaper: Ultrathin Wristwatch
Casio Computer

Casio Computer had decided to develop the world's thinnest plastic-case wristwatch when Noriaki Shimura, managing director of the company's R&D division, looked around him and examined the competition—particularly the low-priced digital watches made in Hong Kong and Taiwan and also in Japan itself.

What was needed to separate Casio from the others, Shimura decided, was a "paper-thin" digital watch, noticeably different from all others on the market and difficult for the others to copy.

What he got after a year of research and development was the Digipaper, a ¥3,900 ultrathin, plastic, digital wristwatch only 3.9 mm thick and weighing 12 g. Its all-in-one case and band were particularly adapted to a high-fashion design—originally in a sporty, athletic black and later in bright colors. Its digital display cuts across the face at a rakish angle.

In addition, the product was manufactured using a process that would require a major financial investment for competitors to duplicate. And, best of all, the Digipaper, introduced in March 1985, became a million-seller by the end of the year—the world's first million-seller watch. During the spring of its introduction, consumers, frustrated by their inability to find a store with the new Casio product left in stock, were calling the company continuously, asking for help.

Digital watches have always had two advantages over their analog cousins: the number of functions possible and price. But the two kinds of watches were often similar in thickness. The

An ultrathin, ultralightweight watch with a new design: the case and the band are one

challenge to Casio was to come up with an ultrathin watch that was also digital.

Much of the work focused on fusing the case and band into a single unit, although they are made of two different resins. Casio approached several plastic-molding-machine manufacturers, asking them to provide a piece of equipment that would fuse the two, but each time, the watchmaker was turned down. So Casio decided to make its own machine. Six months later, the company had a band and case fused so tightly that company employees could not break the bond no matter how hard they pulled.

Then Casio faced the problem of assembling the new wristwatch. The works of both digital and analog watches are usually dropped into the case as one piece, but that method tended to make a digital watch thick. After a long search, the company developed a method that allowed the parts of the Digipaper to be inserted one at a time from the back of the case using an automatic-assembling device that placed the parts at predetermined locations.

Digital watches also have fewer parts than analogs, and the Digipaper has 30% fewer than a conventional digital—which helped hold down its cost.

The new wristwatch tells the wearer the month and day and whether it is AM or PM—in addition to the hour, minute, and second—on a face canted at an easy-to-read angle. Its automatic calendar is set at twenty-eight days for February.

The Digipaper is accurate to ±15 sec per month, and its super-small battery lasts two years.

1985 High Award for Excellence

Voice Note: A Voice-Recording Wristwatch
Hattori Seiko

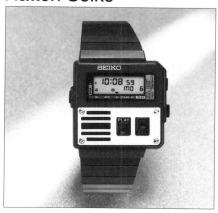

A voice-recording wristwatch

The Seiko LCD, digital, quartz Voice Note (sold as Calibre M516 abroad) is the first wristwatch to record and play back the human voice. Hattori Seiko, a leader in the wristwatch industry, is a pioneer in turning digital watches into information machines.

Seiko miniaturized the speaker-microphone, making it about the size of a human fingernail, and combined its functions with two 16-Kbit static RAMs. The Voice Note watch can be set to record or playback for either four or eight seconds—enough time for the watch to be used as a simple memo pad. The wristwatch will replay its message at the touch of a button or at a selected alarm time.

Selling for ¥25,000, the Voice Note also functions as a stopwatch and a calendar. It is enclosed in a lightweight, carbon-fiber-reinforced plastic case, and has a thickness of 7.8 mm, including the battery, which will last up to two years.

1983 Award for Excellence

DB-1000: Data-Bank Digital Wristwatch
Casio Computer

This wristwatch is an example of the successful evolution of digital watches into information tools. The DB-1000 from Casio Computer can store fifty names and telephone numbers of up to twenty characters each in its data bank. The information to be stored is written on the face of the watch with the finger and read by sixteen transparent electrodes. An LSI circuit stores the information, and an editing function automatically alphabetizes it. The DB-1000, marketed abroad as Tele-Memo 50, also works as a calculator, stopwatch, and alarm clock.

In developing recognition software for letters and numbers, tests were conducted to determine how the shape of handwritten letters and numbers varies among Japan, the U.S., and Europe. It was found that there are six ways to write the number "7," depending on differences in the stroke order and shape. Software was developed that classifies and analyzes characters according to the number and order of strokes; it can also recognize some individualistic methods of writing.

1984 Award for Excellence

To input data, write on the glass face with a finger

TV-Watch
Seiko Epson

A 1.2-in screen; the headphone unit is on the right

In 1980, when Seiko Epson announced that it was test manufacturing a pocket-sized, LCD television watch, it did not get much response. Nevertheless, it continued with development, confident that there was a future for LCD televisions.

Many years of research into LCD panels for displaying numbers on digital wristwatches put Seiko Epson in an excellent position to develop this kind of product, a better position than household-appliance manufacturers who specialized in televisions.

The TV-Watch went on the market in 1982 at a cost of ¥108,000 for the basic model. For viewing, the 80-g watch was attached to a separate 185-g TV and FM receiver. The black-and-white screen contained nearly 32,000 LCD elements.

In 1983, the product disappeared as appearance of pocket-sized, portable, LCD televisions took over the market. But it was the television-watch that had acted as a catalyst for the subsequent development of the product that displaced it.

1982 High Award for Excellence

CCD-M8 Handycam: 8-mm Video   Camera-Recorder
Sony

The CCD-M8 uses a compact (95 × 62.5 × 15 mm) 8-mm cassette tape

In the beginning of the first big video war a decade ago, there was Beta and VHS. Sony's Betamax format video-tape recorder went up against the VHS format VCR made by Victor Co. of Japan (JVC), competing for the disposable incomes of consumers who want to watch movies at home and record TV programs for later viewing.

Then, two years ago, the battlefield shifted. The contest now focuses on video camera-recorders—"camcorders," as they are sometimes called—designed to allow amateurs to shoot their own TV pictures at home.

But the combatants remain the same: Sony with its 8-mm video camera-recorder and JVC committed to camera-recorders using a modification of the VHS half-inch cassettes familiar from VCRs.

Sony's champion in the new battle is the CCD-M8, dubbed the Handycam and introduced in September 1985. It is light, small, and swift—the smallest and lightest 8-mm camcorder in the world at the time of its introduction. Weighing in at 1 kg, the CCD-M8 is about the size of a paperback book. Its simple three-position focus system (close, medium distance, and far) allows a photographer to put the camera to his eye, point, and shoot without a lot of adjustments.

Cassettes used in the Handycam are smaller than audio cassettes and run up to a maximum of 120 minutes on a recorder built into the camera. The Handycam costs ¥198,000 and comes with a small, separate playback machine for viewing what has been photographed. In a later generation of the Handycam, the camera itself plays back a tape when plugged into a television set.

The issues in the latest video war are size and weight, and also familiarity. JVC's champions—its C-Series of camcorders—are also lightweight; but they record on a smaller version of the familiar VHS cassette. Inserted into a special carrier, the cassette can then be played back on a VCR.

Japanese companies have not yet chosen sides in the new video war. Matsushita (National) and Hitachi make both VHS and 8-mm video camcorders and sell them to other companies for sale under their brand names, and Sony sells its 8-mm camcorders to Fuji Photo Film and Kyocera for sale under their brand names.

Over the last two years, sales of the 8-mm camcorder has come to account for 60% of the video camera-recorder market worldwide. Sony is betting on its continued success because the format makes even smaller cameras possible without shortening tape time.

The 8-mm cassette is also especially adaptable to players small enough to be installed in automobiles and boats. "Have you ever driven across Kansas in a car?" asks a Sony spokesman. "I have, and it was in a car with a 9-in TV and an 8-mm cassette player. It was great."

The small 8-mm camcorders are also popular with women. "The husband may go looking for a camcorder to buy, but he often takes his wife and children along," says a Sony spokesman. "Our salesmen are finding that when the camcorder gets in the hands of the woman, that's when the decision to buy is made."

1985 High Award for Excellence

Format: 8-mm video format
Audio recording system: Rotary head FM recording
Recording time: 120 min (when using P6-120 tape)
Imager: CCD solid filming element
 (250,000 pixels)
Viewfinder: Optical viewfinder
Lens: f1.6 / 3-position zone focus

JVC HR-C3: Compact Video Cassette Recorder
Victor Co. of Japan (JVC)

The HR-C3, the first compact, portable VCR, uses cassettes about the size of a deck of cards—about one-third the size of ordinary VHS cassettes. Compact cassettes were the key to developing a lightweight, portable machine that could be used anywhere. Besides allowing direct playback, tapes recorded on the HR-C3 can be played back on a standard VHS-format VCR by inserting the compact cassette into an adapter the size of standard cassettes.

According to the head of JVC's Video Products Division, an "inordinate amount" of effort was required to make this idea technologically feasible. JVC changed its design to use numerous integrated circuits, and developed an unusually small, flat motor. The end product was the HR-C3, which, at 2 kg, weighed about one-half of existing machines. Known as the HR-C3U abroad, it features an automatic editing function that backs up the tape about

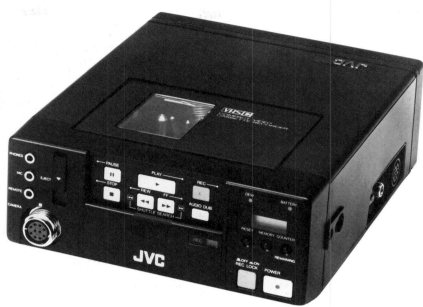

The HR-C3 uses a compact (92 × 59 × 23 mm) VHS-C tape

thirty frames between takes for smooth joining of different scenes.

1982 Award for Excellence

Epson Televian: Pocket-Sized LCD Color TV
Seiko Epson

The Televian came on the market about a year and eight months after Seiko Epson marketed the TV-Watch, the first wristwatch with a built-in, black-and-white, LCD television screen. Measuring 80 × 160 × 31 mm and weighing 450 g, the pocket-sized Televian, sold in the U.S. as the EIF, is the next logical step after the TV-Watch.

The development of a color LCD television owes a great deal to the precision production techniques used in watch manufacturing technology. Reception of the Televian's clear color image is made possible by 52,800 picture elements and thin-film transistors inserted in the 2-in diagonal LCD screen. A single defective transistor can impair picture quality, so very precise wiring technology was required.

The Televian sells for ¥84,800 and can also serve as a VCR monitor. It operates on five AA-size batteries; an AC adapter, a rechargeable battery pack, and a car-battery adapter are also available.

The Epson Televian uses an LCD panel only 2 mm in thickness

1984 High Award for Excellence

Yamaha LV-X1: Laservision™ Player
Nippon Gakki

When Nippon Gakki scanned the competitive market of videodisk players, looking for a vacuum to fill, there was only one. No company had yet produced a machine targeted at the young, movie- and music-hungry videophile, combining low price with superior picture, sound quality, and more features than a Swiss army knife.

So, in November 1985, Nippon Gakki did it. After more than a year of work, the company introduced the Yamaha LV-X1, a high-quality videodisk player priced at under ¥100,000 in a market where the average price was over ¥150,000.

In the LV-X1, a picture as sharp as a razor is created by 400 lines of horizontal resolution. Before the LV-X1, the most sophisticated videodisk player had only 370 lines.

Sound quality in the LV-X1—both hi-fi and stereo—compares favorably with the audio CD players Nippon Gakki also makes. The machine features a wireless remote control and on-screen display of the picture even when the player is rewinding or fast forwarding. Movies can be viewed at normal speed, as stills, frame-by-frame, or up to twelve times normal speed.

Another feature allows a viewer to hop directly to a scene without the bother of fast forwarding or rewinding. The disk player will also automatically repeat one side of a disk or a segment of one side.

The laser LV-X1 also plays any of the approximately 4,000 laserdisks on the market in Japan today. And it doesn't wear them out. Unlike conventional stylus players, the laser technology avoids friction on the disk.

To make something special took a combination of carefully altered technology, wise manufacturing decisions, and creative management techniques.

Engineers, for example, cut the number of parts in the LV-X1 to half that in similar equipment. The size of its printed circuit board was reduced to 60% of that in other equipment. Both changes translated into more and better functions at lower cost.

The development process used to bring the LV-X1 to the market was typical of Japanese business practices, but with a twist.

In the summer of 1984, Nippon Gakki formed a team to create the new product. First, the team anticipated all the problems it might face in the devel-

opment process and then made a plan to counter them. Then it addressed the product—everything from design of the machine to the selling season in which it should be introduced.

Next, the team took a step unusual for a Japanese company concerned about competitors and the risk of leaks. The team decided to share some information about the player with employees elsewhere in the company. The goal was to increase goodwill and also increase information about the product.

The head of the development team, Minoru Ogita, now credits that last decision with much of their Laservision player's ultimate success: "Our success was made possible by the positive support we received in such areas as purchasing, quality control, and manufacturing."

1985 Award for Excellence

Form: Philips MCA-style Laservision system
Playing time: 30-cm standard disk (CAV), 1 hr; 30-cm long-playing disk (CLV), 2 hr
Rotational speed: Standard disk, 1,800 rpm; long-playing disk, 600–1,800 rpm
Dimensions: 435 (W) × 116 (H) × 410 (D) mm; wt: 9.4 kg

Nippon Gakki's remote-control Laservision player, LV-X1

CLD-9000: Compact-Disk/LaserVision™ Player
Pioneer Electronic

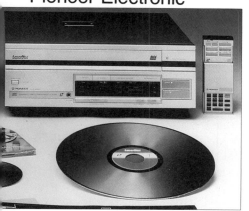

A compatible player for both CDs and VDs

The idea of joining a CD player and a LaserVision videodisk player into one machine came to Pioneer directly from the front lines. One day an electrical-appliances store manager told Pioneer director Shigeyoshi Yanagi it would be convenient to have a single player that could play both LaserVision video-disks and CDs.

Yanagi immediately issued instructions to develop such a player and the result was the CLD-9000, the world's first combination player.

Although the idea seemed simple enough, it took the company one year longer than expected to bring the new product to the market. Two major problems had to be solved: the rotary mechanisms for the two kinds of disks were different and needed to be reconciled; and standards for digital-sound LaserVision disks had to conform to those of the patent holder.

Still, the timing of the CLD-9000, priced at ¥249,800, turned out to be ideal. Released in September 1984 during the CD boom, it quickly became a popular item.

1984 Award for Excellence

D-50: Portable CD Player
Sony

When the Sony D-50 appeared on the market in November 1984, it hurdled two major obstacles to large-scale consumer purchase of compact-disk players. One was size, the other, price.

Sony wanted to make a CD player that could be held in one hand, but to do so would involve large expenditures for research and development. The company proceeded, gambling that a small CD player would sell well, eventually recouping investment.

The D-50's small size was achieved by using a single microchip for its integrated circuit and reducing the space

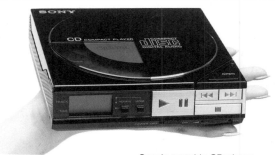

Sony's portable CD player

used for the laser to read the signals by two-thirds.

The new product was put on the market at ¥49,800, a price far below that of other CD players, and became an immediate hit with students. The low price led to an explosion in demand, and mass production meant a profit for Sony. In 1985 it continued its development of this market when it introduced the D-50 Mark II, known as the Discman.

1984 Award for Excellence

CDP-101: Compact-Disk Player
Sony

Compact-disk players differ from conventional record players by using digital instead of analog signals in the playing process. Compact disks, however, recorded with digital signals, reproduce sound extremely clearly, and they do not warp or deteriorate.

Sony and the Dutch firm Philips originally pursued digital sound research independently, but they joined forces to develop the CD format. Because there was no precedent for the product, development presented numerous difficulties. Tests had to be conducted over and over to

The first CD player

ensure the micron-level precision of optical devices, such as the lens that reads the digital signals and semiconductor lasers. The diameter of the disks even caused a major debate.

When the first compact-disk players went on sale in October 1982, the price of ¥168,000 was too high to generate mass sales. Now, however, as the price has dropped, production of CD players exceeds that of compact analog phonographs.

1982 High Award for Excellence

GP Series: Plate-Type Sealed Ni-Cd Cells
Japan Storage Battery

As electronic products have become lighter and more compact, they have required similar, lighter, and more compact cells.

Sony, in an effort to reduce its fourth-generation Walkman cassette players to about the same size of the cassette itself, asked Japan Storage Battery in October 1983 if it could design a flat, thin battery unlike conventional cylindrical cells.

Japan Storage Battery agreed, but had reservations concerning whether or not it would be able to develop such a revolutionary cell within the one year that Sony had requested. Also, the company knew that if the cell were a commercial success, it would have to install an entirely new production line in order to meet the new demand.

The biggest problem facing the engineers at Japan Storage Battery was the structural weakness of a plate-type cell compared with a cylindrical type. When a cell is charged, oxygen is emitted, increasing the inside pressure. Although a cylindrical cell can withstand this increase, a rectangular cell cannot and tends to become deformed. Use of a thicker cell case solves the problem, but at the sacrifice of the cell's energy density. Sony's insistence on a thin, plate-type battery forced the engineers to find a way to decrease the interior pressure, as well as a way to strengthen the battery's seals.

Japan Storage Battery began by using the same negatively charged cadmium plate employed in previous cells to absorb oxygen. It then developed a special treatment for the surface of the electrode to increase its ability to absorb oxygen better and decrease internal pressure. It also developed a method of laser welding, since it is impossible to seal a plate-type cell by crimping. To prevent damage in case the amount of gas in the interior of the cell should suddenly increase, the company developed a miniature terminal with a resealable vent mechanism

Rectangular-shaped batteries in which steps have been taken to control the generation of oxygen; the inner structure is shown at left

SL-800: Ultrathin Calculator
Casio Computer

The aim of Casio engineers in developing this product was to create a calculator with the actual dimensions of a credit card. Calculators roughly that size had already been produced, but the thinnest was 1.6 mm thick. They all used glass for their solar batteries and liquid crystal displays, and screws to join the parts together.

For the light, slim SL-800, Casio hit upon a completely different method for making calculators. It turned the calculator's LSI, solar battery, and LCD panel into a series of films and attached the parts with ten different adhesives. As a result, the "Film Card" calculator, as it is nicknamed, will not break when dropped and can also withstand some

A solar-cell-powered Film Card

to allow the escape of excess gas.

The resulting battery, retailing for ¥1,000, is a mere 5.6 mm thick, about the size of a stick of gum, and uses 30% less space than a conventional cylindrical cell. It also has a higher energy density than conventional cylindrical cells. Like ordinary cells, the flat type can be recharged. Both standard and rapid-type recharging are possible.

Japan Storage Battery completed a prototype that met Sony's technical criteria within thirteen months of having accepted the challenge.

When the fourth generation of Sony's Walkman with its plate-type cell came on the market in October 1985, it had a revolutionary effect on the small-electronics industry. Other makers scrambled to start production of Walkman-type players using GP Series cells.

Initial production of the cells was 200,000 units per month. In January 1986, Japan Storage Battery established a 50-50 joint venture company, GS-SAFT, with SAFT of France.

1985 Award for Excellence

Dimensions: 16.4 (W) × 66.5 (H) × 5.6 (D) mm;
wt: 23 g / Voltage: 1.2 V
Capacity: 450 mA
Recharge time: 15 hr/8 hr (high speed)

bending. It is also put together on an automatic assembly line for greater precision than with the hand labor used in the past.

The SL-800 sells for ¥5,900 and performs the four basic mathematical and constants calculations, percentages, square roots, and others.

1983 High Award for Excellence

Donvier: A Home Ice-Cream Maker
Nippon Light Metal

When Nippon Light Metal, an aluminum manufacturer, was trying to break into the home consumer market, it decided to produce a home ice-cream maker that requires neither salt nor ice

Enjoy making ice cream with Donvier

nor hours of churning.

The key to the development of the Donvier ice-cream maker lay in the cooling element in the aluminum container. It has a refrigerant, trade-named Chillfast, permanently sealed between its walls. When kept in a freezer for at least seven hours, the pot will freeze liquid poured into it in about fifteen minutes. The Donvier, which gives the ice cream a smooth and non-grainy texture, costs ¥4,800 and makes about 500 cc of ice cream.

The *Los Angeles Times* hailed the Donvier as the "next biggest hit after the Walkman." Nippon Light Metal launched a very assertive advertising and sales promotion campaign for the new product. Between its appearance and 1986, over 2 million Donviers (including newer models) were sold in Japan alone; and in 1985–86, 2.8 million were sold abroad.

1983 High Award for Excellence

Karamanbo: Automatic Washing Machine
Hitachi

This fully automatic washing machine combines features of both Japanese and American washers—the pulsator type and the agitator type—to create a large-capacity machine that washes large loads gently.

When development began in April 1980, the Hitachi machine, unlike American products, had no center post. Then it became clear that the post reduced the tangling of clothes, so it was added to the design. The machine's pulsator was also enlarged and made to turn slowly.

Eventually the post and its properties were responsible for the name—and much of the success—of the new washing machine. When a campaign was held to name the new machine, Karamanbo, referring both to the post and the lack of tangles, was chosen. It turned out to be very popular with young consumers.

Since its introduction in 1982, twenty models have been developed

and, as of October 1986, 1.5 million machines have been sold. The three original models sold from ¥68,000.

1982 Award for Excellence

Hitachi's popular Karamanbo washing machine

α-7000: Autofocus SLR Camera
Minolta Camera

The Minolta α-7000 is the most successful automatic-focus, single-lens-reflex camera ever put on the market. Two central processing units built into the camera body—not the lens, as had been the case with previous cameras—calculate the distance to the subject. This information is used by the motor, also built into the body, to automate focusing. The extensive line of interchangeable lenses allows even a beginner to experience the excitement of sophisticated photography.

The world's first autofocus SLR

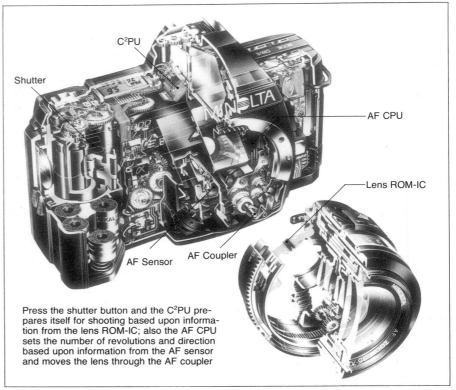

Press the shutter button and the C²PU prepares itself for shooting based upon information from the lens ROM-IC; also the AF CPU sets the number of revolutions and direction based upon information from the AF sensor and moves the lens through the AF coupler

Tokuji Ishida, of Minolta's Research and Development Department, is the man who perfected the autofocus mechanism. He remembers: "When CCDs [charge-coupled devices] appeared back in 1981, we were really excited. We realized that CCDs would make fully automatic focusing possible. The problem, though, was price. If CCDs were too expensive, commercialization would be out of the question. I guess you could say that development of the α-7000 began with our repeated visits to the integrated circuit manufacturers, asking them to lower the price of their CCDs. What makes our autofocusing mechanism possible is that the microprocessors instantaneously read and calculate the distance to the image being photographed, and then automatically focus the lens." The α-7000 has two 8-bit microprocessors built into the camera body and also employs seven custom-designed ICs in the 16-to-24 kilobit class.

Minolta was the last of Japan's major camera manufacturers to produce an autofocus model. The first appeared in 1981, but none had taken a very big market share. They were all designed with a focusing motor built into each interchangeable lens, making the lenses bulky and heavy. Furthermore, the companies gave users a choice of only two or three lenses. A big factor behind the success of the α-7000—sold in North America as the Maxxum 7000, and elsewhere outside Japan as the 7000—was that in appearance and weight it was about the same as a conventional SLR camera and that the focusing motor was built into the body. A line of twelve slim, lightweight lenses was already available when the new camera went on sale.

Shifting the focusing motor to the camera body meant designing a new drive system to handle complex information exchanges between body and lens. That required an overall redesign of the mount used to attach a lens to the body, but a new lens mount would render useless all the lenses a camera owner had previously accumulated. Since Minolta had long advertised "the unchanging Minolta mount," adopting a new mount was an issue hotly debated within the company.

Hideo Tashima, president of Minolta, described the decision-making process: "We had long considered how to move to automatic focusing, the greatest innovation in the industry. But since we weren't the industry leader, a cautious approach would expose us to the danger of dwindling sales. Consequently, we decided to gamble. In our eyes, the future of Minolta depended on taking a large risk and going beyond the others to create 'the camera for the twenty-first century.'"

1985 High Award for Excellence

Autofocus system: TTL position phase-detection method
Photometry system: TTL release center emphasis average photometry
Shutter speed: 1/2,000 sec to 30 sec
Film speeds: ISO 25 to 6,400
Dimensions: 138 (W) × 91.5 (H) × 52 (D) mm; wt: 555 g (without lens or batteries)

TW-300: Tele-Wide Compact Camera
Fuji Photo Film

The fully automatic TW-300

Until now, compact cameras have only allowed photography with wide-angle or standard lenses and no telephoto option to bring subjects close. Fuji Photo Film has changed the situation with the introduction of TW-300, an automatic-focus compact camera offering a telephoto—wide-angle switchover system. The wide-angle lens, appropriate for scenery, can be replaced at a single touch by a telephoto lens intended for photographing details from a long distance.

Market research on compact cameras revealed customer dissatisfaction at the absence of a simple telephoto option. In a survey carried out by Fuji Photo Film in 1982, 54% of the 1,000 respondents listed the telephoto function either first, second, or third on the list of desirable functions for compact cameras. This sentiment was especially common among parents who photographed their children at sports meets or class-day events. Unable to get close due to space restrictions, they would be disappointed with the final photograph, unable to distinguish their child from the surrounding mass.

It was clear that there was a potentially huge market ready for exploitation. Fuji began development of the TW-300 in the spring of 1983. The company had built a similar camera five years earlier, but the bulkiness of the lens and the fact that it was not fully automatic limited its appeal. Technology developed in the meantime promised to eliminate these drawbacks.

The greatest technological stumbling block was linking the viewfinder switchover to the lens switchover. Changing between a wide-angle and a telephoto lens is useless if the view-finder that shows the scene to be photographed is not adjusted, too. Fuji's technical team installed two finders with differing predetermined magnifications and a mechanism that shifts the finders the instant the lenses are switched.

The difference in magnification ratio between the telephoto and wide-angle lenses also presented a problem. Ideally, the focal length of a telephoto lens should be as long as possible in order to produce a clear contrast to wide-angle. The lens size, however, is limited if a compact camera is to be compact. The result of the balancing act was a camera with 38-mm wide-angle and 65-mm telephoto lenses—a 1.7 magnification ratio suitable for both scenery and portraiture.

Fuji offered the TW-300 for ¥57,800 when most compacts sold for ¥30,000 to ¥40,000, and many at Fuji feared this price exceeded the acceptable threshold. These fears were swept away as soon as the product appeared on the market. Consumers flocked to buy the TW-300. The camera was selected as the best among twenty-seven autofocus compact cameras in the September 1986 issue of *Consumer Reports* magazine. With the introduction of the TW-300, compact cameras have taken a step closer to approximating the functions of the sophisticated single-lens-reflex cameras. Other companies followed Fuji's lead, and switchable compact cameras now represent nearly 40% of the market.

1985 Award for Excellence

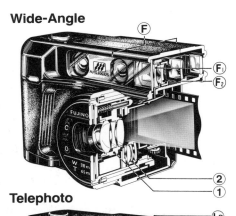

Wide-Angle

Telephoto

A wide-angle/telephoto convertible lens linked with finder optics

[When using wide angle]
Shooting optics:
Shooting is carried out (1) with a 3-component, 3-element f3.5 38mm structure, or (2) with a rear converter (image enlargement lens) that moves out of the light path and takes no role in photographing
Finder optics:
(F) The wide-angle viewfinder is a 4-element, 0.39X-magnification finder

[When using telephoto]
Shooting optics:
When (LS) lens selector is turned to the left, the wide-angle lens (1) comes forward, and the rear converter (2) takes the rear position, to formulate 6-component, 6-element telephoto lens (1.7X magnification telephoto)
Finder optics:
(F1) front lens (No. 1 lens) retreats out of the light path, and at the same time the second (F2) lens (No. 2 lens) pulls back to formulate the 3-element 0.61X magnification telephoto finder

OM-4: An SLR with Multispot Metering
Olympus Optical

Most light meters built into single-lens-reflex cameras measure the average brightness of the entire area to be photographed. Thus, when a subject is backlit, it invariably appears too dark in the photograph. A deliberately shadowy subject is often reduced to overall blandness.

Olympus gave control of picture tone back to the photographer with the introduction of the OM-4, which allows the measuring of multiple locations with its built-in exposure meter. Light can be measured in as many as eight different spots, and then the proper exposure is calculated in the meter's microcomputer memory. The recording and calculating functions are fairly complicated.

Now, the new OM-4Ti, the latest in an SLR, with its newly developed titanium body (wt: 510 g), sells for ¥129,000. Even though the computer element has been expanded, the over-all size of the camera is about the same as that of its less sophisticated predecessor. The OM-4 weighs 540 g without a lens attached and sells for ¥109,000.

1983 Award for Excellence

The multispot photometry structure OM-4

Nikon FM2: An Ultrafast SLR
Nippon Kogaku

Nikon set out to make a camera with an ultrahigh-speed shutter in response to requests from professional photographers who wanted to take pictures at a flash sync speed higher than 1/125 sec.

Using a flash under such conditions would require a single-lens-reflex camera with an ultimate flash sync speed of 1/200 sec.

The weight of the shutter was the critical element in increasing speed. Steel, which had been used in the past, was too heavy, and plastic resin, another candidate, was soon abandoned because it was not durable. The company also considered and rejected aluminum as being too soft, and beryllium because it produced a toxin during processing. Titanium was chosen, and its strength increased by a special treatment of the surface.

The choice of titanium, coupled with an etching process to make the shutter thin, reduced the shutter weight by 60% and made the FM2's 1/4,000-sec shutter speed possible.

1982 Award for Excellence

An ultrafast Nikon FM2 professional SLR camera

SPORTS, LEISURE, AND SUNDRY ITEMS

Omnibot: A Multifunction Toy Robot
Tomy

From Doraemon and Astro Boy to Gandam and Transformers, the word "robot" evokes many images for Japanese children. While the images take many forms, the expectations for robots and their "powers" are many and high, often higher than real-life technology allows. The gap between image and reality was the first challenge faced by engineers at Tomy when they set about to design a toy robot.

They began in 1982, at a time when many in Japan were encouraging a "science boom," in anticipation of the 1985 Tsukuba science and technology exposition. Several new magazines using graphics extensively to explain science to the layman came to the market. Industrial robots were gaining a foothold in factories, and robotics companies were grabbing the limelight among high-tech industries.

Meanwhile, toy manufacturers were in trouble as they tried to expand markets. Tomy's approach to this problem was to turn to the manufacture of robots as toys with a large potential appeal. Yet there was that gap between popular expectations and limited technological capabilities; surveys indicated that even young children held very sophisticated ideas of what robots should do.

Engineers struggled with the problem of making real robots that were also toys easily accessible to the average consumer in price and operating simplicity. Then one of them proposed combining robots and cassette tape recorders. The unprecedented combination led to a breakthrough that turned robots into a consumer product.

The built-in recorder was designed to serve not only as the robot's ears and mouth, but also its brain. A major function of the robot is to move in response to remote-control commands, and the tape recorder enabled it to "learn" and repeat such movements.

To this was added an alarm and a timer function, so that movements could be programmed in advance. When the toy also received amplifying and sing-along equipment, Multifunction Robot Toy #1 was born. It was dubbed Omnibot, the robot that could know and do all—and was put on the market in September 1984.

In marketing the Omnibot, Tomy departed from its standard sales practices. Tomy had confidence in the product; wholesalers and retailers were also enthusiastic. So Tomy decided to reverse the usual process of reaching customers through retailers. The company made a direct appeal to consumers in an advertising and publicity campaign, counting on a high rate of inquiries from customers to give retailers confidence that the robots would sell.

The strategy worked so well that Tomy was able to expand its sales network to include volume appliance stores, bookstores, and mail-order houses. The Omnibot sold more than 200,000 units from September 1984 to April 1986, 80% of those overseas. In 1986, Tomy consolidated the design and reduced the functions to offer a low-priced model for just ¥14,800.

1985 Award for Excellence

Omnibot: the robot that can wake you up with a "Good morning!"

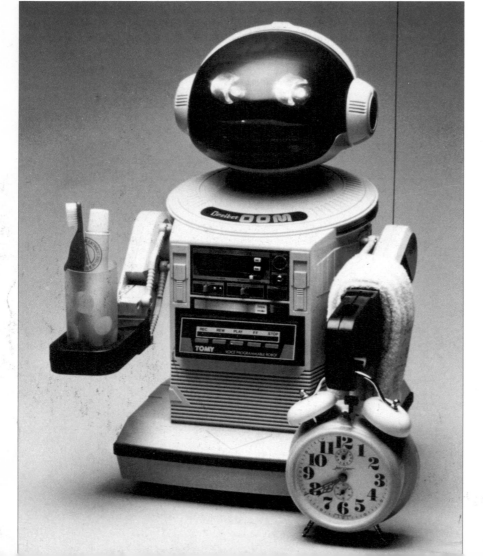

Hang-On: Motorcycle Video Game (Riding Model)
SEGA Enterprises

Hang-On is a video game with a twist: it allows the player to feel like he is actually driving a motorcycle. The player straddles a model motorcycle and holds onto a pair of handlebars while looking at the road on the video screen. Meanwhile, sound effects, from the rumble of exhaust to the blast of passing cars, come out of four speakers. Hang-On adds a new dimension to the world of ordinarily operated video games, by involving the player's whole body in the adventure. With dimensions of 199 (L) × 161 (W) × 133 (H) cm and a weight of some 240 kg, Hang-On, employing two 16-bit and one 8-bit IC devices, retails for ¥1.6 million.

SEGA's research and development department chief points out that it "took pains to replicate the angles at which a bike body leans. A great deal of effort was spent on software processing in order to mimic the sounds and sensations of a real motorcycle, essential to a motorcycle game."

Hang-On is not just an amusement machine. A major factor in its commercial success was its usefulness as a sales promotion tool. Bridgestone, for example, displayed the game to great popular acclaim at West Germany's Frankfurt International Motor Show, at the Brussels Automobile, Motor, and Cycle Exhibition in Belgium, and at other fairs. At a motor show in Italy, Turmac, the advertising agent for the English tobacco maker Rothmans, showed two models that were designed in tandem, in order to boost Rothman's image as a racing bike sponsor. Amusement and motorcycle-related businesses keep up a steady demand for the machines.

In addition to the straddle-type model, Hang-On is made in two other versions that can be played while standing or sitting. Sales for these have exceeded 10,000 units. In the commercial video game market, where games that sell 2,000 or 3,000 units are considered highly successful, Hang-On has been unusually popular.

In Japan, video games are generally designed to be played with ¥100 coins, but Hang-On requires ¥200. However, judging from the game's popularity, SEGA, as a designer of game machines, has reason to be confident in the viability of high-cost machines.

In September 1985, a contract for the knockdown assembly of Hang-On machines in Ireland was signed with the video-game maker Atari, Ireland. Because sales agreements between SEGA Enterprises and dealers in Europe have now been firmly solidified, SEGA has made Atari, Ireland its production base for the European market.

Based on the success of Hang-On, SEGA Enterprises has started selling Hang-On Mini, a compact unit that fits in the palm of the hand. The mini version is increasingly popular among middle and elementary school students who cannot yet ride motorcycles. The success of the mini version has allowed SEGA to expand sales to the consumer through toy stores, household appliance stores, and department stores.

Hang-On is not the only game that gives the player the feeling of "being there." SEGA released its fourth "body sensation game," one called Out Run that imitates a car, in September 1986.

1985 Award for Excellence

Screen color: 32K colors
Program memory capacity: 192 K bytes
Stereo sound: DA sound system with
 4 built-in speakers
Power consumption: 100 VAC 190 W

Hang-On provides plenty of thrills

Family Computer
Nintendo

In Japan, the family game computer is known as *famikon*, an abbreviation of *famiri konpyutā*. The game computer produced by Nintendo, accounting for 99% of the domestic home video-game market, has almost come to define *famikon*.

Nintendo's *famikon* began its march to the market in the early 1980s when the company's best-selling toy, the Game & Watch, a hand-held LCD game with a watch function, was still in its heyday. In the midst of success, the company began looking for a new product.

In the United States, video games were already home items that were making small game computers popular. The latter had been available in the U.S. since the 1970s, but not until games such as Nintendo's own Donkey Kong and Namco's Pac-Man captured the attention of America's children was there a demand for them.

Nintendo took note and in October 1981 began planning the new product. The company acquired samples of two hot American products—Atari's 2600 and Coleco's Coleco-Vision machines —and analyzed them thoroughly. "We learned what we could about every aspect of the software, from handling noise to calculating circuitry for program control," says Masayuki Uemura, Nintendo's research and development manager.

About the same time, a technological breakthrough in LSI manufacturing allowed semiconductor manufacturers to supply toy companies with a large volume of chips at reduced prices. "We received word that LSIs would be available at a price Nintendo wanted, so we decided to go ahead and do it," says Uemura.

Nintendo began full-scale product development in January 1982. Critical to the process was its decision to keep the *famikon*'s price low.

Reducing the cost of its *famikon* to less than ¥15,000, Nintendo was forced to compromise as it designed. Both the quality of color and the

sophistication of movement for the figures in the games suffered. Still, the resulting product struck a successful balance between price and quality, a balance that eventually attracted nearly 10 million customers. "The reason that the *famikon* has sold so well is because the ratio between price and performance is so much superior to other pastimes," says Uemura.

Nintendo also realized that at such a low price for hardware, its success lay in the continuing sale of games software. As Nintendo President Hiroshi Yamauchi says, "We sell software, not hardware."

Early in 1986, Nintendo began selling a disk drive to extend the uses of its *famikon*. The new product has three times the memory of a game

cassette, and sales of both the disk drive and its software have been very good.

The success of Nintendo's *famikon* has not gone unnoticed by other Japanese companies, especially now that it includes the disk drive. Early in 1987, Nintendo and Nomura Securities, Japan's largest securities company, announced plans to develop a system allowing investors to use their *famikons* to read market information and to buy and sell stocks at home.

1985 Award for Excellence

Measurements: 150 (W) × 220 (D) × 60 (H) mm
Weight: about 620 g (including two controllers)
Screen size: vertical 240 × horizontal 256 pixels
Scroll function: 1 dot square unit scroll
Animation: 64 animation/1 screen
Colors: 52 colors
Power requirement: use of special AC adaptor

The "Super Mario Bros." game has rekindled the family-computer fever

Yamaha PS-1600 (Keyboardissimo): A Portable Electronic Keyboard
Nippon Gakki

A professional-use, digital instrument

The primary factor in the quality of musical instruments nowadays is determined neither by the technique of the expert craftsmen, nor by large-scale manufacturing capability. It is the result of the use of a single LSI, as is the case in Nippon Gakki's Yamaha-brand electronic keyboard, PS-1600.

This portable keyboard operates on both an FM and PCM sound source. An all-digital system was realized by increasing the amount of information the LSI can process, and, as a result, the sound source can handle forty-two varieties of instrumental melodies and harmonies, and twenty-one percussion sounds. The cost of this microchip is one-fifth that of usual LSIs.

Electronic keyboards are generally incapable of subtle variations in the quality of sound. To overcome this drawback, Nippon Gakki developed a carbon-based pressure sensor that translates subtle variations in pressure on the keys into corresponding variations in sound. This allows portable keyboards to produce the highest quality of music.

1984 Award for Excellence

MSX Personal Computers for Home Use
ASCII

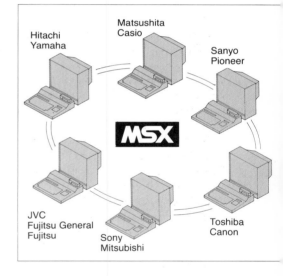

Mainframe computers and personal computers share the characteristic that the software developed for different machines is usually incompatible. The American software developer Microsoft, in conjunction with the Japanese maker ASCII, overcame this problem by offering uniform standard software to Japanese personal-computer makers. Dubbed MSX, this software was designed for use with 8-bit MSX home personal computers. Manufacturers were then able to design their machines in line with the MSX standards and thus ensure software compatibility.

A retail battle involving the MSX-based personal computers began in October 1983. More than ten companies, including Matsushita (marketed under the Panasonic brand in the U.S.), Sony, and Toshiba, joined the MSX camp, and the systems sold quite well during the Christmas rush. Since the end of 1986, more than 2 million MSX machines had been sold in the world market. The significance of MSX lies in its having set an example for future software and hardware developers to follow.

1983 Award for Excellence

Tutor: A 16-Bit Graphic Computer Toy
Tomy

The world's first 16-color graphics system

Tutor is a home video-game console, priced in the ¥50,000 range, that has earned the right to be called a personal computer.

When connected to the family TV set, Tutor's sophisticated graphics capabilities allow it to paint up to sixteen colors at the touch of a key. This means that children can not only reproduce a version of the Mona Lisa, they can also put a moustache on her.

A variety of cartridges for playing games—such as Frogger, Scramble, and Bombman—or teaching elementary arithmetic have been designed for the console. With the addition of an optional tape recorder, children can also design their own games, creating original pictures and charts.

Research and development on Tutor was slow. At a critical moment, however, an American company, Texas Instruments, introduced a 16-bit microprocessor with graphics capabilities. Tomy recognized that it could use this chip and was able to bring Tutor to the market; sales figures have proved the effort worthwhile.

1982 High Award for Excellence

Youzo: A Voice Message Device
Wagner Shokai

A high-tech memo pad

Writing memos, notes, and telephone messages can be both a time-consuming and tedious process, but with a Youzo you can not only forget such bothersome details but can also leave a personalized, verbal message. The Youzo is a voice recorder in a small box measuring 13 cm in height and 7 cm in width. It is equipped with a simple tape recorder that acts as a voice message board. The user talks while pushing a button, and records a message that can be up to 20 sec long. The message replays when the box is picked up. Youzo is popular with consumers who do not like the cold impersonality of written memos and who prefer to communicate through the warmth of the human voice, and is steadily making its way into homes and offices.

The tape mechanism was originally designed in 1983 for Melody Motion, a doll that plays a melody. In the process, designers began considering other possible uses for the recorder.

When production of the doll proved too costly, the company was left with only the recorder as an inexpensive, marketable device. The president of the company, while mulling over possible applications of the recorder, thought of the familiar sight of family members scribbling telephone messages to one another. "Wouldn't it be great to dispense with that and just speak to the person?" he thought. This idea was brought to the designers, who quickly set about applying it to the recorder they had on their hands. With the simple addition of a recording function to the tape recorder, they brought forth Youzo.

More than anything, the simplicity of the product accounts for its success. Consumers can use it in a variety of ways—mothers leaving directions for their children, sweethearts passing on affectionate words, or office workers simply relaying messages to their fellow employees.

Wagner Shokai also hopes to market it as a promotional giveaway product. Until now businesses have been limited to cigarette lighters and memo pads inscribed with company names, but these have become so commonplace that they make little impression on customers. Youzo is already playing an active part in corporate promotion for a large frozen food and candy maker

Gore Racing Wadrak: New Fabric Skiwear
Descente

The requirements placed on skiwear in Japan are particularly stringent since Japan's ski slopes have a higher degree of humidity than those of the West.

Gore-Tex, produced in the United States, is a new material that satisfies Japanese standards. It is particularly well suited for skiing, since it releases the moisture generated from body warmth, but keeps water out. It is used on the outside of Gore Racing Wadrak skiwear, while the inside is lined with light polyester cotton to maintain body temperature. Gore-Tex fits the requirements that skiwear ensure comfort, mobility, warmth, and durability, and yet still be fashionable.

The greatest difficulty in manufacturing this product was the sewing process. The holes made in stitching usually allow water to penetrate ski clothes, undermining their effective-

ness. Descente solved this problem by using waterproof thread on the outside, and by developing a new seaming process that sealed the material completely.

1982 Award for Excellence

The latest in skiwear

Yamaha YFG-45: An Oversized Tennis Racket
Nippon Gakki

The YFG-45 is a tennis racket designed for beginners. Its frame is 27% larger than that of a standard racket, and therefore it has a larger sweet spot (the area of maximum rebound). This makes it easier to handle, and improves the performance of weak players. The frame is an ideal blend of carbon for strength and fiberglass for pliancy. Carbon-based rackets are usually costly and inappropriate for beginners, but the extensive use of fiberglass in the YFG-45 has reduced the cost. The YFG-45 is the first carbon-based racket to drop below the ¥20,000 level.

Even though the demand for oversized rackets has settled down, the use of new, lightweight, inexpensive materials has allowed Nippon Gakki to go that had already been using the device at their company.

In March 1986, new models with a parrot comic character painted on the body of the unit were introduced, and Youzo has made inroads into the toy market. Since the toy market is a lucrative one, the company hopes to develop the product as a children's plaything. This toy market is increasingly dominated by electronic goods, particularly high-tech products such as *famikons*, family game computers. Children are considered an ideal target group since they are eager to play with new products and are receptive to new technology. The Youzo recorder is especially attractive, since it allows children broad range for creative expression. This should be appealing to adults who are worried about their children becoming passive video-game addicts.

1985 Award for Excellence

Computer—Talking Teacher: An Educational Toy
Takara

This talking machine is an educational toy that enables children to learn new sounds as they grow. The machine, which utilizes an LSI sound synthesizer, emits a sound and presents several cards to the child, who then must search for the corresponding card and insert it into the machine. The machine then informs the child whether or not the response is correct.

The idea for this "computer teacher" was developed in 1982 as Takara was also searching for ways to improve the quality of electronic toys. The company considers the greatest measure of its success the reports of teachers that the communication of autistic and linguistically handicapped children has greatly improved with use of this toy.

One unexpected difficulty in developing the product was the selection of the appropriate material for the cards. Paper was too weak, and injection-molded plastic was rather expensive (too expensive a price is a fatal drawback for a toy). After tests with various materials, a thick synthetic resin board was deemed suitable.

1983 Award for Excellence

Ten different word games for children ages three to six

on to produce its popular **α**-Series of lighter, easier-to-swing rackets.

1982 Award for Excellence

The easy-to-use, top-light type YEG 45

Whisker Rod: A High-Strength Fishing Pole
Daiwa Seiko

The Whisker Rod is the most advanced fishing rod available today. Three types of rods were developed: one that employed silicon-carbide whiskers; another, a carbon-fiber-reinforced resin; and another, an amorphous metallic fiber. Fishing rods have progressed from bamboo to fiberglass to carbon, but this silicon-carbide-whisker-reinforced rod is lighter and stronger than other carbon rods.

Tokai Carbon's successful mass-production of this silicon-carbide whisker prompted Daiwa Seiko to make use of it as a reinforcing material. The company's biggest problem was determining the correct percentages of carbon-fiber-resin base and silicon-carbide whiskers to use in the rod. It ultimately came up with a suitable combination and managed to hold the price down with an efficient manufacturing process.

Daiwa enjoys annual sales of ¥10 billion, and at present, the Whisker Rod has a two-thirds share of the market, which continues to expand.

1983 Award for Excellence

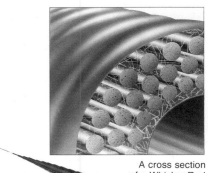

A cross section of a Whisker Rod

All Target 11: A Well-Ordered Set of Golf Clubs
Bridgestone Sports

Bridgestone Sports has developed a set of golf clubs designed to solve one of the most common problems the average golfer encounters with conventional clubs, that of choosing the proper club for middle-range distances. Conventional clubs are divided into woods, for long drives, and irons, intended for shorter drives, and each type requires a different swing. Amateur golfers frequently have difficulty with long irons, which approach the shorter range of the woods. Many players have problems adjusting their swing to the long iron, finding it difficult to drive long distances consistently with the club. This makes it difficult to choose the proper club, long iron or short wood, for this range, and Bridgestone decided to design a new set of clubs that solved the problem.

After some experimentation with redesigning conventional woods and irons, the company's engineers decided to abandon this approach altogether,

and rethink the fundamental nature of golf-club design. Their answer was a well-ordered set of eleven clubs in a continuous series that maintains a systematic change in the shape of the head, the length of the shaft, the angle of the loft, and the position of the center of gravity. The distance and trajectory that the ball travels therefore change by the same increment from club to club, and all clubs swing alike. Thus the new clubs eliminate the uncertainty in club selection as well as the need to master a different swing for woods and irons.

Bridgestone achieved this by combining the latest technology in materials with conventional design. The All Target 11 clubs are made of metal, and the surface of the head is coated with a baked enamel. A slight bulge in the faces of the new clubs that correspond to traditional long irons yields greater accuracy and longer distances.

The designers tried to follow con-

ventional design as closely as possible, since they doubted that players would accept a radically different club. To test golfers' reactions to the new clubs, Bridgestone took them to Orlando, Florida, in 1985. There the clubs were exhibited in a hotel near a trade fair for American golf products. The appearance of the new clubs, then called ARX, caused quite a stir, and Bridgestone was deluged with questions concerning their performance and the development process.

Word of American interest in the new product reached Japan before it was placed on the Japanese market. Before it went on sale, consumers were asked to select a name for the product. Thereafter, it was sold in Japan as All Target 11. Bridgestone reports that

---

Carboniron: Carbon-Graphite Golf Club
Yonex

The Yonex Carboniron golf club is an iron that allows golfers to increase the distance of their shots by 10–15% compared with driving with conventional clubs. This feature has made it a particularly popular item among golf-

ers who have weaker strokes.

The secret to the power of this club is its head. Conventional irons have heads made of stainless steel, while the Carboniron head is compression molded of high-quality carbon graphite. Yonex used an ultrahigh-temperature manufacturing process to produce the club. The supertough layers of carbon graphite produce a club face that maximizes the coefficient of repulsion, for power play. In designing the head, Yonex reinforced the material with long, continuous fibers that are soft, but highly resistant. Thus, the carbon head makes a strong, cushioned strike against the ball, holding it longer than does a conventional club. This produces a shot that travels correspondingly higher and farther.

1984 Award for Excellence

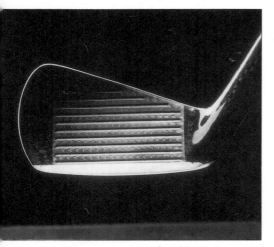

Yonex's popular Carboniron club

Altus: A Double-Layered Golf Ball
Bridgestone

The Altus golf ball is composed of two layers: a highly elastic core of polybutadiene rubber covered by a strong ionomer resin. The advantage of this ball

The low-spin and wind-resistant Altus

although consumers were skeptical at first, the fact that scores improved with the new clubs spread by word of mouth. Because All Target 11 has become so popular since its appearance on the market, other companies in Japan and the U.S. have developed similar clubs. By the end of 1985, the U.S. manufacturer Spalding was selling its version of the clubs in Japan, and Bridgestone began exporting its product to the United States the following year.

1985 Award for Excellence

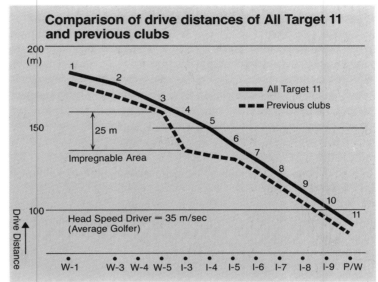

Comparison of drive distances of All Target 11 and previous clubs

— All Target 11
--- Previous clubs

25 m

Impregnable Area

Head Speed Driver = 35 m/sec (Average Golfer)

Drive Distance

W-1 W-3 W-4 W-5 I-3 I-4 I-5 I-6 I-7 I-8 I-9 P/W

over the traditional golf ball is that less friction occurs when it is hit by a club. Thus, the ball can travel longer distances without spinning. Additionally, the outside covering is stronger than that of a conventional ball, and does not damage as easily.

A double-layered ball was first developed in America for golfers who wanted a ball that would travel farther. Recognizing that this was an important innovation, Bridgestone set out to develop its own version of the ball. It established a team to start research and development from scratch, and invested ¥300 million in a new production line in Yokohama.

Professional golfers started to use Altus soon after it appeared on the market, and a boom in sales ensued. Altus's popularity has helped to boost the share of double-layered balls to over 70% of Japan's golf ball market.

1982 Award for Excellence

Vanguard The First: Graphite Wood Golf Clubs
Mizuno

These new Vanguard woods from Mizuno feature heads made of a carbon-fiber-reinforced resin. Golfers have found that they are good for beginners and produce longer, more accurate drives on the fairway.

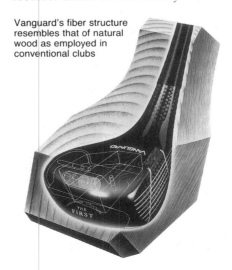

Vanguard's fiber structure resembles that of natural wood as employed in conventional clubs

Dubbed "the scientific clubs" because of the technology and computers used in their design, the Vanguard The First clubs have heads composed of high-quality graphite hardened with resins. This composition allows for considerable freedom in designing the shape of the heads and results in better performance. The specific gravity of the carbon is twice that of the more traditional persimmon wood. The new clubs are also constructed with a hollow head, filled with polyurethane. The combination of the heavy outside and lighter core means that the Vanguard head has a larger sweet spot, the area that provides the optimum force for a golfer's swing. There are five woods in the Vanguard series, ranging in price from ¥50,000 to ¥120,000.

1982 Award for Excellence

Team-Demi: A Mini Stationery Kit
Plus

The Japanese are known for their ability to take a product, make it compact, and package it well, but even by Japanese standards, Team-Demi has made its mark in this world of miniatures. Team-Demi is a small-scale stationery kit that contains the world's smallest stapler, scissors, tape measure, a cutter, water-based glue, transparent tape, and ruler, all in a small plastic case of 12 × 9 × 4 cm. The ruler even has holes every 1 cm so that it can also be used as a compass. Available now in nine colors, Team-Demi is extremely popular in fashion-conscious Japan.

Plus, a leading manufacturer of office furniture and stationery items, faced great difficulties in the early 1980s since the demand for stationery items was dwindling. With the hope of attracting general consumers, it developed the Demitasse, a stapler measuring 18 × 35 × 19 mm. Despite its compact size, it holds fifty standard-sized staples and can attach papers the thickness of twelve sheets of newspaper. Although its price was nearly 65% higher than that of the average stapler, the Demitasse sold well. Based on its success, Plus decided to launch an entire set of miniature stationery items.

Plus began developing this set in early 1983. In April, when college graduates traditionally enter Japanese companies, Plus decided to include three young workers fresh out of college on its project development team. Until this time, Plus had only used its young and inexperienced employees in sales. Only after years of experience were they allowed to work in product development. Plus had also chosen to include a woman on this team, hoping that she could provide fresh, exciting, and innovative ideas.

The company's hopes were not unfounded. The young woman came up with the idea for a miniature stationery set in a compact case, and after working with a designer, developed a prototype. Her work was not finished at this point however, since she had to find manufacturers willing to produce the miniature stationery items. Since the product was experimental, the number of units made was very small and producing items to match the designer's specifications was difficult. The scissors, for example, posed particular problems. The manufacturer claimed that if produced according to specifications, they would break when cutting something thick. The final product has thicker and stronger blades of 6 mm and a still-thin body of 7 mm.

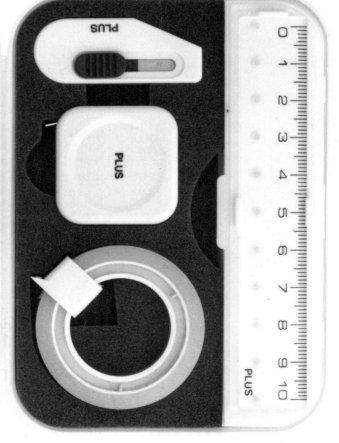

The actual size of Team-Demi

When Team-Demi went on sale, it was an immediate success and, priced at ¥2,800, the mini stationery kit is now one of Plus's best-selling products. The fact that a young woman was behind the development of Team-Demi received considerable media attention in both newspapers and magazines. By the end of June 1986, just a little less than a year after Team-Demi was put on the market, an astounding 4.5 million kits had been sold. In addition, the product's success prompted many other companies to manufacture miniaturized sets of items, such as tool kits and cosmetic kits.

1985 Award for Excellence

Arston 15: Zirconia-Based Ceramic Scissors
Ars Edge/Toray Industries

This is the first pair of scissors to use a zirconia-based ceramic in its blades. To date, ceramic scissors have been alumina-based, but zirconia-based scissors are stronger. The Arston 15 can even cut aramid fiber, which metallic scissors cannot do.

The properties of zirconium oxide (ZrO_2) led to the development of these scissors. Compared with aluminum oxide (Al_2O_3), ZrO_2 is stronger and more shock-resistant, and therefore better suited to cutting. A major drawback of aluminum-oxide scissors is that they are too brittle. While the average steel scissor is sharp enough to be used 100,000 times, the zirconia-based blade is still sharp enough to cut gauze even after being used 1 million times. Furthermore, the blade is smooth, heat- and rust-resistant, and does not conduct electricity.

The hardest problem to overcome turned out to be the finishing of the blade. After repeated failures, the makers were able to form a blade that satisfied all the requirements for durability and cutting.

1983 Award for Excellence

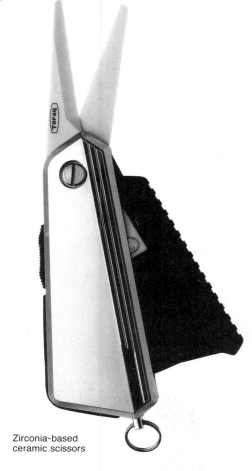

Zirconia-based ceramic scissors

Etona-01: The ¥100 Stapler
Etona

Setting out to win a greater share of the Japanese stapler market, Etona decided to develop a product with the same capabilities as existing staplers, but one that would catch the attention of consumers with its extremely low price. Recalling the popularity of ¥100 lighters, Etona chose ¥100 as the optimum selling price. However, the only way to achieve this goal was to make a stapler out of plastic.

Except for the anvil, the spring, and the driver that pushes out the staple, all the parts of this stapler are made of plastic resin, ABS, and polyacetal resin, which costs less than one-third the price of metal. Plastic has the additional advantage that it allows the entire body to be produced in one piece, further lowering the price. To reduce abrasion at the mouth of the stapler, glass fiber was mixed with the resin to strengthen it. Etona was worried that consumers would regard plastic as weaker than metal, but four months after its introduction, the Etona-01 obtained a 25% market share.

1983 Award for Excellence

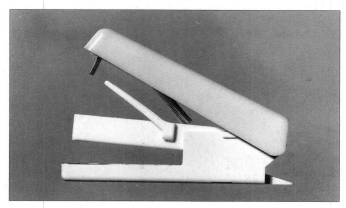

The Etona-01 can be used more than 60,000 times

Household Deodorizers Series
Morishita Jintan

Morishita Jintan, previously known only as a maker of thermometers and of breath-freshening candies, gambled the future of the company on the development of an entirely new product line. In December 1983, Morishita Jintan inaugurated a 12-woman project team, called the Jintan Woman's Lab, whose task it was to generate ideas for products that would appeal to consumers. The first product that this team conceived—a household deodorizer—became a major success.

An important element in the Household Deodorizers Series is the deodorizer base Anico. Unlike other deodorizers, which employ activated carbon that physically absorbs an odor, Anico is a chemical deodorizer that neutralizes odorous particles by chemically transforming them. The deodorizer is sold along with a questionnaire

postcard and a pamphlet entitled "The Science of Odors." This establishes a channel of communication with consumers, and the group receives fifty to sixty replies a day.

The next task was to design the deodorizers to be aesthetically appealing and easy to use. This proved to be a challenge for the team, since it was their goal to develop many different designs for each deodorizer. The team planned to produce eleven different varieties of deodorizer, including ones for the car, toilet, household cupboards, shoe cabinet (present at the entrance of every Japanese house, since it is customary to remove one's shoes before entering the living area), and sports locker. One reason for the popularity of the series is its innovative package design. The toilet deodorizer, for example, comes in the form of a

sheet imprinted with a picturesque fairy-tale scene that enlivens the restroom area. It is available with fourteen different pictures. The locker deodorizer comes in nine different trendy cloth bags that can be hung from a hook, while the cupboard deodorizer folds so that it can fit into the corner of a shelf. Until now such products were combinations of air fresheners and dessicants, but the Household Deodorizers Series is the first product to be sold purely as a deodorizer.

With no experience in the market, the company placed great reliance on the judgment of the Woman's Lab and encouraged its members' complete involvement in product development, from conception and marketing research to retail sales planning. Their enthusiasm at being so closely involved in the development of a product even

---

Sterapore Mashimizu: A Portable Water Purifier
Mitsubishi Rayon

Sterapore Mashimizu is a portable water purifier that immediately provides potable water. It evolved from a purifier designed by Mitsubishi Rayon for hospital use. This portable version for travelers consists of a plastic case with a capacity for one liter, a hand pump pressurizer, and a cartridge divided into two sections. Water is passed through the bottom portion of the cartridge, which contains layers of silver-treated activated carbon. Organic and chemical materials are filtered out at this point by means of absorption and decomposition. Pressure from the hand pump then pushes the water into the upper portion of the filter. This consists of a hollow-fiber membrane that traps many ultramicro particulates, including bacteria and rust.

The idea for this purifier came from the president of Mitsubishi Rayon who, affected by bad water while on a trip to Mexico, recognized the need for a water purifier that could be taken abroad. Its light weight (420 g) and low

price have made it very popular with travelers.

1984 Award for Excellence

A truly portable water purifier

Bub: A Bath Tablet for Good Health
Kao

Bub is a new type of bath tablet that promotes good health and relaxation. Its development began in 1981, when Kao's R & D division began testing the effects of carbon dioxide (CO_2) in hot water upon blood circulation. It is well known, for example, that CO_2 springs have long been popular in Europe for the treatment of circulatory diseases. Thus, Kao's household products' planning and development division joined forces with the R & D division to develop a new kind of bath tablet.

The greatest problem Kao faced was how to get CO_2 into the household bath. After numerous tests, Kao decided to add succinic acid to sodium hydrogen carbonate to create a mixture that would release CO_2 when it came in contact with water. The mixture is shaped by a tablet-molding machine into tablets about 25 cm^2. The tablets are individually wrapped for long shelf life, and packaged in a gaily colored brought them into retail stores on weekends to help promote the company's sales campaigns.

Despite the rather familial aspect to the development of these deodorizers, Morishita Jintan regards this market as an important one. Before the Household Deodorizers Series appeared on the market, sales for refrigerator and toilet deodorizers alone amounted to over ¥13.4 billion. The series was started with the goal of obtaining a 30% share of the domestic deodorizer market. While producing such a highly diversified range of products inevitably increases costs, Morishita Jintan is willing to gamble for what it sees are high stakes.

1985 Award for Excellence

A team of women developed these deodorizer products

gaily colored box. Sales totaling some ¥8 billion in 1984 have contributed to a sizable increase in the bath-tablet market.

1984 High Award for Excellence

Enjoy a CO_2-bath in your own tub

Moony Disposable Diapers
Uni-Charm

Disposable diapers first appeared in Japan in 1978, when Procter & Gamble Far East introduced Pampers. Uni-Charm's contribution to this field is a disposable diaper that, unlike its competitors, does not leak. These diapers have two features that distinguish them from similar products. There is an extrathick layer of absorbant pulp in the middle, and a 3-cm length of gathering along the leg holes near the crotch. The gathering is made of polyurethane rubber, and thus does not cause pain to the baby or leave any marks on its legs. As a result, the product has answered the main complaint of mothers—that disposable diapers leak—to make the diapers a hit and give Uni-Charm the No. 1 share in the Japanese market.

The company later increased its market share by introducing a specially reinforced product for nighttime use in 1985, causing a severe price war with its biggest domestic rival, Kao. Disposable diapers represent one of the expanding areas in the toiletries market.

1982 High Award for Excellence

Paper diapers that do not leak

Lady '80 BIO Lipstick
Kanebo

Shikonin is an extract from the root of the *Lithospermum erythrorhizon*, a plant that has been used for medicines and dyes in Japan since ancient times. It has antibacterial, anti-inflammatory, and skin-moisturizing properties, as well as a deep, rich color.

Since, however, it is found in only very small amounts in nature (only 1–2% of the root is extractable as Shikonin), a research team at Mitsui Petrochemical Industries decided to produce it biotechnologically.

Kanebo took advantage of the resulting low price of Shikonin and used the material in some of its cosmetics. The name BIO Lipstick was chosen to suggest the high technology embodied in the product. That was then followed by an advertising campaign featuring a popular singer using the lipsticks that was a tremendous hit in Japan. In 1984, over two million lipsticks, or ¥6 billion worth of merchandise, was shipped, an unparalleled success in the Japanese cosmetics industry. This is an eloquent testimony to the rightness of Kanebo's marketing strategy.

1984 High Award for Excellence

A moisturizing lipstick

The Mitsukoshi Shopping Bag
Mitsukoshi Department Store

The typical department-store shopping bag in Japan usually has a solid color, is rather subdued (with the store's name prominently displayed), and is gratis. Mitsukoshi, however, decided to introduce a shopping bag of striking design and sell it as a separate product, instead of simply giving it away with any purchase. The bag is extremely popular, especially with younger customers. It has a bold pattern of yellow, blue, white, red, black, and green horizontal stripes, and is available in three sizes. Since the beginning of sales in 1983, it has been at the height of fashion, especially with young women.

The two female members of the staff of the design department of Mitsukoshi who were directly involved in the bag's development said that the choice of colors, the shading, and the arrangement of the colors was a difficult process. The six colors were selected by an analysis of the most common colors of flags of the nations of the world, on the assumption that national flags usually reflect people's favorite colors.

1983 Award for Excellence

Colorful shopping bags

Non-Brandname 22" Bicycle
Seiyu

A no-frills bicycle

Seiyu has developed and sold over 1,100 different generic products—goods sold under the Non-Brandname brand name. Although it is rather unusual for a supermarket to sell a large consumer good as a non-brandname item, one of its most popular private brands has been the Non-Brandname bicycle, which went on sale in September 1982.

The concept behind the non-brandname products is the minimization of costs by simplifying the production process and dispensing with fancy packaging. This bicycle is a model of success in this respect. The no-frills equipment conforms to legal and safety standards, and the lamp, basket, mud guards, and luggage rack are sold separately as options. Consumers express satisfaction at its low price and at the fact that they can paint the bicycle any color they like (it is white when bought) and add equipment according to their own tastes. Sales of the bicycle have been very high, prompting retailers to reconsider their concept of generic products.

1982 High Award for Excellence

CLOTHING, FOOD, AND HOUSING

Physical Stretch Pants: Stretch Slacks for Business
Kashiyama

Businessmen have a definite need for trousers that can be worn for long periods without showing creases or sags. Stretch slacks for golf, made of a mixture of polyurethane and polyester, have been available for some time, but Kashiyama's Physical Stretch Pants are the first stretch slacks for business use that are made primarily of wool. The wool is blended with polyester, which normally ruins wool's special appearance and texture, but Kashiyama obtained the assistance of Gunze, a textile manufacturer, in developing a spinning process that preserves the characteristic qualities of wool.

Physical Stretch Pants are made of a blend of 60% wool, 35% polyester, and 5% polyurethane, a rubberlike fiber that makes the fabric stretchable. Thus, Kashiyama's stretch pants are both functional and fashionable.

The most difficult part in developing the pants was retaining the special look and feel of the wool. Slacks are a fashion item, so if they are to sell, they must not only be functional but also look attractive.

With the cooperation of Gunze, Kashiyama developed a solution to this problem in the spinning stage of production. It selected thick polyester fibers and thin woolen ones and spun them at high speed, using centrifugal force to create a fiber with wool on the outside, polyester on the inside, and polyurethane in between.

Sales of the new slacks far exceeded the marketing goal. In the spring and summer of 1985, the company had sales of 14,500 pairs and in 1986, some 45,000 pairs. Kashiyama decided to develop several more articles of stretch clothing. The next product put on the market was a blazer, and then samples of a winter model of the slacks were released. The company worked hard to develop these slacks, which were of a heavier fabric and more complicated weave and cut than the summer slacks. The samples were very well received and the winter slacks were soon sold nationwide. The next item to follow was a suit made of the new stretch material.

There is a phrase in Japanese, "the sewer-rat look," that refers to businessmen who wear drab and dark navy or grey suits. In the past, most men bought suits off the rack and paid little attention to fashion. With Japan's recent economic prosperity and an accompanying reexamination of the quality of the basics of daily life, it seems that businessmen are now paying more attention to their work clothing.

Hence, more fashionable business wear is now in demand. Japanese men are abandoning the monotonous, monochrome designs in business suits for more fashionable individualized wear. But these lines have been developed mainly by smaller makers. The major apparel manufacturers, such as Kashiyama and Renown, have long continued to put the major emphasis on comfort and practicality, as well as on appearance and cost. Most of Kashiyama's Physical Stretch Pants are sold for ¥14,900, a price that makes them affordable for many salaried workers.

1985 Award for Excellence

A blend of three different fibers (inset) is the secret of Kashiyama's stretch pants

Kumikko Kaekko: Mix-and-Match Bras
Wacoal

Designed for girls in their teens, this mix-and-match bra series offers the fun of putting together components of different patterns and colors. Its cups and straps can be separated and combined as desired.

The idea for a mix-and-match brassiere was derived from a pair of sneakers that was sold with a choice of laces. A member of a company team planning new teenager brassieres for the spring and summer seasons mentioned that she had seen such sneakers for sale in a shoe store and that they appeared to be popular with young people. The idea seemed to appeal to the playful spirit and fashion-consciousness of teenagers, and the members of the team reasoned that this might be applicable to underwear as well.

Developing the product for manufacture was not technically difficult, but choosing colors and patterns suitable for a brassiere stumped the designers at first. Since it was firmly believed in the underwear industry in Japan that most teenagers wanted their underwear in a plain white or off-white fabric, the Wing Division at Wacoal was truly taking a new direction.

Strong colors and loud patterns would be necessary to make the mix-and-match bra series stand out, but it was felt that young girls would hesitate to wear such flashy underwear.

The designers finally ended up with three patterns—plain, stripes, and polka dots—in three colors—pink, pale blue, and off-white. Thus, they were able to offer nine varieties of convertible cups and shoulder straps.

In initial marketing tests, the first sample group was lukewarm in its evaluation of the bra, and subsequent exposure at trade shows and exhibitions only further deflated expectations for the product. Nevertheless, the new line went on the market in February 1985, and Wacoal distributed this product to about 600 stores across Japan. Within about two months, orders began to pour in from retail stores, and reports relayed by sales promotion staff dispatched to shops revealed that the item was gaining popularity.

The division immediately stepped up production. It secured the company's in-house production line and delayed the manufacture of other lines that could wait, and in July and August even subcontracted manufacturing to outside factories.

By the end of the summer season, sales of the bra had exceeded the expected target by more than 300%.

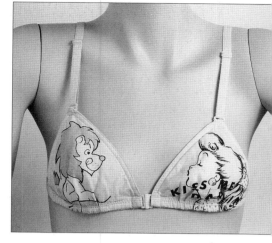
The latest in teenage underwear

The division continued to develop new features, coming out with reversible cups with different patterns on each side, and a set of cartoon faces (girls on one side, boys on the other) called Kiss Me. These, too, became topics of conversation among teenagers, and sales again exceeded expected levels. The mix-and-match bras have already become the Wing Division's most successful product. They are an example of a great success born from a small idea.

1985 Award for Excellence

Cross-Cut Girdles
Wacoal

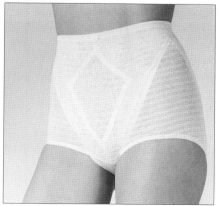
A cross-cut structure for comfort

These girdles were developed to eliminate the uncomfortable pinching of the inner thighs often caused by full-support girdles. An inner and an outer layer of material are crossed at the inner thigh, just at the places on each leg where an ordinary girdle would pinch. These layers redistribute pressure from the thigh to the lower stomach and crotch, thus allowing for more comfortable movement.

Most girdles, although sold in several sizes, take only the hip and waist sizes into account, and do not allow for variations in thigh size. But even among women whose hip and waist size may match the size of a girdle, there are many cases where thigh sizes differ considerably. These Cross-Cut Girdles are designed to give the best fit and the greatest freedom available in a girdle.

Wacoal, which puts emphasis on quality and function, is known for spending considerable time and money on research and development, resulting in products of very high quality. This girdle, three years in development, is an example of Wacoal's excellent workmanship.

1983 Award for Excellence

Xing: Simple Knit Goods
Scoop

Scoop's mix-and-match knits provide variety and style

The Xing (pronounced "Crossing") brand, jointly developed by Scoop, an apparel maker popular with young people, and Marui, a large department-store chain, was an attempt by two major forces in the world of women's clothing to introduce a new fashion concept. They designed a line of mix-and-match knits. Designer wear is usually sold in specialized sections in department stores, but Xing is sold at Marui's regular counters.

To make this new line of coordinated knitwear a success, Scoop employed dramatic new sales methods. Video-disk systems were installed near the department-store counters where this line was sold. By watching the screen, customers could see the variety of ways that these clothes could be mixed and matched. Customers are asked to program personal data, which enables the company to send them highly personalized mail concerning its products.

The Xing line has been a great success and in 1985 a Xing men's line was introduced.

1983 Award for Excellence

Planned: Machine-Washable Woolen Sweaters
taka-Q

Woolen sweaters, although comfortable and fashionable, cannot be washed by machine without shrinking, and sometimes fading as well. A leading fashion chain specializing in men's and women's clothing, taka-Q, together with the International Wool Secretariat, developed a special process by which resin is soaked into woolen yarn, allowing a sweater knit from that yarn to be washed in a machine without shrinking.

After developing a machine-washable sweater, the next problem the company faced was that machine washing caused the color of the darker-colored sweaters to fade. However, taka-Q came up with a new method of treating the yarn that helps make even those colors that fade easily more colorfast. Another problem was that the type of knitting employed limits the variety of sweaters that can be made. This has not affected the popularity of the Planned sweaters, though, as sales have been encouragingly high. In the 1985 fall/winter season, 60,000 sweaters were sold.

1982 Award for Excellence

A machine-washable sweater made of yarn

Kanecalon: Artificial Fur
Kanegafuchi Chemical Industry

Kanecalon is quite popular among young Japanese women. The acrylic fiber used in this fur was developed by Kanegafuchi Chemical Industry. In 1957 the company entered the synthetic fiber field and developed Kanecalon, an acrylic fiber that it used in men's suits and blankets. In 1971 it developed a longer fiber using Kanecalon appropriate for use in items such as artificial furs, stuffed animals, and carpeting, and by 1975 the first artificial furs made of these fibers were available on the market.

These artificial fibers can be processed to resemble mink, fox, and many other types of furs, and their flexibility and sheen give the finished product a high quality unusual in artificial fur. They can also be dyed unusual, breathtaking colors.

Artificial furs are currently a success not only among those who object to wearing real animal hides, but also among those who enjoy wearing vivid colors and designs.

1982 Award for Excellence

Artificial fur that feels authentic

Hicellent: Fermented Milk Drink
Calpis Food Industry

Hicellent is a concentrated beverage made from skimmed milk fermented with lactic bacteria and then once again with wine yeast and white grape juice. It is prepared by adding four parts water to one part Hicellent concentrate. With an alchoholic content of less than 1%, it has a taste somewhat similar to wine-flavored yoghurt. The drink was created by Calpis Food Industry, which had been known for its Calpis, another fermented-milk concentrate that has been a popular drink and household word since its invention in 1919. The rather unique name is a combination of "cal," from calcium, and "pis," from *sarpis*, a Buddhist word for "superior taste." Calpis has been a success for so many years that it was only in the 1980s, when sales suddenly declined, that Calpis Foods saw a need for a new product. For a company whose profits depended nearly entirely on one product, diversification presented a significant challenge.

Since Calpis is inexpensive and particularly popular with children, in its new product, Calpis Foods wanted to develop a new beverage that would be slightly more upmarket. Drawing on its long history of research in lactic bacteria fermentation methods acquired over the years spent on the production of Calpis, the company developed a new product. By 1982 a prototype for Hicellent was ready, using similar production methods to Calpis and then adding wine yeast and white grape juice. This gave it a more sophisticated flavor in comparison with Calpis. In order to give its product a quality image, Calpis Foods named the product Hicellent: "hi" from high, and "cellent" from excellent.

Rather than adopting standard advertising techniques using mass media, Calpis Foods decided to reach customers directly through a taste-testing campaign. The campaign was launched in 1984, and within one year over 50,000 people in Fukuoka prefecture had sampled Hicellent. In 1985 Hicellent was put on the market all over Japan. By the end of 1985, 1 million people had sampled the drink. Although it has yet to surpass Calpis in popularity or sales, demand for this beverage is growing steadily.

In addition to marketing aimed toward general consumers, Calpis Foods also decided to try and penetrate the gift-giving market of Japan. In Japan it is customary to give gifts, not only on special occasions, but when making social calls. Standard gifts are food, beverages, soaps, towels, or other daily necessities and household items. Calpis Foods, recognizing that Hicellent had potential for this substantial gift market, conducted marketing research. Its research in Fukuoka indicated that 74% thought Hicellent an appropriate drink to offer guests or to give as a gift item, and 31% thought it a good beverage to enjoy with friends. In order to accommodate the gift market, Calpis Foods designed, in addition to the original 550-ml Hicellent bottle, a 90-ml bottle sold in boxes containing two, three, four, or five bottles. It is available in plain (yoghurt), muscat grape, blueberry, and orange flavors.

1985 High Award for Excellence

More than a million people have tasted Hicellent in a thoroughgoing, all-Japan campaign

Green Tea Drink: Canned Japanese Tea
Ito-en

Hot green tea, the traditional drink of Japan, has been rapidly overwhelmed by foreign competition since the end of World War II. Coffee, black and Chinese teas, fruit juices, and carbonated drinks are now the favorite beverages of the Japanese. In fact, the ratio of those who drink coffee to those who consume green tea has been completely inverted in the last forty years.

Ito-en set out to reverse this trend with the introduction of canned green tea. One problem the company faced was the question of whether consumers would actually pay money for such a product, since green tea is usually served for free in Japanese restaurants. However, Ito-en's recent success with unsweetened canned oolong tea led it to believe that the Japanese market was ready for another canned, sugarless, calorie-free drink.

Technical problems with product development delayed the introduction of canned green tea to the market. There are three major varieties of tea: black tea, in which the tea leaves are completely fermented with an oxidizing enzyme; oolong tea, in which the enzymes of the tea leaves are partially

fermented; and green tea, in which the leaves are quickly steamed in order to prevent oxidation. When green tea is left to stand after brewing, its color gradually changes from green to brown and the flavor changes because the tannin within the tea oxidizes. As a result, canning a green tea drink was long considered almost impossible. Ito-en, however, developed a packaging method which prevents oxidization by removing iron from the water and minimizing exposure of the liquid to oxygen during the canning process.

After conquering the technical problems, Ito-en moved on to the question of the tea's flavor. The flavor of green tea varies greatly with the locale where the tea leaves are produced and the way in which the tea is brewed. Yet Ito-en had to produce a palatable flavor suitable for mass consumption. A survey of 10,000 consumers was conducted in order to determine the best flavor, which was then reproduced in Ito-en's brewing process.

Usually, hot green tea is served in homes or in offices, but the company intended to make its green tea drink a year-round beverage that could be con-

sumed virtually anywhere, hot or cold, and has largely attained this goal. Canned green tea is now considered a suitable beverage for such outdoor activities as hiking, fishing, or playing tennis. In order to achieve these results, the tea was targeted at young people, especially singles. This strategy has proved successful, as evinced by high sales at lunch-box stands and convenience stores.

One unexpected result has been that even older people, who already drink green tea regularly, have also started to drink Ito-en's canned green tea because of its convenience. Instead of brewing their own, they can simply warm up the canned green tea. Thus, Ito-en has succeeded in making a canned green tea drink that is popular with all age groups. Although canned green tea represents only 1% of the total green tea market, this figure grows by 40% every year.

1985 Award for Excellence

Green Tea Drink—Japanese tradition in a can

Can Chu-Hi: Light Drinks in Cans
Takara Shuzō

A refreshing, low-alcohol drink

Drinkers in Japan are beginning to show a preference for lighter alcoholic beverages. The traditional drink of the lower classes—*shōchū*, an inexpensive distilled white liquor—forms the base of this new product, which has recently become very popular among Japan's younger drinkers. Takara's Can Chu-Hi was responsible for starting this trend.

Takara, a major producer of *shōchū*, added it to carbonated water and natural fruit juices and packaged it in aluminum cans to make a drink that is light in taste and low in alcohol (8%). It comes in flavors such as lemon, plum, grapefruit, and lime. Takara also markets a lighter line (4%).

The name derives from the words *shōchū* and "highball," thus, Chu-Hi. Chu-Hi is sold in attractively decorated aluminum cans, with fashionable designs intended to appeal to young people. The price has been kept low, and in the first year that the product was on the market 5.8 million 24-can cases were sold.

1984 Award for Excellence

Marunama: A Round, 1.8-L Draft Beer Container
Suntory

Suntory, known primarily for its whiskey rather than its beer, has been waging a fierce battle to win customers away from Japan's Big Three brewers—Kirin, Sapporo, and Asahi. One way it has been able to attract consumer attention is through the innovative designs of its beer containers.

The container for Marunama is almost a perfect sphere—quite an eye-catcher when on the shelf with other brands of beer. The name of this product itself—Marunama—is also quite a distinctive attention-getter, as "maru" means round and "nama" means draft.

Draft beer that stays fresh longer

This shape, which has never before been used for draft beer, has numerous advantages for the consumer, according to Suntory, such as minimizing the surface area relative to volume, which reduces the escape of carbon dioxide, and keeping the beer fresh and cool longer.

Although Suntory has not managed to break into the ranks of the Big Three brewers, it has consistently maintained the lead in the beer-packaging war.

1983 Award for Excellence

Alcock Light Cocktail: A Powdered Alcoholic Drink Mix
Sato Food Industries

It just did not work when Sato Food Industries tried to develop a powdered form of white soy sauce. The alcohol, which is needed to give soy sauce its characteristic flavor, kept evaporating during the powder-making process.

What did work, however, was the technology gained from the experiment to make a powdered alcoholic drink mix—the Alcock Light Cocktail.

Since 1967, Sato Foods has sold powdered alcohol for industrial use in candies, hams, cake mixes, and similar foods. It knew that dextrin, a starch hydrolyte, would dissolve in water but not in alcohol. Combining the two "secrets" resulted in the powdered cocktail. When the light cocktail reached the market, one six-month period saw sales of 1.2 million packets.

Since then, sales of the Light Cocktail have been curtailed in Japan. Domestic legal restrictions complicated its sale abroad. Sato Foods has since gone on to produce a best-selling line of various spray-dried instant teas.

1982 Award for Excellence

Powdered cocktail mixes

Soybean Protein Sheets
Hanamaruki

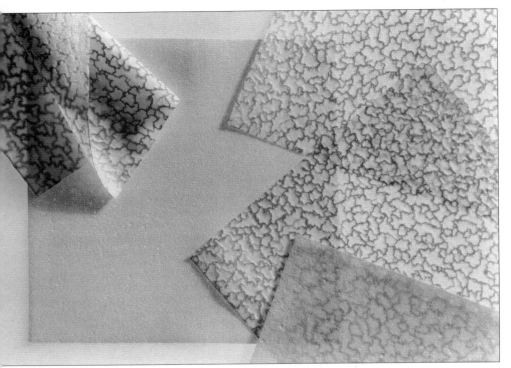

A variety of different soybean sheets

Soybean products such as tofu and miso (bean paste) have been mainstays in the Japanese diet since the seventh century when they were introduced from China. Miso is a soybean paste that serves as a base for soup. This soup, known as *misoshiru,* is an indispensable part of Japanese-style breakfasts. Although these soybean products are usually considered to be traditional foods, in recent years new forms of soybean foods have been introduced.

A crepe made without eggs

Pal Sweet $\frac{1}{60}$: A Low-Calorie Sweetener
Ajinomoto

Pal Sweet $\frac{1}{60}$ is an artificial sweetener that contains a new amino-acid sweetening agent, aspartame, that is 200 times sweeter than sugar. Aspartame is a combination of two amino acids: aspartic acid and phenylalanine. The sweetener was originally developed in 1965 by the American pharmaceutical company, G. D. Searle, a division of which was renamed NutraSweet in 1986. This company has worked since 1970 with Ajinomoto, which established a production technique for the sweetener. Ajinomoto is the largest manufacturer of monosodium glutamate (MSG) and amino-acid products in the world.

Unlike cyclamate and saccharine, aspartame is thought to be a noncarcinogenic artificial sweetener. The product was officially approved by the American Food and Drug Administration in 1981, and by the Japanese Ministry of Health and Welfare in 1983. It is available for consumer use in granule and tablet form, with only one-sixtieth the calories of sugar.

1984 High Award for Excellence

Low-calorie sweetener

Jagamaru-kun:
A Low-Calorie Snack
Seven-Eleven·Japan/ Nakamuraya

Jagamaru-kun is a low-calorie snack that has started a trend for such foods in Japan. It consists of potatoes, mashed and then baked without their skins. Nakamuraya, a long-established food manufacturer, developed this product, which consists of mashed potatoes filled with a ground pork and vegetable filling. The mashed potatoes are molded and baked so that they resemble a baked potato in appearance. The product is sold exclusively by Seven-Eleven, an extremely successful convenience-store chain in Japan. This was the first time a major Japanese food manufacturer and a major convenience-store chain joined forces to create a product. Their efforts met with great success.

After appearing in April 1984, some 25 million Jagamaru-kuns were sold in

Hanamaruki, the second-largest Japanese miso manufacturer, is at the forefront of development of new food products, one of which is its soybean protein sheets. These sheets, made of soybean protein, water, vegetable oil, salt, and preservatives, can be produced in a variety of flavors, aromas, and colors. Continuous rolls 40 cm wide and 0.1 mm thick, the sheets resemble crepes or egg-roll skins, which in fact were the inspiration for the product. When Shichirō Niwano, head of product development at Hanamaruki, visited a plant that produced the thin wheat-flour skins for egg rolls, he had the notion that a similar process could be duplicated using soybean derivatives to produce continuous roll sheets.

The idea of soybean protein sheets seemed simple enough—*yuba*, a sheet-type soybean protein, had long been an element of the Japanese diet—but Hanamaruki encountered consider-able problems in development of a soybean protein product only 0.1 mm in thickness. If the mixture contained too much water, bacteria could collect and cause spoilage, but if it were too dry, the sheets would be too brittle to roll or stuff. After considerable experimentation, Hanamaruki decided on a 15% water content. Another problem was to determine the best method of dehydrating the soybean protein. At first it experimented with direct heat applied to a drum roll by gas burners, but eventually discovered that indirect heat conducted through electrically preheated drumrolls was the best means of drying the soybean proteins. Producing thin and continuous rolls of protein sheets also presented difficulties. It decided to use a rotating drum, but regulating the speed of rotation of the drum and the thickness of the sheet required great accuracy. The research and development behind the creation of this new food took three years.

Hanamaruki is now using a similar process in making sheets of dried seaweed, another popular food item in the Japanese diet.

Soybean protein sheets can be used for rolling, wrapping, stuffing, or spreading. They can be boiled, baked, fried, or served as is. They can be produced mixed with spinach, pumpkin, and other food. Two hundred such combinations have already been tested. Currently the sheets are being used by confectionery and frozen-food manufacturers and restaurants for Western foods such as crepes and icing for cakes. Take-out sushi chains use the sheets in place of thin fried eggs. Nutritious and inexpensive, low in calories, carbohydrates, and cholesterol, these soybean sheets are a multipurpose food that can be used in both Western and Japanese dishes.

1985 Award for Excellence

---

their first year on the shelves. This is quite a sales record when one considers that they were sold only at 2,200 Seven-Eleven outlets.

The product's great success derives from its being an easy-to-eat, low-calorie snack food.

1984 High Award for Excellence

An easy-to-eat potato snack

Captain Cook CUT and PLUS: A Line of Health Foods
Daiei

Captain Cook CUT and PLUS started as a line of fifty-one health-food items in November 1982. Daiei, Japan's largest supermarket chain, hoped this product would increase consumer interest in health foods. The name "CUT and PLUS" derives from the idea of cutting down on unhealthful ingredients and increasing healthful ones.

Conventional health foods, although nutritionally well balanced, are generally expensive and do not always taste good. Daiei paid a great deal of attention to overcoming these two drawbacks. The most popular items in this line are low-fat milk, additive-free pickles, low-fat yoghurt, wheat-germ bread, calcium-supplemented sausages, low-salt miso paste and soy sauce, and low-sugar jam.

This is the first instance in Japan of a large supermarket chain developing its own line of health foods, and they have proven to be popular. The number of items has now grown to sixty-eight.

1982 Award for Excellence

Natural, healthful foods

Sea Dish: Canned Fish Paste

Nippon Suisan

Imitation foods are not unusual in Japan, especially those that imitate seafoods, which are costly and yet central to the Japanese diet. Imitation crab, scallops, squid, salmon roe, and other imitation fish products are produced. Most imitation foods are made of a paste produced from Alaskan pollack. Emphasis is placed not only upon reproducing taste, but also on shape, texture, appearance, and smell. Prices are from one-tenth to one-third those of the original foods.

Salmon and herring roe are also popular imitation foods, and they are made from salad oil enclosed in a membrane derived from seaweed; but by far the most commonly produced imitation food is crab. It is used in sushi, soups, tempura, and other traditional dishes.

Sea Dish is a crab-flavored fish paste developed by Nippon Suisan. Although in general the canned food market in Japan is in a state of decline, Sea Dish enjoys brisk sales due to its taste, packaging, and marketing. Its ingredients—Alaskan pollack, snow-crab meat, wheat flour, soybean oil, salt, and monosodium glutamate—are ground and then processed into a fiberlike texture that resembles that of crab meat.

Although various imitations of crab meat are available in Japan, Sea Dish has a taste that is closest to the real thing, since its contents actually include 20% real crab meat.

The taste of Sea Dish is further improved by the fact that it is packaged in aluminum rather than tin, since food canned in aluminum does not absorb the metallic taste of the can, as is sometimes the case with tin. The outer surface of the Sea Dish can is entirely covered with multicolored designs, with the exception of the bottom surface which is a pull-off lid. Nippon Suisan also offers other canned goods with pull-off lids.

Nippon Suisan employed unique marketing techniques for Sea Dish. Although food manufacturers usually rely on wholesalers for the distribution of their products, Nippon Suisan brought its Sea Dish directly to supermarkets and other food stores when it sponsored fairs and food-tasting sessions. In addition, it arranged for Sea Dish to be displayed not only with other canned goods, but also in the vegetable section, with the hopes of encouraging its use in salads, as well as in the fish and egg sections. In order to further broaden the appeal of the product, Nippon Suisan introduced recipe cards that suggested uses for Sea Dish in salads, soups, dips, and hors d'oeuvres.

The success of Sea Dish prompted Nippon Suisan to package and market other products in a similar manner. In its Cooking Diary Series, geared toward young adults in their twenties, seventeen different kinds of sea foods and seven kinds of meats are now available. Furthermore, Nippon Suisan eventually plans to can all its foods, including its strongest-selling products, bonito and tuna, in aluminum cans.

1985 Award for Excellence

Sea Dish arranged with a variety of Chinese-style cold vegetables

Thin Slice: Superthin Cold Cuts
Nippon Meat Packers

The taste and consistency of sliced meat vary considerably according to its thickness. A committee of housewives that Nippon Meat Packers consults regularly for product development ideas suggested that ham sliced to only 0.5 mm—about one-quarter the thickness of ordinary sliced meat products—would sell well. Nippon Meat Packers, basing its decision on this advice, decided to market a line of thinly sliced meat products, but it took one year for the project team at the company to develop a satisfactory mass-production method for slicing the meats consistently. Particularly important in this system was steady temperature control, which is crucial for maintaining meat's good flavor during processing.

The housewives' advice proved right, and the Thin Slice line caught on quickly with consumers, especially for use in salads and sandwiches. The company now makes five varieties of Thin Slice. With distinctive pink and green packaging, it stands out on supermarket shelves.

1982 Award For Excellence

A rosette of superthin ham

Kikō Ramen: Instant Gourmet Noodles
Myojo Foods

A staple of the Japanese diet

Ramen is to Japan what the hot dog is to the United States. Ramen noodles are a favorite food throughout the country, and each region has its own way of serving them; the most common one is in a soy-sauce-flavored broth, often with slices of roast pork for variety. In Osaka, ramen noodles are prepared with a lighter soy-sauce; in Sapporo, with a miso (soybean paste) broth seasoned with ground sesame seeds; and in Hakata, with a pork broth. Dehydrated and packaged instant ramen, prepared by simply adding boiling water, is becoming a standard household food.

Myojo Foods, with a slightly expensive but tastier instant ramen, had 15% of Japan's market share, and with the hopes of gaining a larger share decided to develop a new ramen line based on regional flavors. The product was an instant ramen success.

In 1984, the packages were redesigned to depict famous sightseeing locales. For the Tokyo ramen, for example, the package depicts a famous temple gate in Asakusa.

1983 Award for Excellence

Wakame Salad: Seaweed Made Delectable
Riken Vitamin

Wakame is a form of edible seaweed used in many traditional Japanese foods. *Wakame* salad combines dehydrated seaweed in three packages with separate dressings, to give the product a modern image. The dressings are American-style tomato, Szechwan-style hot, and Japanese-style miso and citron.

Riken Vitamin, a major producer of natural vitamins and food additives, has expanded its scope to develop products in which *wakame* seaweed is the main ingredient. It has devised an excellent process for dehydrating seaweed, and thus was able to produce a packaged salad in single servings that would be acceptable to consumers. Riken conducted extensive market surveys among working women, with favorable results, before placing *wakame* salad on the market. With this convenient product, strips of dehydrated seaweed are soaked in water for five minutes, which produces a fresh salad. The user then applies the dressing and has the satisfaction of being able to enjoy an individualized product.

1983 Award for Excellence

A *wakame* seaweed mixed salad

Chicken McNuggets: Deep-Fried Boneless Chicken
McDonald's (Japan)

The number of fast-food restaurants in Japan has increased greatly in recent years. Fast foods, particularly hamburgers, now occupy a significant percentage of the booming ¥19 trillion restaurant industry in Japan. The Japanese hamburger market is especially competitive, and fast-food chains vie with one another to win customers.

In February 1984, two years after McDonald's in the United States began selling Chicken McNuggets, the company introduced this deep-fried boneless chicken product to Japan. It was an immediate success. According to a McDonald's official, the reason for its popularity is that it can be eaten without soiling the fingers.

Chicken McNuggets played an important role in increasing McDonald's 1984 total sales in Japan to the ¥100 billion mark, an unprecedented achievement in the Japanese restaurant industry. Other fast-food outlets, family restaurants, supermarkets, and convenience stores soon followed suit by introducing similar fried-chicken products.

Chicken nuggets for the mass market

1984 Award for Excellence

Flavono: A Breath-Freshening Gum
Lotte

Flavono is a breath-freshening gum made with a flavonoid, an extract of green tea. This substance eliminates bad breath by attacking odor-causing sulfides, aldehydes, and amines. This gum is a more effective breath freshener than the usual chlorophyll gum.

Lotte began development of Flavono at a time when the prospects for a new gum were poor, since the market already appeared saturated. However, surveys revealed that consumers might be receptive to such gums as those that fight bad breath, tooth decay, and drowsiness. After two years the company was able to come up with a more effective breath freshener than existing chlorophyll gums.

Flavono sold well from its introduction to the market in June 1983, and reached sales of ¥2.1 billion within two years. Much of its success can be attributed to its popularity among consumers over twenty years of age, a group that had previously consumed little gum. Thus, with Flavono, Lotte introduced a functional gum suitable for adults.

1984 Award for Excellence

Lotte's new breath-freshening gum with a flavonoid

204

Arch Development Trust System
Sumitomo Trust & Banking

In Japan, where land prices are among the highest in the world, developers find it difficult to acquire land on which to build. This land trust system was devised in which a landowner trusts land to a bank, which then constructs a building and gives a portion of the operating receipts to the landowner. The land reverts to its owner after the trust period is over.

This system is gaining popularity in Japan as a way for the private sector to utilize land more efficiently. Since cap-

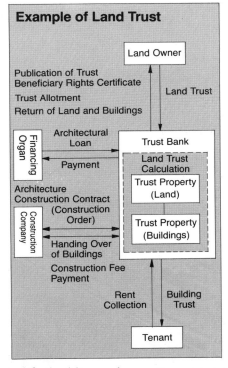

Example of Land Trust

Land Owner

Publication of Trust
Beneficiary Rights Certificate
Trust Allotment
Return of Land and Buildings

Land Trust

Financing Organ

Architectural Loan

Payment

Trust Bank

Land Trust Calculation

Trust Property (Land)

Trust Property (Buildings)

Architecture Construction Contract (Construction Order)

Construction Company

Handing Over of Buildings

Construction Fee Payment

Rent Collection

Building Trust

Tenant

ital for building and operating costs is provided by the trust company, the owner is able to have a sizable building erected on his land without involving himself in the concomitant financial and legal difficulties. In October 1983, after approval to implement land trusts was granted by the government, Sumitomo Trust and Banking immediately began approaching potential customers. Since then, Sumitomo has led the field in the land trust business in Japan.

1984 Award for Excellence

WELS: Welding System
Kajima/Kobe Steel

Fires on construction sites often occur when few people are present, such as at lunchtime or at night. This is often attributable to sparks thrown during the welding process that linger unnoticed on flammable material and burst into flames later on.

Kajima established a team to examine welding techniques and find a way of reducing the risk of fire. It soon become obvious that the conventional welding rod had been designed to favor strength and efficiency at the cost of control of sparks. Kajima then approached Kobe Steel, a major manufacturer of welders, and asked it to develop a welder suited to new specifications. They set as their goal a 70% reduction in the amount of sparks and a 50% reduction of the radius of the spark scattering area.

After thorough testing, which involved simulating the speed at which a spark falls and its changes in temperature, Kajima and Kobe Steel were able to develop a new welding system that reduces the possibility of fire by more than 90%.

1982 Award for Excellence

The WELS system increases safety on the construction site

P-less: A Pipeless Construction Method
Miura Engineering

Conventional construction methods require steel pipes or rods to support the plywood molds while concrete is hardening. This new method employs Miura Engineering's special plywood—

Miura's method does away with traditional reinforcement pipes

twice as thick as conventional plywood—and its P-less ("pipeless") tie-panel fasteners, doing away with the traditional reinforcement pipes. Because of the exact measurements of the fastener, this method also allows for more accuracy in construction.

The idea for this method resulted from the depression following the oil shocks of the 1970s. Faced with the spiraling costs of materials, companies tried to reduce expenditures. Miura Engineering calculated that, on the average, a building of 30,000 m² requires 200 tons of steel pipes for cement-mold reinforcement. The already-high cost of this material is increased by transportation, installment, and removal costs. By substituting extrastrong plywood and P-less ties for the conventional method, Miura succeeded in reducing total construction costs by 30%.

1982 Award for Excellence

Kokugikan: Multipurpose Sumo Hall
Kajima/Sugiyama & Associates/Japan Sumo Association

Outside view of the new Kokugikan, from front

The new Kokugikan, located in Ryogoku, home of Tokyo's sumo tournaments, is a giant, multipurpose hall designed not only for sumo but also for a wide range of events, from concerts to exhibitions. While its external appearance and interior furnishings embody Japanese tradition, the Kokugikan boasts many modern features, including a retractable sumo ring.

Exactly three years before it opened, the Japan Sumo Association chairman, Kiyotaka Kasugano, summoned the president of the Kajima construction company and the head of the Sugiyama architectural firm. Kasugano told them of the Sumo Association's intention to replace its aging hall with a new one, and enjoined them to come up with a design for a building that would be worthy of the name Kokugikan (Hall of the National Sport).

Kasugano had only one specific request to make concerning the design. The Sumo Association, he said, wanted the new building to reproduce the soaring domed roof with its exposed steel frame that was the hallmark of the original Kokugikan.

The design teams at Kajima and Sugiyama went to work to come up with a plan for a sumo stadium fit for the twenty-first century. However, by the time the basic plan was finished, support had grown in some quarters for building a hall that could be used for other events in addition to sumo.

The designers could muster little enthusiasm for this idea, fearing that the building would end up as a bad compromise between a sumo arena and a multipurpose hall. They also knew that to redo the basic design would be a major task. Eventually, after factors such as the promotion of business in the surrounding community and high maintenance costs were taken into consideration, it was decided to modify the original design in favor of a multifunctional facility.

The plan that was finally decided on called for a floor area of 40,000 m² and a hall capable of accommodating a wide variety of events. Since the hall would hold audiences of some 10,000, the air-conditioning and safety facilities would have to be extraordinary.

Kajima employed both computer simulation technology and its considerable construction experience to develop a climate control system for the vast space. The building features a rainwater collection system that keeps 250 tons of water on hand for fighting community fires, and a layout that allows crowds a quick exit from the second floor in emergencies.

The builders intended to finish the facility in time for the May 1985 sumo tournament. Then they learned that Kasugano had told the emperor that it would be ready in time for the New Year's tournament of 1985.

The new deadline of January 1985 meant that the builders would have to shorten that term by five months; promises made to the emperor had to be kept. Kajima exerted great efforts to speed up the construction. On the basis of a detailed analysis of every phase of the building process, it identified all operations that could be completed simultaneously. The company managed to complete the job with time to spare.

1985 High Award for Excellence

Size: 140 (W) × 39.6 (H) × 94 (D) m
Seating capacity: 11,098
Number of floors: three above ground and two under ground
Multipurpose utilization: sumo, boxing, Judo and Kendo, tennis, basketball, concerts, etc.

A Shinto-style roof hangs over the sumo ring

No. 2 Mitsui Bldg: Mitsui Real Estate Development

The automation of offices has advanced remarkably in the last decade, but the buildings accommodating them have not kept pace with these changes. In the spring of 1984, however, Mitsui Real Estate Development began a pioneering project—completed in February 1985—that became the first intelligent building in Japan to rent office space.

In an intelligent building, communication and services within the building are regulated and monitored by a central computer that not only creates comfortable working conditions but also rationalizes costs by conserving energy. Security, too, is automated, reducing manpower requirements.

The greatest gain in efficiency comes from improved interoffice communication. Individual pieces of office equipment can be linked to the building's internal LAN (local-area network) to allow these machines to be in constant communication with one another. Word processors, personal computers, fax machines, telexes, and telephones can all be connected to the LAN, which in turn is connected to a mainframe computer. Thus, a single instrument such as a personal computer can have access to enormous data banks.

Mitsui selected as its guinea pig the No. 2 Mitsui Building in Tokyo; first it demolished the old building and then built an entirely new one to a new design. One of the biggest problems was deciding the amount of high-tech equipment to be adopted. A large capacity for information processing or electric circuitry would increase construction costs and push up rent. Yet, in order to cope with rapid innovations in technology, it was necessary to include the capacity for future expansion. This was achieved within a reasonable cost by installing a comprehensive wiring system running throughout the building. Optical-fiber trunk lines were run vertically from floor to floor, while tenants on the same

The No. 2 Mitsui Bldg: Japan's first intelligent office building

floor were connected with coaxial cables running in a horizontal direction. The pipes used to conduct the cables were made large enough that the wiring volume can be increased or the cables changed easily at any time. The electrical capacity of conventional buildings in Japan is 80 VA/m^2 of floor area, but Mitsui increased this capacity to 130 VA/m^2 to permit a long-term increase in the volume of office automation equipment available to the tenants. Despite the apparent complexity and sophistication of this network, the installation costs amounted to only 1% of total construction costs for the building. The savings expected from increased use of the LAN will more than offset this outlay.

The efficiency of the LAN network used in the intelligent building depends on its speed, which Mitsui enhanced by using high-speed fiber-

optic cables and PBX (public branch exchange) digital switching technology. Working together with NTT, the Japanese national telephone company, Mitsui redesigned the building to allow it to function with the most up-to-date technology available. Using NTT's digital PBX system, the intelligent building even provides free telephone exchanges for all of its tenants.

1985 Award for Excellence

The new control center on the 1st floor

The Takenaka Dome
Takenaka Komuten

Lighting unnecessary during daytime hours

The new Tokyo Dome, a multipurpose dome in Tokyo, will be the first indoor stadium in Japan. It will be covered by a gigantic air dome—made of a clothlike material of Teflon-coated glass fibers stretched over a frame—that spans some 200 m and is supported by interior air pressure kept higher than the pressure outside. The tensile strength of the covering is about 150 kg/cm, matching the strength of steel.

Till now, this construction method had been used only with temporary structures that were slated for demolishment within one year of use. With the aid of the Ministry of Construction and the Japan Architectural Center, Takenaka was able to adapt this technology for permanent structures. This type of construction makes construction costs considerably less than those necessary for a conventional steel-framed roof.

Construction of the Tokyo Dome began in May 1985; it will be completed by March 1988. The dome will have a capacity of 50,000, the largest of any building in Japan.

1984 Award for Excellence

Ace-Lite: Artificial Wood
Onoda Cement/Onoda Chemical Industry

Compared at equal weights, wood is stronger than iron. However, wood has the disadvantage of being flammable, of warping, and of rotting. Onoda sought to develop a product that would be free of these drawbacks and still retain wood's useful qualities.

Onoda cured calcium silicate at high pressure and temperature and produced an extremely pure inorganic material called xonotlite. Glass fibers were added to improve its flexibility. The resulting material was given the name Ace-Lite, and was put on the market as an inorganic artificial wood product. It is heat-resistant to temperatures of up to 1,000° C, of a bulk density similar to that of lumber, and resistant to water or moisture.

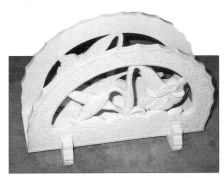

Artificial wood for use in furniture and interior decoration

The demand for this product at present is for use in goods that call for detailed finished work, such as furniture parts or interior decorations. Ace-Lite is not yet strong enough to be used for beams and pillars in housing, but Onoda is continuing further research.

1983 Award for Excellence

The Nisetai: A Two-Generational Dwelling
Asahi Chemical Industry

In Japan, it is still common for several generations of a family to live in the same dwelling. The Nisetai ferroconcrete residences are designed to allow two generations of a family to live together while respecting each other's privacy. The space is organized to permit a variety of uses, responding to the changing needs (and ages) of inhabitants, with a "core living space" where the two generations can share a common living space that functions both as a place of interaction and as a space that respects the independence of each generation. A no-step floor allows easy mobility for residents in wheelchairs.

The percentage of elderly persons in Japan is increasing rapidly, so there will be growing interest in housing with sufficient space and function to allow the elderly to live as independently as possible, while at the same time enabling the younger generation to be close at hand when care is needed. At present approximately 20% of the housing units sold by Asahi Chemical are two-generational dwellings.

1983 High Award for Excellence

Two families; one roof

INDUSTRIAL
AND CONSUMER
MATERIALS

Anico: A Deodorizer
Minato

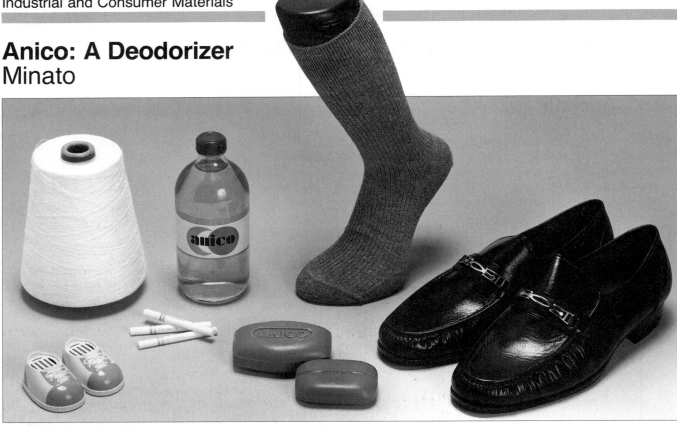

Anico is a deodorizer that comes in numerous forms and is used in many products

Chiaki Ōhama, president of Minato Industries, usually performs a little prestidigitation for visitors to his company. First, he puts ammonia in a plastic bag and sprinkles in two or three drops of perfume. The stench from the bag is almost overwhelming. Then he drops a postage-stamp-sized piece of cloth into the bag, shakes it a few times, opens it again, and voila! The reek of ammonia has vanished, leaving only the scent of the elegant perfume. "Our visitors are always amazed," says Ōhama.

The secret to this trick is the small bit of cloth. It looks like an ordinary scrap, but it actually contains Anico, a deodorizing material developed by Ōhama in conjunction with MITI's Agency of Industrial Science and Technology.

Minato's original business, industrial waste disposal, led Ōhama to investigate the technology of deodorizing. Employee turnover at Minato was high because of the terrible smells at work. Looking for a powerful deodorizer, Ōhama found that the only material available was activated charcoal, which is of limited effectiveness. So Ōhama plunged into the quest for a new, more effective deodorizer.

After three years, Ōhama's efforts paid off. He discovered that combining iron and L-ascorbic acid (vitamin C) would make bad smells disappear chemically. Activated charcoal is a physical deodorizer: it adsorbs odiferous particles into the countless tiny holes in its surface. Anico, by contrast, is a chemical deodorizer that alters odorous molecules by decomposing them in a chemical reaction. This has enormous advantages over physical deodorizers. In particular, it can remove a much greater volume of odor than activated charcoal can. For ammonia, its deodorizing power is about 100 times greater. It also kills odors selectively, reacting only with bad smells and not with the large-moleculed scents of perfumes. Since Anico consists of iron and vitamin C, the substance is harmless if ingested or otherwise absorbed by the human body. The vitamin C also serves to control the growth of microorganisms and maintain freshness, readily penetrates fibers and other materials with little loss of effectiveness, and is flame retardant.

Anico is an extremely versatile product that comes in liquid, powdered, and granular form, and can be incorporated into objects made of fibers, paper, or plastic. Anico has been used in a host of predictable products such as garbage bags, bird cages, disposable diapers, cigarette filters, clothing, chewing gum, and air cleaners. The U.S. Department of Defense is said to be considering the use of this deodorizer inside submarines.

By the end of 1986, some 200 different products using Anico were on the market. Minato's sales of the deodorizing material reached ¥2 billion in 1985.

1985 High Award for Excellence

Hamakicon: A Pheromone Agricultural Pesticide
Shin-Etsu Chemical

Working more efficiently and safely than conventional agricultural pesticides, Hamakicon, a synthetic pheromone developed by Shin-Etsu Chemical, uses the sex hormones of insects to protect fields of precious tea from pests.

Hamakicon, like other pheromone products, disrupts the mating of insects by making it difficult for males to identify females, mate, and produce larvae. The larvae of the tea tortrix and smaller tea tortrix moths are the major threat to tea plants.

Synthetic pheromones control insects without many of the disadvantages of conventional pesticides. Hamakicon and similar products are not toxic to man. They attack only the pests they are designed to affect and do not harm other beneficial insects. Synthetic pheromones are also effec-

tive against insects already resistant to conventional insecticides. Another advantage of synthetic pheromones such as Hamakicon is that their residue does not remain in the environment or in crops.

Hamakicon is applied simply by hanging thin polyethylene tubes containing the substance on the tea plants themselves. The tubes then release the pheromone for up to 200 days, depending upon weather conditions—in hot summer weather, for example, the tubes release the pheromone for about 100 days. The product is especially effective over large areas and as a preventative before insects emerge.

While synthetic pheromones are expensive compared with conventional insecticides, only small amounts are required for large areas.

Although Shin-Etsu is a chemical

company, it had no experience with agricultural chemicals until eight years ago. At that time, the company was converting its production method for PVC from the acetylene method to the ethylene method and sought to develop new applications for acetylene.

The research team realized it was possible to produce pheromones cheaply with the company's technology. Spraying was carried out at a 700-hectare tea plantation along the Oi River in Shizuoka Prefecture, the heart of Japan's tea-growing district, with Hamakicon bought from Shin-Etsu Chemical. Test results showed that the insect breeding rate dropped by 85%.

When Hamakicon was introduced to the market, sales were extremely vigorous in the first year. Countries as varied as the United States, Australia, Italy, Egypt, the People's Republic of China, Pakistan, and Mexico have requested samples for testing.

Over the years, Shin-Etsu has synthesized more than 100 pheromones to be used for pest control. Uninterrupted sales growth is not, however, guaranteed for pheromone agricultural pesticides, since farmers often have little experience using them. Still, Shin-Etsu expects that as concern about environmental pollution from conventional pesticides grows, so will interest in Hamakicon and similar products.

1985 High Award for Excellence

The 20-cm long Hamakicon dispenser is installed by hanging it on a branch

Shikonin: A Plant Dye
Mitsui Petrochemical

Shikonin is a plant dye with a very rich color ranging from red to purple and blue, and with antibacterial, anti-inflammatory, and other pharmacological properties, making it useful in cosmetics and medicines. It is derived from the root of a medicinal herb found in various countries in northeast Asia. However, the five or more years required for cultivation has precluded its mass production. Japan, where the herb is nearly extinct, has long relied on imports of the root from China (PRC) and North Korea, where it is also dying out.

Mitsui Petrochemical decided to take advantage of the material's qualities by mass-producing the dye on an industrial scale with biotechnology. It did so by culturing cells of the plant root so that they grew in a crystal form. The Shikonin extracted from the cells produced by this plant-tissue culture method has a concentration more than ten times higher than that found in nature. It is also uniform in quality and free from offensive odor, making it very useful commercially.

1984 High Award for Excellence

Shikonin from cultured crystals (above) is used in cosmetics

Continuous Production of Ultrathin Metal Foil
Takeuchi Foil & Powdered Metal

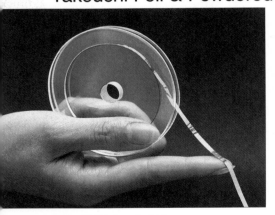

A metal foil 1.5 μm in thickness

Metal foil, commonly used in the food industry in the form of aluminum foil, and used in decorative applications as gold leaf, is now being widely used in electronic parts. Takeuchi Foil and Powdered Metal is a pioneer in this field. In 1983, the company developed a method for the continuous rolling of three types of metals—titanium, stainless steel, and beryllium copper—for the manufacture of ultrathin foils to be used in electronic parts. This method produces foil with a length of 1,500 m, a thickness of 1.5 μm, and a width of 60 mm.

Formerly a wholesaler of gold foil for Buddhist altars, the company turned to the production of ultrathin foil for industrial use. Using a high-precision, reversible, 20-level cold-rolling machine imported from West Germany, Takeuchi was able to produce ultrathin foil of an almost incredible single micron in thickness. This new line of ultrathin foil was first used for spacers between VCR magnetic heads. It is now being used by almost all magnetic-head makers.

1983 High Award for Excellence

Pullulan: Edible, Pliable, Imprintable Film
Hayashibara Biochemical/Osaka Kagaku Gokin/Toppan Printing

Pullulan is an inexpensive, non-polluting, nontoxic, noncaloric, and naturally occurring polysaccharide; like other dietary sugars, it is broken down and absorbed by the body when consumed. The water-soluble exudate is produced by a microorganism known as *Aureobasidium pullulans*. Hayashibara Biochemical's researchers developed Pullulan for use as a substrate in measuring enzyme activity. It was found, however, that it had certain properties that could be of commercial use. In particular, it is soluble in water,

Edible film can even be used on ice cream

but not in alcohol or oil, and it is extremely adhesive.

It was a simple step to turn this polysaccharide into an edible film that can wrap foods and hold in their flavor and freshness. Consultations with Osaka Kagaku Gokin, a sausage-casing maker, and Toppan Printing led to the perfection of such a film. It can be printed upon, colored, and flavored; it can also be used as an antioxidant for foods or as a casing for pharmaceutical products.

1982 Award for Excellence

Bathcal: Antifungal Wall Covering
Pharaon

Bathcal is an interior wall covering that kills mold and bacteria and also inhibits their future growth. The most distinctive feature of the material is that it is actually paint in sheet form that is applied to the wall in the same manner as wallpaper and results in a painted appearance.

A mold suppressant of low toxicity to humans is coated on the outer surface of the wall covering, and a strong antibacterial, antifungal agent is spread on the surface that will face the wall. The product is very effective for long periods of time, even in places where mold is likely to proliferate, such as in bathrooms and food factories.

The development process began with work on ways to make paint in sheet form and required four years of joint effort with paint materials experts. Finally, they discovered that it was possible to create it by mixing polyester and acrylic fibers with paint.

Pharaon calls this new antifungal wall covering "the third form of paint," the other two being liquid paint and powdered paint.

1983 Award for Excellence

Paint in sheet form

Zirconia Oxygen Sensor
Hitachi Chemical

Remaining stable and efficient for more than 10,000 hours of continuous use, this new oxygen sensor dwarfs the performance of other oxygen sensors, which can run continuously for only

Long-life oxygen sensors using zirconia

3,000 hours and even then only with diminishing efficiency. The new sensor design is based on three advanced aspects of heat-resistance technology.

A major obstacle in the development of this sensor was the electrode peeling caused by repeated temperature extremes ranging between room temperature and 800°C. Simultaneous zirconia and platinum electrode sintering eliminated this problem. In addition, electrodes were protected from the sulfur component in heating oil and natural gases by the application of a coat of zirconia film to the electrodes. Finally, precisely calculated amounts of additives such as yttrium oxide and calcium contributed significantly to heat resistance. It was these three technological breakthroughs that made the development and the production of the long-life zirconia oxygen sensor possible.

1982 Award for Excellence

Hoya GLS25C: A Slab Lens for Optical Communications
Hoya

The Hoya GLS25C slab lens represents the first time a lens has made practical use of the molecular-stuffing principle developed in the United States in 1976. It was found to be more effective than the conventional ion-exchange method employed by lens makers for large-diameter-beam focusing at a fixed refractive index.

The Hoya microoptics lab recognized that a gradient refractive-index lens had a wide range of potential applications, including use in optical communications as well as in miniature copiers. It set out to develop such technology and perfected the rod lens in 1983. A year later, the lab was trying to develop a slab lens for use in optical communications. The work in the molecular-stuffing process was painstaking in the extreme. It required cutting special glass to extremely fine specifications; subjecting it to repeated heat and chemical treatments; making minute changes in the temperature settings as well as in the relative concentrations of chemical solutions; cutting slab after slab in thicknesses from 500 to 900 µm; and testing each sample for uniform refractive-index gradient.

The lab's efforts paid off in the emergence of a remarkably versatile lens.

The GLS25C is a one-directional, gradient-index slab lens, in which the silicon-oxide base is permeated with special alkali oxides to alter the refraction index. Incident light is refracted in a single direction and emerges in a straight line in a new direction. Thus, the lens can be used as an optical connector to transmit light to optical ICs and other components more efficiently in the form of beam lines, rather than beam spots. It can also function as a branch connector device, allowing a single optical fiber to branch into multiple optical fibers.

In the past, branch circuits for optical communications, particularly in LANs (local area networks), have mainly taken the form of complex assemblies of rod-shaped lenses. These have been difficult to build and extremely expensive. In contrast, the slab lens facilitates optical fiber branching with an ease equal to that in electrical circuitry branching.

Performance characteristics of Hoya's slab lens are stable even after several weeks of exposure to temperatures of 600° C. The lens is also impressively resistant to acids and water, suffering little optical loss. The standard lens is 3.4 mm thick, 3 to

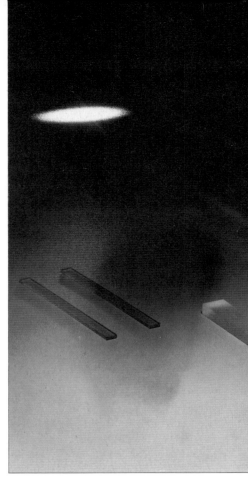

One-directional gradient-index slab lenses

5 mm wide, and 17.8 mm long and retails at ¥20,000.

The ground-breaking significance of the lens was confirmed when the company received an invitation to GIOS, the prestigious international microoptics conference on gradient-index optical-imaging systems, asking it to introduce the lens. Further exposure was obtained when Hoya entered the

EskaExtra: A High-Performance Plastic Optical Fiber
Mitsubishi Rayon

PMMA-type optical fibers in the field of short-distance fiber-optic data transmission

Mitsubishi Rayon, a top maker of methyl methacrylate (MMA) monomer, employed transparent polymethyl methacrylate (PMMA) to produce EskaExtra, a highly versatile optical fiber. The company was only able to develop this fiber through the integration of a number of sophisticated technologies—such as the continuous process designed to manufacture EskaExtra directly from MMA monomer, and a significant improvement in the clarity of the fluorinated polymer used for cladding.

Although its transmission distance

Orientcore HI-B:
Grain-Oriented Electrical Steel Sheets
Nippon Steel

In Japan, the annual core loss from transformers equals the amount of power generated by a 1.3-million-kW power station operating at full capacity for a year. The search for low-core loss electromagnetic steel sheets has therefore been a constant concern of the steel industry. Initial efforts to reduce core loss focused on controlling the grain orientation of the crystal that forms the steel plate, or by using thin gauge, but both of these methods are limited.

In 1983, Nippon Steel developed grain-oriented electromagnetic steel sheets, Orientcore HI-B, that reduced iron core loss by 20%. The company employed a laser to mar the surface of the steel plate in order to increase its magnetic characteristics, and thus to reduce its core loss substantially.

The superior performance of these sheets is now widely acknowledged.

1983 High Award for Excellence

A steel plate that has (upper), and has not (lower), undergone laser processing

lens in a laser-related products show in January 1985. The response was tremendous; Hoya now expects market expansion in the field of optical branch connectors. This use will complement both the growth of fiber-optic networks and the increasing use of optical information processing devices.

1985 High Award for Excellence

of 180 m is shorter than that of quartz optical fiber, EskaExtra's advantages lie in the fact that it enjoys the lowest attenuation, the lowest cost, and the highest durability and heat resistance of any plastic optical fiber.

Because of the handling difficulties and high price of quartz optical fiber, Mitsubishi Rayon believes that the potential for other future uses of the EskaExtra optical fiber is high, and thus it is continuing its development efforts.

1983 Award for Excellence

Electroconductive Powder
Mitsubishi Metal

Mitsubishi Metal has developed a new weapon in the war against static electricity. Previously, carbon black granules were used on materials to prevent electrostatic charges from forming, but

Transparent antistatic material

these could not be used on materials of every color. Thin films applied by the sputtering method were also effective, but their cost was prohibitive.

Mitsubishi Metal's antistatic material is a superfine powdered co-oxide of tin and antimony with a grain diameter of 0.02 μm, a fineness that renders it transparent, making its use possible on all colors. The biggest development problem was reduction of the grain diameter. The company initially achieved a grain diameter of 0.2 μm for a white electroconductive powder using the fine-powder production technology long employed in the production of cadmium and titanium oxide pigments. Further reduction produced a transparent material suitable for many uses. Mitsubishi Metal is now exploring new applications in such fields as LSI production.

1982 Award for Excellence

Fukuyo Shape-Memory Implant: Artificial Tooth Root
Seishin-kai Medical/Furukawa Electric/Nitto Kogyo

A major problem with artificially implanted teeth has been that they tend to work loose after a while. This artificial tooth root utilizes a shape-memorizing alloy that allows it to cling to the jawbone 30–40% more tightly than do other artificial tooth roots.

The nickel-titanium alloy from which this tooth root is made was developed in the United States about twenty years ago for use in airplanes. It was subsequently used in other applications; but even before this group of three Japanese companies started working with it, many had put it to other medical uses.

The special characteristic of this alloy is that when heat above a certain temperature is applied to it, it will regain its original shape regardless of what other shape it was given later.

Many Japanese first learned of this unusual alloy in 1981, when a spoon made of it was shown on television. No matter how much this spoon was bent or twisted—within certain limits—it would resume its original shape when placed in hot water. The television exposure generated considerable interest in the alloy, and many people started thinking about other commercial uses for it. Among the people whose imagination was excited was Dr. Sekio Fukuyo, chief director of Seishin-kai Medical in Nagoya.

A dentist with considerable experience in artificial-tooth implants, Dr. Fukuyo had concluded that in order for artificial teeth to remain in place more tightly, it would be necessary to find a method whereby the bottom portion of the roots could be spread after insertion—perhaps by using a shape-memorizing alloy—enabling them to adhere to the jawbone more securely.

Meanwhile, Furukawa Electric had also been experimenting with what it calls "shape-memory" alloy. It joined forces with Dr. Fukuyo and Nitto Kogyo, a general trading company, to work on an improved tooth root.

The major problems were making the alloy strong enough to bear the pressures that would be put on it and determining the ideal temperature at which the shape change should occur.

Nickel-titanium alloy is by nature a comparatively soft metal. But a tooth root has to withstand hundreds of kilograms of pressure during chewing. Furukawa Electric solved this problem by devising a method to harden the alloy by means of a special heating procedure.

Establishing the ideal temperature for bringing about the shape change was quite complex. When the nickel content of this alloy increases by even 0.1%, the temperature at which a shape change occurs drops by 10°C. Thus, it was necessary to regulate the composition of the alloy with extreme precision. Finally, it was possible to produce an alloy that would change shape at body temperature. Establishing this temperature for the change made surgery easier.

Extensive clinical tests were conducted by Dr. Fukuyo, and finally the Ministry of Health and Welfare granted approval for the use of this product, paving the way for other medical applications of shape-memorizing alloy.

1985 Award for Excellence

A shape-memory implant (right), which has sunk less than an ordinary implant (left); the drawing shows the configuration of deformation

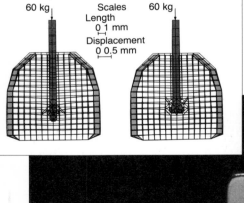

60 kg   Scales   60 kg
               Length
               0 1 mm
               Displacement
               0 0.5 mm

When heat is applied, the shape-memorizing implant spreads to stabilize itself in the jaw

Anthron Bypass Tube: Surgical Tubing
Toray Industries

Toray's development of a special resin tube that prevents blood clotting during temporary bypassing of blood vessels has significantly eased problems posed by organ removal and surgery requiring use of aortic bypass.

Surgical treatment of cancer of the major organs is extremely difficult, since it often entails combined excision of the portal vein or some other major vessel, and consequently the fatality rate is very high. In the case of pancreatectomy, surgery is possible only if the portal vein is temporarily ligated. Halting the flow for more than twenty minutes, however, results in congestion and necrosis of the intestines. Toray's Anthron Bypass Tube aids this situation by releasing minute, steady amounts of the anticoagulant heparin into the blood from its surface, thus both eliminating the need for a large systemic dosage of heparin (which causes extensive bleeding) and allowing extended surgery through superior mesenteric-femoral bypass.

1984 Award for Excellence

A bypass tube that has made long-term portal-vein interception possible

Esmedica-V: A Plasticizer-Free Flexible PVC Compound
Sekisui Chemical

Although conventional flexible PVC resins are transparent and easy to use, bleeding out of the plasticizer and other ingredients has made them unsuitable in many fields, especially that of disposable medical equipment. Esmedica-V is a PVC resin with plasticity and durability comparable to that of conventional flexible PVC compounds. While free of plasticizers such as DOP, it remains highly malleable.

Development stemmed from an urgent need brought to the attention of Sekisui Chemical by physicians. Surgical tubes are made of PVC compounds that have formerly contained a plasticizer. But there were many reports of tubes hardening inside a patient's stomach. The cause of this was attributed to the dissolving of the plasticizer by the gastric juices. The emergence of Sekisui Chemical's Esmedica-V has eliminated this danger.

In 1982 the company set up a factory capable of producing fifty tons of Esmedica-V per month, and it is now being used in many fields.

1982 High Award for Excellence

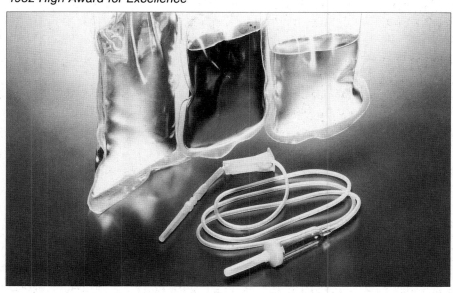

Esmedica-V is used in medicine for such items as IV tubes and blood bags

Silicon-Carbide-Whisker Reinforced Aluminum Alloy
Mitsubishi Aluminum

The lightness, flexibility, and rust resistance of aluminum have put it in great demand. It is being used in a variety of products, ranging from sashes and appliances to automotive and airplane parts. Aluminum has the drawback, however, of being a relatively soft metal with low resistance to heat. It cannot, for example, be used for pistons and other automotive applications, since it cannot withstand severe friction. The quest for a lighter and stronger form of aluminum gave birth to Mitsubishi's silicon-carbide-whisker reinforced aluminum alloy.

The company's research sought a material that would eliminate the previous problems of aluminum alloys by increasing its durability without compromising its lightness. There are three recognized methods for the creation of new materials in the metal industry. One combines various metals to create a high-strength alloy using a casting method. The second entails a metallurgical technology that employs a rapidly solidifying aluminum powder. The third method involves mixing aluminum alloy with fibers or a ceramic powder to create a metal-matrix composite (MMC). Mitsubishi Aluminum decided to pursue this third approach, one in which its R&D lagged far behind that of the other two methods, but which showed the greatest promise for general-purpose applications.

In 1982, when development began, the first step was to select the material to be mixed with the aluminum alloy. After considerable research, Mitsubishi decided on silicon-carbide whiskers. With a tensile strength of 2,000 kg/mm^2, they provided an excellent overall performance.

Although an American company, Arco, had already successfully developed an aluminum-carborundum-whisker MMC, its production method required expensive and hard-to-produce aluminum alloy powder as a raw material. Mitsubishi needed, therefore, to develop its own more cost-effective production technology.

The company identified high-pressure casting and forging as the least expensive method. In this method, preforms of silicon-carbide whiskers are first made, and molten aluminum alloy is then poured into the preforms and solidified under high-pressure conditions. Research soon uncovered a major problem. When the whiskers were exposed to high temperatures for an extended period of time, the carbon atoms reacted with the aluminum atoms, resulting in a reduction in the durability and heat-resistant properties of the whiskers. After testing a wide range of casting conditions, Mitsubishi came up with a method that ensured consistent product quality. The properties of the resulting fiber-reinforced alloy are superior to other aluminum alloys in almost all areas, including durability. In addition, it is possible to manufacture MMC billets in diameters of up to 200 mm. The success of Mitsubishi Aluminum's reinforced alloy has prompted other companies to begin research in this material. As other companies enter the field, prices are expected to drop, leading to an increase in demand for this alloy.

1985 Award for Excellence

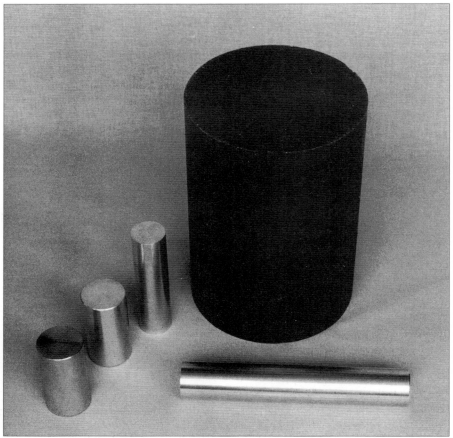

Silicon-carbide whiskers

1μm

Round sticks and a 200-mm-diameter billet

0   50   mm 100

Taimal: An Aluminum Alloy
Showa Aluminum

Aluminum alloy products made of Taimal

The light weight of aluminum alloys accounts for the extraordinary variety of their industrial applications. Low resistance to abrasion, however, prohibits their use in machine parts exposed to considerable friction. Taimal is 100 times more resistant to abrasion than a regular aluminum alloy, while still retaining high malleability.

Silicon is commonly used to increase abrasion resistance in aluminum, but the amount added must be very carefully controlled, since too much rigidifies the material, while too little may produce no significant change. By adding strontium phosphate to the alloy, Showa Aluminum has been able to limit the amount of silicon required. Strontium phosphate causes fine silicon particles to be dispersed throughout the aluminum evenly, thereby ensuring a metal that is both abrasion-resistant and easy to manipulate. Using various additives, Showa Aluminum is creating a series of alloys that are being used in such varied products as VCR cylinder heads and compressor parts in air conditioners.

1984 Award for Excellence

Soldus: Solderable Stainless Steel
Delta Research

0.005-μm plating has made soldering possible

Stainless steel is hard, flexible, and rust-resistant; various other properties that inevitably result from production methods, however, inhibit its usefulness in electronics.

Steel is made by adding chromium to iron, and this results in the formation of a surface film on the finished product. This film, unfortunately, impairs the steel's conductive abilities; it also renders soldering impossible.

In its efforts to upgrade stainless steel for use in electronics, however, Delta Research has developed a special chemical process that removes the surface film and simultaneously covers the exposed chromium atoms with an ultrathin layer of a precious metal, such as gold or palladium, which makes it possible for the alloy to be soldered. This development has greatly diversified the applications of stainless steel for electronic parts such as lead frames.

Delta Research, a company with about ten employees, is now supplying its technology to large corporations.

1983 Award for Excellence

Lubrite FM: A High-Performance Soft Magnetic Material
Sumitomo Electric Industries

Lubrite-FM products

Lubrite FM is a new type of high-performance, sintered, soft magnetic material that can be used with an alternating current. Previously, sintered magnetic material could be used only in direct-current applications (e.g., as cores for direct-current motors and measuring devices). Sumitomo Electric, however, broadened the applications of the material by processing raw powder of high purity with refined sintering techniques to reduce the amount of impurities that impair soft magnetic properties. Lubrite FM, marketed outside Japan as Code FM, is now widely used in dot-matrix printers, word processors, and personal computers.

When Lubrite FM was first developed, there were no commercial applications for it. Sumitomo Electric asked its salesmen throughout the country to find users for the new product. Stressing its superior magnetic characteristics and the fact that it can be used with an alternating current, the salesmen were able to find a market among makers of stepping motors as well as of automotive parts.

1983 Award for Excellence

Ceraborex: An Advanced Boride Ceramic
Asahi Glass

This ceramic is exceptional for its heat resistance (it has a melting point of 3,060°C) and strength (it is twice as hard as Al_2O_3). It also has a high ability to conduct an electric current (its specific resistance is $10^{-5}\Omega \cdot cm$). Asahi Glass began development of this product in 1982. Following repeated experiments synthesizing various materials, it came up with zirconium diboride (ZrB_2). It then developed a process that enables mass production of ZrB_2 with both hot pressing and normal sintering, and transformed the material into a ceramic. With a high conductivity equal to that of iron, Ceraborex can be treated with electrolytic polishing for precise machine processing.

Ceraborex is used in numerous products—from fireproofing devices to electronic parts

Additionally, the range of user demands has prompted the company to develop seven different varieties of this ceramic, including some that are harder or more shock-resistant. Although the ceramics are now relatively expensive, Asahi Glass hopes to lower prices by increasing their variety and applications.

1984 Award for Excellence

Lumiflon: A Fluoropolymer for Paints
Asahi Glass

Lumiflon is suited for use in such applications as outer-wall coverings for buildings

Lumiflon is a solvent-soluble fluoropolymer designed as a paint resin. It is a fluororesin that hardens at room temperature, and that can be applied like regular paint, without baking. Resistant to heat and weather, it can be used on building exteriors (not only to extend the life of the materials but also to reduce the operating costs of the buildings), as well as on bridges and on automotive, aircraft, and marine vessel surfaces (to prevent corrosion caused by the elements).

Since the melting point of conventional fluororesins is between 255° and 270° C, their use in paint is limited. Concentrating on temperature research, Asahi Glass began work on Lumiflon in 1977. The success of its product lies in the development of macromolecular structures with uniform side chains, permitting the resin to be applied like paint at room temperature.

Although Lumiflon is more expensive than urethane paints, Asahi Glass expects that a growing demand and a high sales volume will ease prices.

1982 High Award for Excellence

MACHINERY

Bearings for Jet Engines
NSK

For NSK (Nippon Seiko), a Japanese bearing manufacturer, the development of a new jet engine for commercial airplanes—the V2500, the most advanced jet engine of its day—represented both a challenge and a long-sought opportunity to get a leg up on the competition.

Major bearing manufacturers in Japan had experience in making bearings for jet engines, mainly for Japan's Defense Agency. As jet engines were produced in Japan under license from European and U.S. makers, most bearing manufacturers learned their technology from Western companies. NSK, however, was different. A jet-engine bearing manufacturer since 1960, from the beginning it developed its own technology by destroying bearings and then analyzing them.

The development of the V2500 engine by a consortium of U.S., British, Japanese, West German, and Italian companies gave NSK, which had always done its own research and development, the opportunity for more independence.

In the words of NSK's managing director Seiho Yamamoto, it was "an ideal chance" for his company to take the initiative in the development of commercial jet-engine bearings.

Two types of bearings were required for the engine: one in front of a high-pressure compressor (No. 3); and the other immediately behind the engine fan (No. 1). The outer diameter of the No. 1 bearing is about 400 mm, making it one of the largest ball bearings ever developed for jet engines. The No. 3 bearing is the highest-speed ball bearing in the world; its dN (d=bearing bore [mm]; N=speed [rpm]) value is over 2 million.

The company began work in 1980 by installing high-speed testing equipment exclusively for jet-engine bearings at its Fujisawa laboratory. Jet engines encounter extreme temperature and load variations at ultrahigh speeds, so their bearings must be able to withstand severe conditions.

As Yamamoto said, "This is the first trial of our own high-speed bearing technology, and no failures can be permitted."

The importance of NSK's participation in the V2500 project is as much in future goodwill and prestige as in immediate sales. Supplying important parts for an important engine attracting worldwide attention is a source of pride and has raised NSK's profile in its field.

According to Yamamoto, "There is great significance in our entry into this field, which up to now has been dominated by European and American manufacturers."

1985 Award for Excellence

The System 10, 11, and 12 Series: High-Performance CNCs
Fanuc

Fanuc Systems 10, 11, and 12 (from left) enable high speed and high precision in manufacturing

These high-performance CNCs (computer numerical-control devices) are used in controlling the operation of machine tools. Using optical-fiber transmissions, 8,000-gate custom LSIs, and a 4-Mbit bubble memory, the manufacturer succeeded in reducing the number of component parts by 30% compared with the number of parts in existing CNCs, while increasing reliability. The enlarged processing capacity of their built-in programmable controllers simplifies the process of adjusting the systems to specific applications.

The series consists of three models, designated by the numbers 10, 11, and 12. In a four-year development effort, Fanuc carried out a thorough conversion of its leading products to CNC. The series has since proved highly successful in Japan, Europe, and the United States.

1984 High Award for Excellence

The No. 1 (right) and No. 3 bearings are used directly behind the engine fan, and in front of a high-pressure compressor, respectively

No. 1 bearing: bore diameter 220 mm, outer diameter 325 mm, width 48 mm

No. 3 bearing: bore diameter 150 mm, outer diameter 213 mm, inner ring width 33 mm, outer ring width 30 mm

Spiral Escalator
Mitsubishi Electric

In the early 1980s, when Japan's escalator industry was experiencing a slump because construction starts had declined, Mitsubishi Electric came up with the idea of a spiral escalator. It felt that a spiral escalator whose arc created an angle of 110°−180° between the top and bottom would both allow riders a wide-angle view and have a tremendous appeal among architects and builders.

The concept of a spiral escalator had long been considered by engineers, but no one had succeeded in building one that worked. The structure required to keep the steps level and yet moving in a spiral was so complex that it was difficult to make it run at a smooth, constant speed. Mitsubishi Electric's engineers finally hit upon a structure with a variable radius. The central section of the escalator moves in a circular path with a 5.1-m radius, while the radius changes to 6.5 m at the top and bottom. Thus, the speed of rotation in the central section is faster, but a constant overall speed of 25 m/min can be maintained.

1984 Award for Excellence

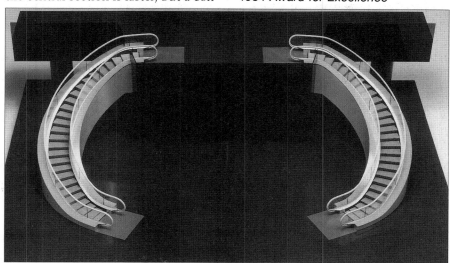

Models of spiral escalators that can transport 6,300 people per hour each

Service Robot:
An Unmanned Conveyor
Dainichi Kiko

This waiter robot, priced at ¥5 million, is one of a number of "amusement" robots that Dainichi has developed for use in restaurants and wedding halls. Performing eight basic operations, including the ability to speak sixteen different phrases, the waiter robot is capable of a wide range of functions. It moves between tables and behaves much as a human waiter would, greeting guests, taking orders, and serving food.

The robot moves on a remote-controlled industrial cart. Electricity consumption has been kept low by using CMOS-type ICs in the control unit. One problem with using a robot in a restaurant is that people often walk about and can inhibit the robot's smooth movements. Thus, the waiter robot had to be designed for quick repair and restarting in the event of a malfunction. The electronic circuit boards in the control device are finely subdivided, and it has been programmed to stop automatically whenever the bumper touches any object.

1983 Award for Excellence

The range of this robot's vertical arm movement is 75°; of the body revolution, 200°; of the head revolution, 180°; and of the head's vertical movement, 100 mm.

ST-77 N: Sushi Robot
Suzumo Machinery Industry

Sushi, one of Japan's traditional dishes, has gone automatic. Suzumo Machinery has produced a robot that duplicates the hand movements of a sushi chef when forming "fingers" of sushi rice. When cooked rice flavored with vinegar, sugar, and salt is placed in the machine, maintaining a constant volume of air content as well as consistent firmness when pressing, it turns out 1,200 uniform fingers of pressed rice in an hour.

Although the sushi topping has to be cut and then added by hand, the invention of this robot was extraordinary, because to Japanese the consistency and taste of the rice is as important as the taste of the fish. The robot received considerable publicity in newspapers, magazines, and on television, since this was the first sushi robot put on the market. Sales were brisk—120 units a month. Subsequently, sales took a downturn, and the company went back to the drawing board to try and produce a sushi robot capable of adding the topping to the pressed rice.

1982 Award for Excellence

A rice finger topped with raw fish

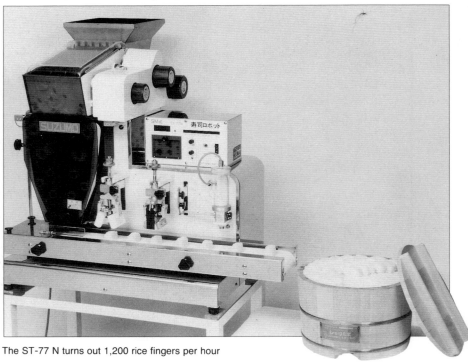

The ST-77 N turns out 1,200 rice fingers per hour

SSR-2: An Intelligent Construction Robot
Shimizu Construction/ Kobe Steel

Work at construction sites such as rock-wool spraying on steel-beam surfaces is highly demanding. The idea that such arduous tasks could be taken over by robots led to the development of the SSR-2 construction robot.

Shimizu Construction, in cooperation with Kobe Steel, developed its first construction robot, the SSR-1, in 1982. Although rather primitive, the robot did prove useful in rock-wool spraying. Using the SSR-1 as a prototype,

The SSR-2: an intelligent construction robot

Shimizu set about developing a self-propelling construction robot with decision capabilities. It employed recent developments to allow the robot to function autonomously.

Since no two construction sites are alike, the robot's designers concentrated on developing software that would enable the robot to cope with the differing conditions at any site. They developed the SSR-3, a multipurpose construction robot, in June 1986. It is intended for use in such new fields as disassembling nuclear reactors.

1983 Award for Excellence

PT-300V: A Welding Robot
Dainichi Kiko

The PT-300V was developed as a low-priced arc-welding robot for small- and medium-sized enterprises that have been reluctant to use industrial robots. Other available robots cost over ¥10 million, but the PT-300V is priced at ¥5.98 million, the first robot to ever cost less than ¥6 million. This lower price was made possible by the use of inexpensive materials for component parts when possible, and the acceptance of a low profit margin that would be offset by a high volume of sales.

The robot has quintuple joints, and can move objects of up to 5 kg. Although it is a small machine, it has an operating area greater than that of a medium-sized welding robot, since its structure was designed so that its movements could cover a dome-shaped area.

It is capable of welding with an accuracy of ±0.1 mm, and can also convey goods with a vacuum-pressure arm attachment. It is easy to program and is suited for numerous operating needs. Actual use has been largely in conveyor applications.

1982 High Award for Excellence

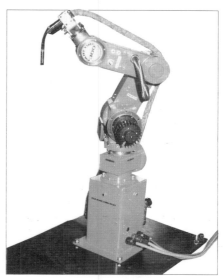

An arc-welding robot with many functions

Multipurpose Process Robot
Hitachi

In anticipation of FA (factory automation) systems that would utilize several robots, Hitachi developed this multipurpose five-pivot-jointed robot capable of performing such functions as

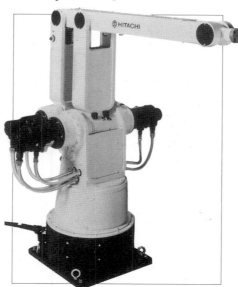

The first robot with a 1-Mbit bubble memory

welding, conveying, and assembling. The job function permits 255 kinds of programs to be arbitrarily combined in up to 99 job divisions. This allows the robot to work more flexibly and efficiently.

The robot contains a 16-bit microprocessor in the CPU of its control unit. It also employs a magnetic bubble memory with a 1-Mbit capacity, the world's first application of a bubble memory. This increased the memory up to 2,000 program points. The control unit is equipped with managing and editing functions and a self-diagnosis function to control program-use, power-input, and robot operating time.

In 1982, the robot was upgraded to a six-pivot type to increase its freedom of movement. When sales of the five-pivot type reached 5,000 units in September 1986, it became one of the best-selling robots ever to be marketed.

1982 Award for Excellence

System One: A Multipurpose Confectionery Machine
Shin Nihon Machine Manufacturing

Even the smallest confectionery store in Japan usually has a dazzling array of items for sale. Confectionery makers are constantly introducing new items in the hope of attracting more customers. Intensified competition has started a trend toward a shorter lifetime for products, and this results in a more complicated production process. In the past, this meant that confectionery makers had to buy new equipment for each new product. Existing machinery,

Cupcakes made by System One

although automated, could not be used to produce a variety of items.

Shin Nihon Machine Manufacturing recognized that there was a great opportunity in this field for marketing new, more versatile machines. It began by improving an automated filling machine that computerized the positioning of the confectionery tray. The company's next challenge was to expand the range of tasks that the machine could perform. Undertaking a systematic study of the baking of various goods, Shin Nihon Machine found that the production of 80–90% of the confectionery items on the market could be reduced to just three basic processes. The project team in charge of developing System One replaced the single nozzle with three different heads, each capable of performing a variety of functions. A couple of conveyor belts were installed to move the trays from head to head to allow uninterrupted preparation of the confec-

tions. For example, when the machine is making cupcakes, the first head puts the waxed-paper cup in the baking pan; the second head fills up the cup with batter; and the third head sprinkles raisins on top of the batter. The heads are interchangeable, and the company designed thirty different kinds of heads for use with the machine. The final product consisted of a main body, a conveyor, a control box with a computer, and three work stations.

The size of the tray has been standardized to 300×210 mm. However, the arrangement of the pieces can be determined on the tray depending upon the product shape and size. Work to be done on the pieces is also programmable.

The great advantage of the machine—which can be used for making various cakes, cookies, and other confections—is that it allows mass production and great variety. System

---

The LSA-6000 Series: 6-Axis Force Sensors
Hitachi Construction Machinery

Most industrial robots presently in use are equipped with position control. This function has recently been supplemented by the LSA-6000 series force sensors. Designed for high-performance robots capable of sophisticated tasks, the LSA-6000 series can detect a given load in terms of six components: the force along the x, y, and z axes, and the three components of torque around those axes. The compact, lightweight sensor is made of three sets of parallel plates of a high-strength aluminum alloy.

The principal structure of these high-precision force sensors was developed by Professor Yōtarō Hatamura; Hitachi Construction Machinery then developed the commercial models, marketed as the LSA-6000 series. Marketing of the sensors, announced in 1984, began in September 1985. The company anticipates use

of the LSA-6000 series in the assembly of precision parts and in force-controlled machine tools for grinding and deburring.

1984 Award for Excellence

A robot using 6-axis force sensors

KAB/E: A Fully Automatic Bean Boiler
Kajiwara Kogyo

Sweet bean-paste, a traditional ingredient in Japanese confectionery, is made from cooked azuki beans. If great care is not taken in cooking the beans, their flavor will not develop fully, regardless of how well the other steps in the preparation are performed.

This fully automatic bean boiler has done away with that tedious job, using a built-in microcomputer to achieve fully automatic, round-the-clock operation. Moreover, since the conditions for boiling are programmed in the microcomputer, the device can consistently produce sweet bean-paste with the same flavor and quality.

It is not possible to boil beans a day in advance, since flavor and consistency deteriorate after a day. It is better to cook the beans overnight, using microcomputer control and

One allows bakers to experiment and create new confections suited to individualized tastes.

At peak production the machine can turn out 2,000–6,000 pieces per hour depending on the confection. Moreover, the conveyor belt moves forward or right and left as programmed by the computer. Having established the machine as suitable for mass production, the company is now challenged to enhance its appeal by diversifying the machine's capabilities even further. This depends on the development of even more heads for the machine. Since Shin Nihon Machine has produced such devices for over 550 different kinds of specialized machines, this should be an easy challenge to meet. A wide choice of heads will allow almost unlimited combinations of functions and therefore an endless variety of cakes.

1985 Award for Excellence

The main body, the conveyor, and the processing head of System One

quiet, highly safe electric heating elements. The simplicity of operating the KAB/E, even for novices, is a factor in its popularity. It is now being exported, even to the People's Republic of China.

1984 Award for Excellence

This machine can boil up to 90 kg of beans, depending on the type

TA-25S: Flexure-Hinge Servo Accelerometer
Tokyo Keiki

Tokyo Keiki, a leading manufacturer of marine systems and navigation equipment, realized that inertial sensor equipment would also have broad applications in high-technology fields such as factory automation, robotics, and artificial satellite communication.

The TA-25S accelerometer is an ultraprecise device that can measure gravity acceleration or inclination. It can detect movements two hundred times fainter than can be perceived by a human. This sensitivity was made possible by the combination of a high-precision-fabricated pendulum with a pair of optical sensors. The TA-25S can measure and control not only linear acceleration on the horizontal and vertical axes, but also vibration and inclination.

Although conventional acceleration sensors have only been used in vehicles, the TA-25S is extremely well suited for use in the arms of industrial robots, for semiconductor production, in vibration analysis for engines and ships, and in inertial navigation systems for aircraft.

1983 Award for Excellence

An ultraprecise accelerometer

Sancron: Automatic Vacuum-Casting Machine
San-ai

Although the testing process of a new product is a major cost burden for any manufacturer, this is particularly true in the plastics industry, where metal casts are used for molding plastic. Metal casts, which are extremely expensive, are suitable for high volume production, but inappropriate when used in small numbers for test models.

The Sancron system is a test-model production system that radically reduces the cost of plastics testing due to the use of silicone rubber instead of metal in making test models. The use of silicone rubber is made possible through the vacuum-casting molding method. Molding, under normal conditions, requires the injection of plastic or some other resin into the mold at a high enough pressure to ensure that the inside of the mold is casted completely. Only molds of metal, however, can withstand such high pressure. With the vacuum-casting method, pouring is done under vacuum conditions, doing away with the need for high pressure to coat the mold with resin and thus making it possible to use silicone rubber molds. In other words, the main resin and a hardening agent are mixed and stirred in a vacuum and then injected into a silicone rubber mold. The resin mixture is then allowed to harden before it is released from the mold. It is then finished and, if required, coated. This permits a cost reduction of almost 90%.

While this method of injection has been known for some time, San-ai had to make numerous modifications before it could be made available commercially. Its most important innovation was the development of a unique urethane-type resin for use in the mold, solving the problem of shrinkage in the plastic products that was caused by the system. This reduced shrinkage to less than 0.3%, guaranteeing precision and product standardization in the test models.

In addition, robots conduct every stage of the process, from mixing hardeners with the melted resin to pouring it into the mold. This eliminates the need for human labor, thereby reducing costs. For San-ai, a subcontractor company, this was a first venture into the development of its own high-tech product.

Recent trends in the plastics industry lean toward shorter product life and rapid cycles of product development and make future prospects for the Sancron system promising. With this system it is possible to produce specialized plastic goods previously not developed due to the high cost of metal models.

It is now possible to use the system not only for test models but also for production in units of several hundred. At present, the company is selling an average of five to seven machines per month, a steady volume that is expected to be maintained in the future. In order to ensure correct usage, San-ai offers a free course at its company training center to those who purchase the system.

1985 Award for Excellence

The Sancron system reduces both product cost and production time by almost 90%

Number formed: 4-5 per hour
Arrival vacuum level: 7.5×10^{-4} Torr
Material insertion volume: 2 L maximum
Maximum formulation dimensions:
  450 (W) × 450 (D) × 400 (H) mm
Power requirements: 200 V (3 phase) 1.2 kW
Outer Dimensions:
  1,100 (W) × 740 (D) × 2,050 (H) mm

IVC-800: Magnetic-Head Winder
Ikari

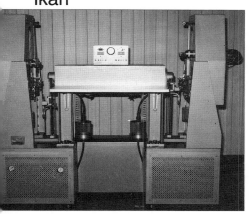

The IVC-800 can wind copper wire as thin as 0.03 mm in diameter

The IVC-800 is capable of automatically winding very fine copper wire of 0.03 mm in diameter through a mere 0.2-mm (diameter) hole in magnetic-head coils used with computers and VCRs. Formerly, this task had to be performed by keen-sighted young women with microscopes.

This product is the first entry into the electronics field by a company whose main area of expertise is environmental hygiene. Ikari is a specialist in rat extermination. The idea for the coil winding machine came from a product it was using for rat control—a pipe through which copper wire was pulled with vacuum force. This amateurish mechanism gave birth to the magnetic-head coil winder.

The company's prototype consisted of a main unit made from several layers of cardboard, to which was attached a pump and the vacuum pipe. Using materials beneath the consideration of large corporations, the company successfully developed a product that large computer and appliance makers had long sought.

1983 High Award for Excellence

LX500A: A Super Wire-Cutting Electrical-Discharge Machine
JAPAX

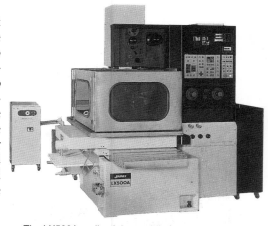

The LX500A realized the world's fastest surface-processing capability

The LX500A is a highly efficient electric-discharge machine that wire-cuts metal at a rate of 200 mm² of area per minute. It is the first machine in the industry to achieve this capacity, a significant advance over conventional capabilities of 120 mm² per minute.

Its high speed and precision (to a degree of 8 μm) are attained by the use of a new computer-controlled non-condenser-type power supply, and through wire tightening by means of DDC (digital direct control).

The product's superiority is not due to its speed alone. It has other useful functions such as a mechanism that prevents wire snapping. This machine is often used in cutting metal for auto parts and home appliances. The company is continuing its efforts to improve discharge machining technology and is already working on the development of a superfast machine capable of handling 300 mm² per second. As of June 1986, JAPAX had introduced the LXR50, a new model capable of wire-cutting metal at a rate of 260 mm² per minute.

1983 Award for Excellence

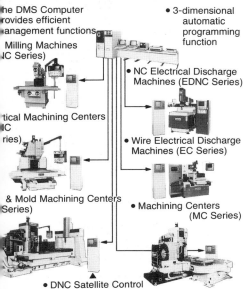

S Die & Mold Machining System

he DMS Computer rovides efficient anagement functions

Milling Machines C Series)

tical Machining Centers C ries)

& Mold Machining Centers Series)

• 3-dimensional automatic programming function

• NC Electrical Discharge Machines (EDNC Series)

• Wire Electrical Discharge Machines (EC Series)

• Machining Centers (MC Series)

• DNC Satellite Control

DMS: A Die-and-Mold Machining System
Makino Milling Machine

The DMS machining system combines a DNC (direct numerical-control) system computer with EDM (electric discharge machining) and other NC (numerical-control) machines to create an overall system that automatically produces dies and molds in three-dimensional complex shapes. By reading dies and molds that have been converted to numerical values by a programmer, the DMS automatically produces a machining program and sends it to the NC machines.

Machining programs for three-dimensional dies and molds are often so complex that one can require up to 50 km of paper tape to record them. Consequently, changing the program tapes for the NC machines has always involved a great deal of manual labor. The DMS system, however, eliminates this task by putting the programming device online with the NC machining systems. DMS was first developed on behalf of Sanyo Electric. It took two years to complete, and caught on immediately with small- and medium-sized die and mold makers.

1982 High Award for Excellence

Sakura Nice Print System: The No-Wash Mini-Lab
Konishiroku Photo Industry

Paper-developing machine (from directly above); installation space of only 7 m²

This low-priced mini-laboratory enables speedy development of photographs by eliminating the washing process. The key to this innovation is the use of a processing agent called Super Stabilizer Ace, which renders water superfluous in the development of film and photo paper. This eliminates the need for water pipes and a boiler installment, reducing the space necessary for installation to less than 7 m². Thus, it can fit easily into a small camera shop.

The system consists of a film developer, a printer, and a paper developer. It is capable of processing 34 rolls of film and of developing 500 sheets of photo paper in one hour. It is priced at ¥6.98 million, a price 30–50% lower than that of conventional developing machines. Since its introduction, the Sakura system has become the mainstay of neighborhood photo shops, and has even been adopted by large photo companies such as Fuji Film, Konishiroku's chief rival. It is marketed outside Japan under the Konica brand.

1984 High Award for Excellence

Vibration-Resistant Nuts and Bolts
Japan Ace

Conventional nuts and bolts have a single spiral groove. Their grip, or ability to hold, results from axial tension produced along this single groove, and once the axial tension is loosened, the hold is loosened from top to bottom. Such nuts and bolts are thus easily susceptible to vibrations, and once loosened can fall apart.

The president of Japan Ace, Masao Kanazawa, identified the need for improvement in the basic design of nuts and bolts. While riding on a Shinkansen bullet train, he noticed a bolt shaking loose, and immediately called his company from the train and ordered it to begin development of this product.

The resulting product has a screw portion with a double structure, each part acting in different directions. When one part of the screw is loosened, the other part tightens, maintaining the axial tension of the entire bolt-nut assembly. This product is six to seven times more resistant to vibration than conventional products.

1982 Award for Excellence

Double-structure screws whose parts revolve in opposite directions from each other

Accuma UL-85: A CO₂-Laser Cutting Machine
Urawa Machine Tools/Miyama

The Accuma UL-85 combines the machine-tool manufacturing technology of Urawa and the laser technology of Miyama to reduce the cost and power consumption of multikind and small-quantity metal-plate machining. It is a good example of what can result when two medium-sized enterprises such as Urawa and Miyama combine their strengths and develop a successful product.

Urawa's main product is a vertical MC (machining center) that can reposition small parts with micron precision and that is widely used in precision machining of both machine parts and metal patterns. The Accuma UL-85 improves upon this machine by replacing the driving axle and cutting tool with a CO_2-laser oscillator. It is able to cut steel plates 3–4 mm thick at a rate of 6 m/min, with a level of precision of ± 2μm. Crucial to Miyama's success in entering the laser field was technical cooperation from an American laser oscillator maker named Coherent.

1982 Award for Excellence

Cuts 6 m of 3–4-mm-thick steel plate per minute

SERVICES: FINANCIAL, INSURANCE, AND ENTERTAINMENT

Index Portfolio Fund
Kokusai Securities

The Index Portfolio Fund is an investment trust designed for customers looking for low-risk investment in the stock market. The fund invests in 300 or more stocks listed daily in the *Nihon Keizai Shimbun,* a group known as the Nikkei 500 or the Nikkei Average (analogous to the Dow Jones Average). The aim of this fund is to provide investors with a margin of profit equal to that of the average prevailing in the stock market. In theory, weighted investment in a large number of stocks should do so.

The idea for such a trust first evolved in the United States in the early 1970s, where it was used for investment of large-scale capital resources, such as company pension funds. In addition to its comparative predictability, it has the advantage of being simple to administer. Since the stocks to be purchased are predetermined, there is no need for pre-investment research on the part of the fund's manager.

In planning the fund, Kokusai Securities had three different indexes from which to choose: the Nikkei Average, comprising 225 stocks; the Nikkei 500, with 500 issues; and the Tōshō (Tokyo Stock Exchange) Price Index, a composite of all the stocks listed on the exchange. The Nikkei 500 was chosen because it corresponds closely to movements in the market and is an up-to-date indicator of trends in the economy. While the 225 stocks listed in the Nikkei Average do not change from year to year, those in the Nikkei 500 are adopted or rejected, based on their previous year's performance. As a result, the Nikkei 500 better reflects changes in economic structure and expected future performance. The Tōshō Index was found unsuitable as an investment instrument since its extremely large number of issues would require the fund manager to research each one before deciding what proportion of the fund should be devoted to it.

The drawback of such a fund is that service fees, taxes, and the necessity of maintaining a portion of the capital in cash to cover withdrawals from the fund damages the otherwise predictable correlation between the respective profit margins of the Nikkei 500 and the stock market as a whole. In a bull market, there is a tendency for investors to be more willing to "put their eggs in one basket" and prefer investment in a few stocks over the security of a fund that provides only average returns. In a bear market, however, the desire for security encourages investors to withdraw from investment trusts with a narrow range of stocks and prefer those, like the Index Portfolio Fund, that are likely to follow overall market declines. Thus, the Index Portfolio Fund managers expect a decrease in investment during a general rise in the stock market, and the reverse during a market downturn. Indeed, in the booming market of the summer of 1986, investment in the fund performed exactly as expected.

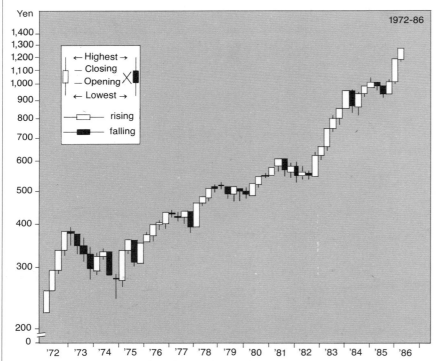

Nikkei 500 Average Stock Quotations (added in quarter periods)

1972-86

Yen

← Highest →
— Closing
— Opening
← Lowest →

□ rising
■ falling

(1) This graph expresses the Nikkei 500 Average stock quotation movements in added quarter periods (logarithmic scale) up to May 31, 1986. Stock prices prior to January 4, 1982, have been compiled from figures from the *Nihon Keizai Shimbun.*
(2) The Nikkei 500 Average stock quotations had been publicized up to this time based upon the Nikkei-Dow 500 Average stock quotations. The name was changed to the present one on May 2, 1975.

1985 Award for Excellence

Saison Mortgage Certificates
Seibu Mortgage Acceptance

The Seibu Saison Group entered the mortgage-securities business in 1984 with the establishment of Seibu Mortgage Acceptance. This was the first mortgage-securities plan to be implemented in Japan. By selling mortgage securities at its Seibu department stores, it changed the image of these securities. Previously directed only at professional investors, they quickly became attractive to small savers.

Saison Mortgage Certificates offer the advantage of automatic transfer of interest to a specified account every six months, as well as the option of accumulating the interest in a high-yield time deposit. The first offering of ¥2.5 billion attracted much attention when it quickly sold out. Initially available in units of ¥1 million, the certificates' appeal to small-scale individual investors was enhanced further with the introduction of ¥100,000 units.

By the summer of 1986 a volume of about ¥10 billion of these securities had been sold. At present, other companies, such as Tokyu, Daiei, and Jusco, are following Seibu's lead.

1984 Award for Excellence

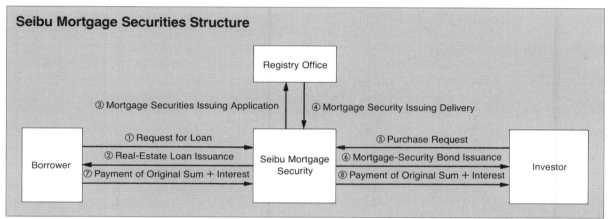

Seibu Mortgage Securities Structure

Sweep Account
Kyoto Shinkin Bank/Daiwa Securities

The cash management account (CMA) was a revolutionary financial innovation in the United States. A Japanese equivalent of the CMA, combining a passbook savings account with a money-market account invested in a medium-term government-bond fund and called a "Sweep Account," was created by the Kyoto Shinkin Bank and Daiwa Securities.

A customer's account at Kyoto Shinkin is maintained at ¥300,000. Any amount above this is swept into Daiwa's money-market fund, which yields high interest. If the balance of the savings account slips below ¥300,000, the bank replaces the funds with a loan up to the balance in the money market. The loan is secured by Seibu Credit.

Savings in Japan have traditionally been placed in bank and post-office accounts. But financial liberalization in the early 1980s resulted in more attractive high-yield instruments. The CMA has now been introduced by other financial institutions.

1984 High Award for Excellence

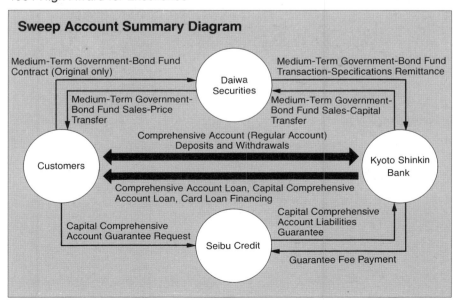

Sweep Account Summary Diagram

Sci/Tech S.A.: A High-Technology Investment Trust
Nomura Securities

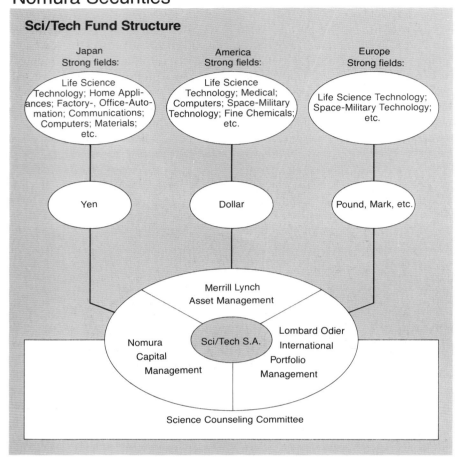

Sci/Tech Fund Structure

Japan
Strong fields:

Life Science Technology; Home Appliances; Factory-, Office-Automation; Communications; Computers; Materials; etc.

America
Strong fields:

Life Science Technology; Medical; Computers; Space-Military Technology; Fine Chemicals; etc.

Europe
Strong fields:

Life Science Technology; Space-Military Technology; etc.

Yen

Dollar

Pound, Mark, etc.

Merrill Lynch Asset Management

Nomura Capital Management

Sci/Tech S.A.

Lombard Odier International Portfolio Management

Science Counseling Committee

The internationalization of financial markets has created a need for investment trusts that can draw on global capital resources. Sci/Tech S.A., developed by Nomura Securities in cooperation with Merrill Lynch of the United States and Switzerland's Lombard Odier, does just that. It invests in high-technology companies in Japan, the United States, and Europe, focusing on pharmaceuticals, biotechnology, telecommunications, and new materials. It pays particular attention to venture capital companies.

Nomura handles stocks in Japan, where approximately 40% of the trust's investment is made, and Merrill Lynch and Lombard Odier take responsibility for the United States and Europe—40% and 20%, respectively.

Soon after the trust was established, total investment reached US$840 million, including approximately US$100 million from Japanese investors. Although capital has subsequently declined, this trust remains significant as an innovation in international investment.

1983 Award for Excellence

Money Capsule: A Government-Bond Time Account
Mitsubishi Bank

In 1983, Mitsubishi Bank devised a method of making it easier to sell government bonds at bank branches to individual, small-scale investors by offering them in conjunction with fixed-time savings accounts. Dubbed the Money Capsule, this high-yield financial instrument, sold in ¥500,000 units, combines a ten-year, long-term government bond with a savings account paying, as of September 1, 1986, an untaxed 5.988% when left for ten years. Sixty percent of the principal is commonly used to buy a long-term government bond, with the remainder resting in the savings account.

In the world of finance in Japan, "cross-products" (products that are the same at all banks) are the rule. As a

result, the Money Capsule's uniqueness makes it an unusual product. Since it was a combination of existing instruments, it required no license

as a new product from the Ministry of Finance.

1983 High Award for Excellence

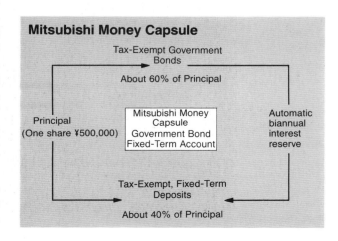

Mitsubishi Money Capsule

Tax-Exempt Government Bonds

About 60% of Principal

Principal
(One share ¥500,000)

Mitsubishi Money Capsule Government Bond Fixed-Term Account

Automatic biannual interest reserve

Tax-Exempt, Fixed-Term Deposits

About 40% of Principal

Jumbo Fund
Yamaichi Securities

The Jumbo Fund, an investment trust introduced by Yamaichi Securities, buys government bonds with five years remaining to maturity and systematically reinvests interest earned instead of paying dividends. Investors must remain in the fund for five years. The annual yield for the first issue, offered in July 1982, was a hefty 9.2%.

As a result, this type of fund caught on quickly not only with the public but also with other securities firms. They were soon offering similar funds, and all were competing successfully with interest-bearing bank debentures and loan trusts. Before the year was out, the competitors included Nikko, Daiwa, Nomura, and Dai-ichi.

With the subsequent rapid decline in interest rates, however, yields on outstanding government bonds have fallen sharply, reducing the attractiveness of such funds. Unless interest rates rise again, the prospects for further sales will remain poor.

1982 High Award for Excellence

Structure of Jumbo Fund

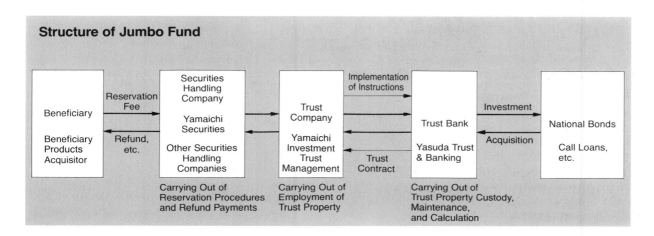

Non-Collateral Community Loans
Mitsui Bank

While conventional business loans rely heavily on financial statements and collateral, this system issues loans to small- and medium-sized businesses using the reputation of the company and the character of the applicant as criteria. The business is required to designate a guarantor, but conventional loan applications are not necessary.

The current loan ceiling is ¥5 million, and interest rates vary according to the lending term. Loans can be used for tax and bonus payments, equipment purchase, stock and raw materials, and the like.

At its peak, about ¥5 billion was loaned out. In 1985, 200 loans were made, averaging about ¥2.5 million each. Undertaking this type of financing has given Mitsui Bank expertise with small- and medium-sized businesses, which it is using to design other

financing systems to meet the needs of other customers.

1982 Award for Excellence

Mitsui Bank's non-collateral loans are designed for small- and medium-sized businesses

Factoring System for Account Settlement
Credit 109

Conventional account settlement between commercial buyers and sellers in Japan, as elsewhere, involves the use of promissory notes. Although the conventional system allows transactions to be completed smoothly without the handling of currency, it can be costly and time-consuming to administer. The factoring system introduced by Credit 109, a consumer finance company in the Tokyu Group, through an agreement with Nichiboshin, Ltd., a financial institution specializing in bill-discount business, does away with promissory notes in transactions between Tokyu Group buyers and their suppliers. This simplifies settlement for all parties, eliminating the expense of clerical work, financing costs, and stamp duty.

As a consumer finance company, Credit 109 is primarily serving such Tokyu Group enterprises as depart-ment stores and travel agencies, which deal directly with consumers and thus conduct many of their transactions through its credit-card business. However, Credit 109 was seeking ways to provide finance-related services to other Group members as part of efforts to use resources more efficiently. When Nichiboshin approached Credit 109 in the fall of 1983 with a new method of account settlement—replacing promissory notes with a factoring system—the finance company accepted the proposal positively.

By April 1986, six of the larger companies in the Tokyu Group—Tokyu Construction, Tokyu Car, Tokyu Agency, Tokyu Trading, Seikitokyu Kogyo, and Shiroki—had been introduced to the new system.

The system involves an agreement among a buyer, a supplier, and a finance company—the factor. Under a general contract for the factoring system, after each purchase the supplier immediately sells the resulting receivables to the factor, and the factor receives a commission for handling settlement of the receivables. In addition to reducing paperwork, lowering collection costs, and speeding up settlement, a factoring system does not require any compensating balance of deposits related to bill discount, so the effective interest rate on factoring can be lower than that on bill discounts although the factor's nominal interest rate exceeds the bill-discount rate.

For companies that issue a small number of promissory notes, however, factoring offers little benefit. Credit 109 estimates that a company must average at least 400 to 500 notes per month to make the factoring system economical for all parties involved. Thus, only six large members of the

Mini-Reservation Member's Loan
Sumitomo Credit Service

An easy-to-fill-out loan form with a limit of ¥300,000

Sumitomo Credit gave buying on credit a boost with the Mini-Reservation Member's Loan, a credit system available to holders of Sumitomo's Visa Card.

When the system was instituted in 1982, cardholders were allowed to borrow freely up to a ceiling of ¥200,000, with repayment in a lump sum or in fixed monthly installments at 18% annual interest. The ceiling was subsequently raised to ¥300,000.

Sumitomo Credit developed this loan as an alternative to Cashing, its so-called instant loan program. Although Cashing allows easy borrowing and is thus extremely popular, it requires a monthly payment of the balance, a heavy burden on family finances often resulting in defaults.

When the Member's Loan plan was introduced, Cashing customers with good credit histories were offered membership, allowing them to apply for loans that can be deposited directly into their bank accounts. In this way, Sumitomo Credit built a pool of reliable credit customers.

1982 Award for Excellence

Tokyu Group elected to try using the system.

Despite the advantages of factoring, several obstacles currently prevent Tokyu Group companies from actually implementing the system. An easy-money policy is now prevailing in Japan, making it easy and inexpensive for companies to raise short-term funds to liquidate their accounts receivable.

Some suppliers are accustomed to settling their own accounts payable with promissory notes received from buyers. Laws are protecting small- and medium-sized companies from disadvantageous payment practices of large buyers. Therefore, there is little room for small companies to raise any objections against the change of payment method.

1985 Award for Excellence

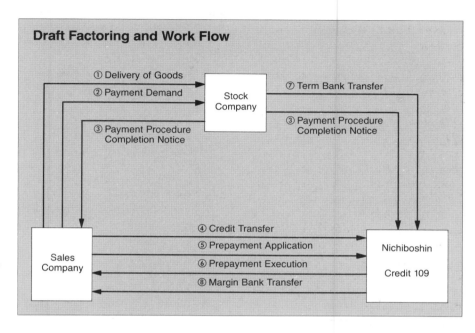

Draft Factoring and Work Flow

① Delivery of Goods
② Payment Demand
③ Payment Procedure Completion Notice
⑦ Term Bank Transfer
③ Payment Procedure Completion Notice
④ Credit Transfer
⑤ Prepayment Application
⑥ Prepayment Execution
⑧ Margin Bank Transfer

Stock Company

Sales Company

Nichiboshin

Credit 109

Speed Plan: A Driving School Course
Marui

Obtaining a driver's license in Japan is no simple matter. Both written and road tests are strict, and require high marks. One way of ensuring success is to enroll in a driving school. If a driving school certifies a student's driving ability, he is exempt from the government's road test and need submit only to the written test and an eye examination.

The cost of a driving school course is high—in 1982, as much as ¥228,000. Marui's package plan offers both enrollment in a driving school and a low-interest loan to cover the cost of tuition.

Students can enroll in a regular course with at least 27 hours behind the wheel and 30 hours of classroom instruction, or they can attend an intensive driver-training camp. These camps are in resort areas and have proven popular with the young.

Marui's first-year revenue target was ¥300 million, but actual revenue soared to ¥2.5 billion.

1982 Award for Excellence

Marui's driving school course can be paid for with its credit card

Dementia-Care Insurance
American Family Life Assurance

What happens to a family when a member suffers from dementia? Feature films depicting the wandering and disorientation of the old, coupled with the stress and financial drain on those who must care for them, have appeared with increasing frequency in Japan. In the fall of 1985, American Family Life Assurance promoted one such film, the critically acclaimed *The Grey Sunset*, to publicize a new policy: insurance to care for dementia patients.

The problem of dementia is a growing one in Japan. According to the Ministry of Health and Welfare, there is at least one family member over sixty-five in a quarter of Japan's 37 million households. Some 600,000 Japanese are elderly and suffer from dementia, and another 500,000 are bedridden. In fifteen years, Japan will have 28 million people over sixty-five.

American Family Life Assurance responded to the statistics and a call by government for services to the elderly with its own innovation. The company, a U.S. firm, started selling a cancer insurance developed especially for the Japanese market in 1974, and was

searching for a new product. American Family's managing director, Hidefumi Matsui, stumbled on the idea of dementia insurance in conversations with two friends who each had a family member who suffered from dementia. They remarked that caring for their relatives was difficult and costly, with no way to ease the burden. Here was the opportunity that American Family was looking for. No dementia coverage existed in the market.

The most difficult problem encountered by the designers of the policy was the sticky question of defining dementia. They agreed that to receive benefits, a policyholder would need a physician's certification of organic dementia and disorientation, and a need for care as a result.

Coverage can begin as early as age 18, when premiums might be as low as ¥1,920 monthly for a male. Benefits include payments for death, severe disability, and dementia. If a policyholder should begin to suffer from dementia for three months or more while still making payments, the policy pays up to ¥5 million. Upon completion of

payments, the policyholder receives "congratulatory" bonuses of ¥200,000 every five years while in good health, and coverage of ¥150,000 per month for ten years if dementia occurs.

In February 1984, preparations for the policy were finalized, and the company applied for permission from the Ministry of Finance to market it. When permission was granted nine months later, sales were expected to be around 1,000 policies per month, but the volume soon reached 1,500 per month. Other insurance companies followed suit with similar plans of their own, firmly establishing this form of insurance in Japan, and American Family could claim credit for a successful innovation.

1985 High Award for Excellence

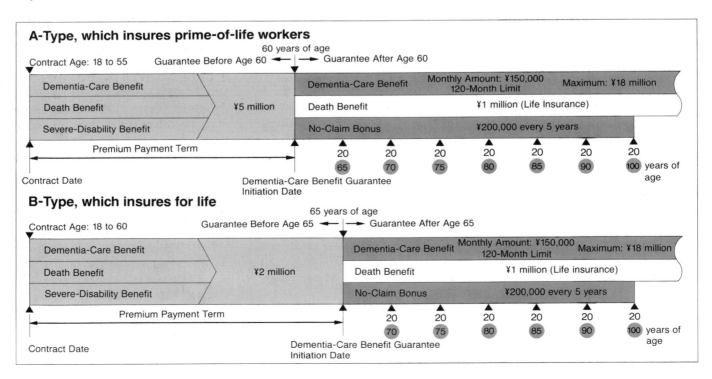

Dream Plan: A Travel, Insurance, and Loan Plan
Japan Travel Bureau/Orient Finance/Tokio Marine & Fire Insurance

This innovative mix of loans and insurance was designed to help travelers explore the world on inexpensive credit. The Japan Travel Bureau, the nation's largest tourist agency, arranged the trip, while the two other companies helped pay for it.

Orient Finance would lend money to cover travel costs and sell a single-premium accident insurance policy from Tokio Marine and Fire Insurance. This insurance, covering plane, car, and ship crashes, was used as collateral; if the customer could not pay back what he borrowed, Orient Finance would recover the money from Tokio Marine and Fire.

The attraction of this plan was that it offered interest rates 4–6% lower than those of competitors' travel loans. The

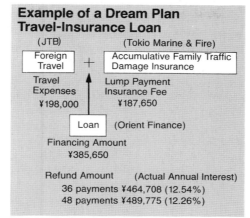

Example of a Dream Plan Travel-Insurance Loan

(JTB) (Tokio Marine & Fire)

Foreign Travel + Accumulative Family Traffic Damage Insurance

Travel Expenses ¥198,000 Lump Payment Insurance Fee ¥187,650

Loan (Orient Finance)

Financing Amount ¥385,650

Refund Amount (Actual Annual Interest)
36 payments ¥464,708 (12.54%)
48 payments ¥489,775 (12.26%)

were possible because the majority refund was returned, not to the customer, but to Orient Finance to defer some of the cost of financing.

The Dream Plan was popular at first, but later was squeezed out of the market when other interest rates dropped and because travelers disliked paying after the trip.

1984 Award for Excellence

Long-Term Ladies' Accident Insurance
Sumitomo Marine & Fire Insurance

A poster for Long-Term Ladies' Accident Insurance

Since Japanese working women generally save more than their male counterparts, Sumitomo's insurance tailored to suit the female lifestyle was an unprecedented hit in the nation's insurance industry.

The plan accumulates savings and also covers accidents in the office, at home, and on the road as well as on the sports field, both in Japan and overseas. It compensates policyholders for such specific liabilities as when their dog bites someone or their bicycle bumps into a pedestrian, or when they, as shoppers, break a valuable in a store. The policy even pays them if they become victims of pickpockets and muggers.

Sumitomo marketed the plan in 1984, and within a year sold more than 100,000 contracts at a value of ¥20 billion. From May 1985, fourteen other companies offered similar policies, attracting 1.1 million women by March 1986.

1984 Award for Excellence

Tabi Tabi: A Travel Savings Plan
Japan Travel Bureau

Tabi Tabi is a vacation savings plan that lets people pay a little now and travel a lot in the future. One of the major appeals of Tabi Tabi, developed by the Japan Travel Bureau (JTB), is that it gives subscribers interest on the money they put into special accounts. A member makes monthly payments of at least ¥3,000 for a fixed period from six to sixty months. At the end of the period, he gets travel tickets worth the total paid plus interest, at rates of 6% for a one-year contract or 8% for five years. Installments can be paid conveniently by automatic transfer from bank or postal accounts.

The program is ideal for students saving for school trips, businessmen organizing company outings, and couples planning retirement journeys. Tabi Tabi has found particular success among housewives in their forties and fifties.

Tabi Tabi—a pun on the Japanese words for "travel," *tabi*, and "frequent," *tabi-tabi*—was the fruit of efforts by a JTB Creative Planning Team set up in 1983. Its seven staffers wandered through every section of the company and considered the mission of JTB in the twenty-first century.

What most impressed this team was JTB's need to respond to potential competition from the "new media." If hotels, airlines, and other transportation services could contact consumers in their homes via cable television and two-way videotex services, why would anyone need a travel agency?

The team concluded that JTB had to step up its personal contact with the public. A Market Development Section was formed in June 1984, and soon enough Tabi Tabi was on the drawing board.

It sends sales staff directly into potential customers' homes and offices to introduce the product and ink contracts. Later they confirm monthly installments and advise subscribers of travel options available. The system also keeps detailed, up-to-date data on the sex, age, wedding anniversary

A brochure for JTB's travel savings plan

dates, and travel hopes of subscribers so JTB can focus its tour campaigns.

JTB put the plan on the market in April 1985. Since then, Tabi Tabi has been so popular that it is considered one of the major successes of Japan's travel industry in recent years. In fiscal 1986, some 340,000 customers bought contracts worth a total of ¥38 billion.

Ironically, the test product for Tabi Tabi was almost its direct opposite and a failure. It called for customers to "travel now and pay later." The Dream Plan was introduced in 1984 by JTB in cooperation with Tokio Marine and Fire Insurance and Orient Finance.

A subsequent survey of consumers, however, revealed widespread resistance to the idea of paying for travel after the fun was over.

The Dream Plan failed, but it did help inspire its reverse. Within six months of Tabi Tabi's debut, three other major travel bureaus followed suit and introduced similar travel savings plans.

1985 High Award for Excellence

CATS, The Musical
Shiki Theatrical Company

In Japan, theater productions have much shorter runs than those overseas. Traditionally, shows run for less than two months, with closing dates fixed before a show opens.

The Shiki Theatrical Company successfully fought this convention with its production of the musical CATS, putting up its own "tent-theater" for a year's run at a total cost of ¥300 million.

Such a large sum was far beyond the current assets of the company, but Shiki gambled that the costs would be recovered by proceeds from the long-run performance—an innovative approach to theater financing in Japan.

Advertising sponsors helped defray some of the costs. Ticket sales were boosted by use of on-line computers—a first in Japan. The company, hoping for repeat customers, also advertised that a multiple-cast system would ensure fresh performances throughout the musical's run. The show closed after the year's run because Shiki had to vacate the rented site.

1984 High Award for Excellence

The CATS theatre built in West Shinjuku, Tokyo

Nakazato Ski Train
Seibu Railways

A popular overnight tour for skiers

With the 1982 opening of the Jōetsu Shinkansen "bullet train" service connecting Tokyo to Niigata prefecture, Japan National Railways (JNR; JR as of April 1, 1987) was forced to decrease its regular train service to the area by one-third as demand fell. Faced with the possibility of further cuts, JNR welcomed a proposal from Seibu-group-affiliated transportation, tourism, and leisure enterprises, to develop an inexpensive overnight tour for skiers to the Nakazato ski resort area.

The package deal, known as Ski Train, originally costing ¥9,300 for adults, consists of reserved tickets on a JNR express train, inexpensive accommodations with breakfast, lift tickets, and a 50% discount on ski rental and lessons. The package is available from January through March and is limited to trains departing three evenings per week.

Ski Train was the first time a private company was allowed to develop services using the JNR.

1982 High Award for Excellence

Tokyo Disneyland
Oriental Land

Japan's largest amusement park, Tokyo Disneyland, covers 82.6 hectares of land outside the city and was built at a cost of ¥150 billion. Oriental Land worked closely with Walt Disney Productions in the United States to create a mood that would evoke the feeling of the U.S. Disneyland. It consists of five theme lands much like its two predecessors. Disney president Ron Miller paid Tokyo Disneyland a high compliment when he pronounced the Japanese version "better than the original."

Since its opening in April 1983, the amusement park has attracted visitors not only from all over Japan, but also from Southeast Asia. At present, over 10 million people visit Tokyo Disneyland annually, generating more than ¥70 billion in revenues. It employs 7,450 full-time and part-time people.

The amusement park has given a boost to the tourist industry in Tokyo. Hotel occupancy rates have risen, and some large chains—Hilton International, Regent International, and Sheraton—are now constructing hotels in the vicinity of Disneyland.

1983 High Award for Excellence

Tokyo Disneyland's annual sales near ¥70 billion

B-BOX: On-Line Job Information
Gakken

The information revolution is posing a danger to small- and medium-sized publishing companies. Electronic bulletin boards, computerized information services and public video display terminals threaten to eliminate the need for much printed information. Gakken, an educational publisher based in Tokyo, has responded to this threat by moving into the computer information field. It provides an on-line, part-time-job information service, called B-BOX, through 150 terminals located in bookstores and other places where youth congregate throughout Tokyo.

The terminals have direct access to the large job-information data base of the Gakken host computer. This link is provided by telecommunications lines reserved exclusively for B-BOX, permitting high-speed transmission of large volumes of data at any time of the day. The data can be supplied to the

terminals two hours after it was collected. This speed is crucial to the success of B-BOX, since it is thereby able to provide more up-to-date information than the job-information magazines popular in Japan.

The B-BOX is easy to use. For ¥10 per use, the job hunter supplies the terminal with his age, sex, and desired working conditions. He can stipulate his working schedule—specifying preferred days of the week and times of the day—and his desired type of labor. The computer will then provide him with up to twenty items per search—information on positions available in seven different categories including office work, light labor, jobs in fast-food restaurants, and part-time work for housewives. B-BOX users can also print out a hard copy of their searches.

Gakken has found that each B-BOX terminal is used as many as 100 times a day. Sixty-eight percent of the users are

men. Nearly a third of all customers are between ages 18 and 20. According to a survey in March 1987, the highest rate of employment among B-BOX users was in the light labor field, with 68% employed. Office work followed, with 57% finding jobs.

In its present state, the system is still basically a computer version of job-information magazines. Gakken has openly acknowledged that it is in competition with such publications. In order to get one step ahead of its rivals, however, the company has decided to expand the menu of service options in the near future.

Its most immediate goal is the provision of an on-line service of employment information for recent graduates—that is, full-time jobs and career positions as opposed to part-time work. In September 1986, Gakken also provided a telephone link that allows personal-computer users

---

Telpost: Videodisk—Telephone Information Service
Chescom

Telpost is a street-box information terminal that connects a videodisk to a telephone. Chescom, the company that markets Telpost and acts as an

information clearing-house, programs the disk with information about hotels, restaurants, bars, movie theaters, and other leisure services. A customer may view information on a 21-in color display screen—with audio in either Japanese or English—until he finds what he is looking for. If he picks up the attached phone, he is then connected immediately to the establishment concerned, so it can provide him with further details.

Chescom, a highly successful telephone-forwarding and answering-service company, established Telpost in response to requests from numerous service companies. It did so under the aegis of Japan Information Systems, a company it formed together with NTT, Japan's domestic telephone company. Chescom is hoping to capitalize on its success with Telpost by developing a computerized town-guide service.

1984 Award for Excellence

Telpost combines a telephone with videodisk

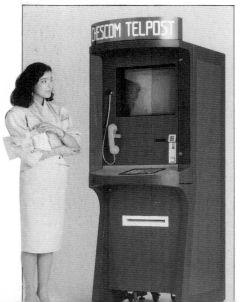

Ticket PIA: Computer Ticketing Network
PIA

PIA publishes the biggest and most popular biweekly entertainment-information magazine in Japan. It has capitalized on its high profile by setting up an extremely successful on-line computer sales system of tickets for plays, movies, concerts, and other entertainment events. The data base is detailed enough to allow a customer to specify even which seat he prefers for a given performance. There are 150 PIA Service Centers in Japan, all linked by video terminals to the central data bank.

A Ticket PIA "station" in Tokyo

B-Box terminals throughout Tokyo provide up to 20 pieces of job-offer information at ¥10 apiece

access to the data bank.

The success of B-BOX has prompted the company to enlarge its expertise in computer technology. Gakken has, for example, developed a teaching computer for children that is modeled on B-BOX, and is planning to expand business operations in the computer field. Gakken's foresight has prepared it well to defend its territory and survive the effects of the information revolution.

1985 Award for Excellence

Demand for such on-line services in the entertainment industry has grown rapidly with the information boom. Ticket sales by this method are already very high.

In April 1986 PIA expanded its activity and established a system with Japan Air Lines, called JAL World Ticket PIA, that allows customers to reserve tickets around the world—on Broadway, at the Opéra—with a single telephone call.

1984 High Award for Excellence

Shinjuku Washington Hotel:Automatic Front Desk
Fujita Tourist Enterprises

The Shinjuku Washington Hotel, which opened in December 1983, was the first hotel in Japan to employ an automated front desk check-in and check-out service and magnetic key-card system. With 1,638 rooms, the hotel needs low room charges to maintain a high rate of occupancy. This need necessitated bold measures to cut personnel costs.

Borrowing from a system in use at the Peachtree Plaza Hotel in Atlanta, Georgia, the management of the Washington Hotel chain experimented with a punch card system at one of its provincial branches. Management concluded that only magnetic cards would permit a fully automatic service.

In conjunction with Omron Tateisi Electronics, a manufacturer of automated bank-teller machines, Fujita developed the desired system. It allows one machine to perform the work of 1.5 humans, thereby eliminating the need for about ten front desk employees.

An automatic front desk

The Washington Hotel's room rates have remained low and its occupancy levels high.

1983 Award for Excellence

243

Happy Wagon: A Low-Calorie Meal-Delivery System
Teishoku

The Happy Wagon home meal-delivery service for diabetics offers four different kinds of low-calorie menus, ranging from 1,200 kcal to 1,840 kcal. Customers may select the menu most suitable to their needs and have it delivered to their residences. Teishoku developed the menus in consultation with both hospitals and doctors. Patients pay a lump sum for joining the program and an additional amount corresponding to the number of calories consumed each month.

Unquestionably, a great need exists for such a service since diabetes is one of the most prevalent modern diseases. There are an estimated 2 million potential diabetics in Japan. Since diet is an essential part of treatment for this disease, diabetics must spend a great deal of time thinking about what they eat. Teishoku's service goes a long way toward relieving this burden.

Aimed also at the general public, Teishoku's low-calorie meal-delivery menus are also advertised as diet menus and healthy menus.

1984 Award for Excellence

Happy Wagon delivers two low-calorie meals and a snack once a day

Merchandise Rental by Phone
Orient Leasing/JCB

Japanese consumers have had a long-standing prejudice against renting or borrowing goods, preferring to buy brand-new goods for themselves. Gradually, however, this prejudice has given way to more practical concerns such as the high prices that have to be paid for little-used goods, and the short-term rental business has begun to grow in Japan.

In 1984, Orient Leasing teamed up with the Japanese credit-card company JCB to provide rental service to card holders. As a result of the high land prices in Tokyo, the two companies decided to forego establishing an actual store. Instead, customers place an order by phone and have goods delivered to their homes.

The most popular items for rental have been expensive goods such as word processors, televisions, and air conditioners as well as other goods for seasonal use, including skis. Rental costs are low because overhead costs have been kept to a minimum.

1984 Award for Excellence

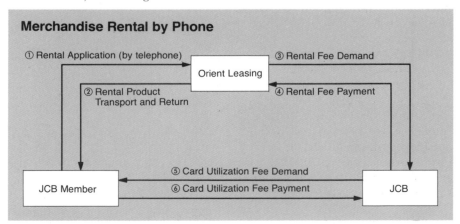

Merchandise Rental by Phone

① Rental Application (by telephone) ③ Rental Fee Demand

Orient Leasing

② Rental Product Transport and Return ④ Rental Fee Payment

JCB Member

⑤ Card Utilization Fee Demand
⑥ Card Utilization Fee Payment

JCB

Golf Takkyūbin: Golf-Club Delivery
Yamato Transport

Golf sets are delivered in a special cover

It is estimated that between 65 and 70 million people play golf in Japan—an astonishing 55% of the population. Most of these devotees must commute to golf courses outside cities, using crowded trains and carrying heavy golf equipment. To save people this troublesome procedure, Yamato Transport started a golf equipment delivery service. With a single phone call, a golfer can contact the company and arrange to have his clubs picked up and delivered to the course the day before playing. The service is available on weekends and holidays as well as on weekdays. A special cover is placed over the clubs to protect them from inclement weather.

Although not the first to provide such a service, Yamato was able to take advantage of its strong nationwide delivery network to become a serious competitor in this business. Since golf courses in Japan are usually located outside the cities, and since the golfing population continues to grow, it is expected that demand for this Golf Takkyūbin service will increase.

1984 Award for Excellence

P-Size Takkyūbin: Small-Parcel Delivery
Yamato Transport

Private companies providing door-to-door small-parcel delivery services by truck are popular in Japan.

In 1983, Yamato Transport, a leading parcel-delivery company, added a new class of parcel—P-Size, or "petite" size, under 2 kg—to its rates. Until this time, its rates for small and petite packages were the same. With this move, Yamato's price of ¥700 for the smallest packages was only slightly higher than those of the Ministry of Posts and Telecommunications (MPT), and Yamato's service is faster and more reliable.

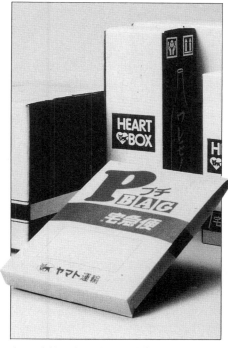

A special bag for delivering P-Size packages

One of the company's objectives in lowering rates was to gain strength in the small-parcel market dominated by the MPT. The other was to force the MPT to acknowledge officially the private parcel-delivery services. The MPT responded not only with a price reduction and improvement of services, but also by establishing upper and lower limits for delivery-service rates, thereby recognizing private delivery services and essentially liberalizing rates.

1983 High Award for Excellence

Phonoprint Express: Transcription Service
Temporary Center

Phonoprint Express, provides quick transcription of minutes of company meetings that have been recorded on tape. In extremely urgent cases, it is possible for Temporary Center's staff to record and process the minutes of a meeting in an adjacent room while the meeting is still in progress, although this is rarely done. The minutes could then be distributed immediately after the conference.

More commonly, a recorded tape of proceedings is sent to the company, whose employees, working at home, then transcribe the minutes. Several employees can work on different sections of the same minutes. Transcribers submit their work by facsimile or via an acoustic coupler using telephone lines. Final proofreading and editing is done at Temporary Center.

Phonoprint Express was the idea of Temporary Center's deputy managing director, Yasuyuki Nambu, who listened to companies' requests for service. Temporary Center charges less than ¥30,000 for a one-hour tape.

1983 Award for Excellence

A quick, efficient transcription service

Prepaid Telephone Card
Nippon Telegraph & Telephone

The prepaid telephone card, developed by Nippon Telegraph and Telephone (NTT), is a magnetic card for use instead of coins in public telephones. Cards are sold in denominations ranging from ¥500 to ¥5,000. When a card is inserted into a telephone, a meter ticks away, showing the amount remaining on the card.

Confronted by obstacles such as problems of durability or fraudulent use of card substitutes, it took NTT researchers nearly ten years to develop a usable product. A tangle of more than 100 new patents were applied for.

The cards can be printed with any surface design and they have become a

A few examples of NTT's popular telephone cards

fad among collectors, similar to postage stamps. The cards have been a huge commercial success, with sales of 200 million cards by February 1987. The company continues to offer new services with the cards, such as free graphic design for corporations ordering in bulk. Cards valued at ¥1,000 and up also offer a discount.

1984 High Award for Excellence

Housecleaning Gift Coupons
Tokyu Department Stores

A housecleaning gift coupon set of ¥500 coupons; there are four sets, ranging from ¥20,000 to ¥70,000, depending on the extent of the housework to be done

By introducing gift coupons for housecleaning tasks, the Tokyu department store chain pioneered the concept of gift certificates for services as well as for goods.

Under the Tokyu system, a professional cleaner is dispatched to the home of the coupon holder to scrub the bathroom and toilet, disinfect the tatami mats (the traditional floor covering present in most Japanese homes), and perform various other cleaning chores.

Currently, four types of cleaning services are available. Two ¥20,000 coupons are for the kitchen or toilet and bath, while two others in ¥50,000 and ¥70,000 denominations include windows, hallways, and bedrooms. All four types have been quite popular, with sales for 1985 reaching ¥80 million on 1,200 orders. The majority of the coupons are purchased for year-end gifts, a time when Japanese traditionally perform their "spring" cleaning.

1984 Award for Excellence

My Doctor: Medical Emergency Alarm
Secom

When Secom, a home and office security company, discovered that many of its customers were using their security alarms in medical emergencies, it realized that customers would welcome a portable alarm system for illness. So Secom began research on a signal device that could be worn at all times and activated in case of a medical emergency.

It proved quite difficult to design a transmitter that was small, error-proof, and easily manipulated, even by the infirm. Secom finally settled on a device the size of a disposable cigarette lighter, to be worn around the neck.

Under the Secom system, an elderly or handicapped person who suffers an attack or fall can send out an emergency signal by simply squeezing the My Doctor alarm. When this signal is received at a Secom control center, medical aid is called and a Secom staff member goes immediately to the site. The service is offered for ¥400 a month to customers of Secom's comprehensive home security system, My Alarm.

1982 Award for Excellence

The My Doctor alarm hangs around the neck

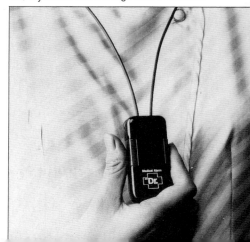

SALES AND DISTRIBUTION SYSTEMS

Fresh System: A Home Delivery Service
Fresh Systems

Fresh System catalogues

Fresh System is a home delivery service providing consumers with groceries and daily necessities as well as clothing, furniture, and other goods. Although home delivery services exist throughout Japan, one that even delivers perishables, as is the case with Fresh System, is unusual. Ten major department stores and supermarkets all over Japan participate in the system on a franchise or joint venture basis.

To place an order, members call a computerized answering service and state their membership and code numbers. A recorded voice then asks for the numbers of the products they wish delivered. The computer records this information and then relays it to a central computer located at a franchised store. The central computer not only records what customers want and when, but it also arranges for payments to be made by automatic bank transfer.

When members join Fresh System, they arrange for deliveries twice a week, choosing from three patterns: Monday and Thursday, Tuesday and Friday, or Wednesday and Saturday, although arrangements can be made for deliveries on other days. Customers do not have to be at home, since Fresh System provides a delivery locker that is placed outside the customer's home. The locker is a simple wooden box. Perishable goods are put in a small ice box that is placed in the locker and preserves the foods for up to eight hours.

Customers select products from two types of catalogues, both prepared by Fresh Systems for its franchise operations. One catalogue, which lists a variety of products ranging from chinaware to bicycles, is the same throughout the country. Other catalogues are tailored for each franchise, listing its products, such as perishables or other foods. These catalogues, which change weekly, show photographs of the products, list prices and product numbers.

Fresh System was developed after considerable experimentation with various methods, such as placing storage lockers inside shops or leaving products in the customer's home and then checking off and receiving payment for what was used, the traditional method by which medicine is sometimes sold in Japan. The current system was designed in response to social changes in Japan, where increasing numbers of women are entering the work force. Fresh System is designed so that the stores reach out to the customers, rather than having customers go to the stores.

Fresh System charges no membership or delivery fee. It began in 1983 with a clientele of 1,000 households. In 1986, it enjoyed a membership of 100,000 households and 10 companies, plus total sales of ¥8 billion.

In order to ensure customer satisfaction, a female representative of Fresh Systems visits members' homes once or twice a month to listen to customers' complaints and requests as well as to explain the telephone ordering system. As the system grows and as more department stores and supermarkets participate and members join, an increasing variety of products will be available at lower prices.

1985 High Award for Excellence

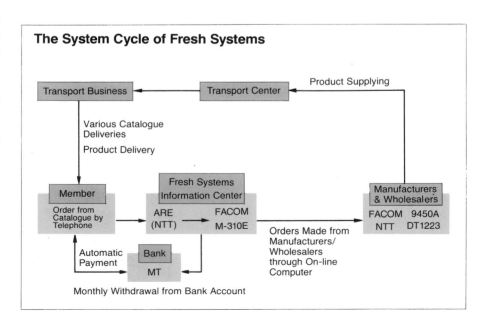

The System Cycle of Fresh Systems

- Transport Business
- Transport Center
- Product Supplying
- Various Catalogue Deliveries
- Product Delivery
- Member — Order from Catalogue by Telephone
- Fresh Systems Information Center — ARE (NTT) FACOM M-310E
- Manufacturers & Wholesalers — FACOM 9450A NTT DT1223
- Orders Made from Manufacturers/ Wholesalers through On-line Computer
- Automatic Payment
- Bank — MT
- Monthly Withdrawal from Bank Account

Aucnet: TV Auto Auction System
Aucnet

Used-car auctions are generally conducted in large open areas, where bidders can view lots to be auctioned one by one. For many used-car dealers this is a great inconvenience, since it requires that participants be present at the auction site. Dealers from remote areas are particularly disadvantaged by this system, since they must travel considerable distances to be present at auctions.

The Aucnet on-line information system was developed to overcome the physical limits imposed by on-site auctions. The president of Aucnet, Masataka Fujisaki, is himself a used-car dealer, familiar with problems of the business. It was his idea to use a computer to tie dealers into a single network, and allow the auction to be conducted by visual transmission. This eliminates the need to bring cars to an auction site, and allows buyers to participate in bidding from their homes or businesses.

Using a laser videodisk sent by Aucnet and a private terminal linked to the Aucnet host computer, member-dealers can study photographs and physical data on automobiles before the auction. Inspectors sent to examine cars before the auction ensure that accurate, meaningful information is supplied to the host computer.

On the day of the auction, bids are made by depressing a button on a joystick attached to the system. The price of the car is raised by ¥3,000 with each touch of the button. The highest bidder for any particular lot is informed of his purchase by a message flashing on his screen. Sellers who feel that the highest price offered is not sufficient have the option of rejecting the offer and keeping their car.

Aucnet was a success in its very first year, signing up almost 1,200 dealers in the Kantō, Tōkai, Tōhoku, and Kansai areas as of January 1987. They rent the computer hardware for ¥29,000 per month and purchase videodisks of cars for sale for ¥2,900 each per week. Despite the large number of used-car auctions held in Japan annually—about 100—Aucnet became one of the country's top five auctioneers within a year, and its profits reached ¥13.5 billion in 1986.

While the company's immediate goal is the establishment of a comprehensive auction system throughout Japan, its long-term aim is export of the system to the United States and Europe. Toward that goal, Aucnet conducted four trial auctions in America in conjunction with a major American automobile manufacturer beginning

The "Start" sign is given to begin the auction

in June 1986. Aucnet exported the necessary hardware and software while the American maker provided the used cars and access to its 13,000 American dealers. Unlike the Japanese system, in which dealers bid from their home bases, the American dealers assembled in one location to bid and practice using the Aucnet equipment. The American maker hopes to use the video auto auction to strengthen its relationships with its dealers. Additional U.S. auctions are planned for the future, with the automobile manufacturer supplying 50,000 used cars per year.

1985 High Award for Excellence

Aucnet System

Information Center
Input of Used-Car Data into Host Computer
Input of Photo Collection into Laserdisk

Auction Participation

Auction Participation

Photos and Data Sent by On-line Computer

Photos and Data Sent by On-line Computer

Auction Participation

Photos and Data Sent by On-line Computer

Used-Car Dealer
Auction Participation with TV Screen and Computer Terminal

Used-Car Dealer
Auction Participation with TV Screen and Computer Terminal

Used-Car Dealer
Auction Participation with TV Screen and Computer Terminal

Participation of Over a Thousand Used-Car Dealers

Milk Joy: Rental Formal Wear for Children
Marie

Marie's rental system allows parents to outfit their children on formal occasions

Japanese parents are known for spending large sums of money on their children, and a surprising amount of it goes for clothing. In Japan, where society places high value not only on ceremony but also on the clothing worn at such times, it is customary for children to dress in formal Western or Japanese attire on occasions such as matriculation and graduation ceremonies for elementary school, piano recitals, weddings, and *Shichi-Go-San* (a Shinto ceremony for the future well-being of children aged three, five, and seven). Since formal clothing is quite expensive and children outgrow clothing quickly, outfitting children for these infrequent events can be a costly venture.

Marie, a children's clothing manufacturer, has designed a retail system that enables parents to rent formal clothing for their children. Although such rental systems are already popular among adults, particularly young women, children's rental is a new concept. The service, known as Milk Joy, provides clothing for three days and two nights at a cost of ¥4,000 to ¥6,000, or about 15−20% of the retail price. Shoes and a full line of accessories such as corsages, necklaces, and hair ornaments are also available for rent, at the nominal fee of ¥500 per item.

Marie was able to develop this system because it is basically a clothing manufacturer. Since the volume of business is relatively low for most of the year, independent rental shops are unprofitable. Instead, Marie offers a franchise option to children's clothing retail shops all over Japan that are already wholesale customers. These stores simply open a rental corner within existing shop space, making overhead costs minimal. According to Marie, the original wholesale purchase can be recovered if the clothing is rented about three times. Since one article of clothing can be used twenty to thirty times, the potential for profits is considerable.

The two peak rental seasons are in the fall for *Shichi-Go-San* and the spring for school entrance ceremonies. The *Shichi-Go-San* demand extends from early October to late November with a peak in the middle. As many as 100 outfits a day are rented for school entrance ceremonies.

Experimenting with sales for one year enabled Marie to analyze consumer rental patterns and to extend its business to some twenty-nine franchise stores by August 1986. Marie found, for example, that there was some resistance in rural areas to the notion of rental clothing. Rental of clothing was particularly rare for more traditional occasions such as *Shichi-Go-San* and school entrance ceremonies, and was limited to events such as piano recitals or weddings.

One difficulty that any clothing rental business faces is in the cost of cleaning returned goods. This is particularly true in children's clothing rental. Marie handled this situation by using easily washable synthetic fabrics for tulle and lace. As manufacturer of the clothing, it is also able to provide franchises with manuals that teach them how to remove stains and clean clothes themselves.

1985 Award for Excellence

Sailors: Limited-Edition Clothing and Accessories
Hudson Japan

Sailors is a line of "character" products for teenagers. Sold at a single shop in Tokyo, their popularity has been such that as many as 2,000 people will visit the store on a Sunday or holiday, often lining up outside to get in.

The Sailors brand name was born when the president of Hudson Japan, Shizuka Miura, printed the sailor emblem from the sign of her Tokyo blue-jeans store on some sweatshirts, as a trial. The fifty shirts sold out in just a week, and Miura decided to develop a series of brand-name products using that logo.

The series includes not only clothing and small accessories, but also tableware, stationery supplies, toothbrushes, shampoo, combs, and watches. The company's intention was to sell a line of products that offered everything a teenager needed in daily life. The Sailors brand now comprises more than 3,000 different products. A sweatshirt, for example, ranges in price from ¥8,300 to ¥13,900.

In the past, efforts by a company to capitalize on a fad via a large marketing campaign only served to bring the boom to an early end. To avoid this, Hudson Japan was determined to limit availability of the products in order to enhance their appeal as "exclusive" items. The volume of production of the clothes is kept low, with only perhaps ten items per color in a style. Subtle changes in color combination or in the details of a design are made to allow constant production of new products in a short cycle.

Sailors are sold in only one store in one location on an alley off a main street in the Shibuya area of Tokyo, already known for its teenage denizens. Hudson Japan has permitted no wholesale selling of the products and no branch stores, so customers know that "you have to go to the shop to buy the items." Teenagers regard possession of Sailors products as a status symbol revealing that not only do they know the "secret" location but they have also been there themselves.

Hudson Japan has also benefited from Sailors' exposure in the mass media. Singers and TV personalities popular with young people frequently appear wearing Sailors sweatshirts, T-shirts, and pants in magazines or on television. Thus, Sailors has ridden the mass media waves to make the product known in every corner of Japan.

As Sailors became a topic of teenage conversation, young people in the outlying areas could not buy them at home. As a result, teenagers on vacation would flock to Tokyo from far and wide just to visit the shop.

The secret to the success of Sailors—with sales of ¥1.2 billion in 1986—appears to rest on a marketing strategy based on a firm grasp of the lifestyle and psychology of today's youth in Japan, coupled with the power of the mass media and word of mouth among teenagers. In that sense, demand for the product has been artificially created to meet a psychological, rather than a material, need and also to provide teenagers with the satisfaction derived from owning something others do not. Also, the clear success of Hudson Japan's strategy of limited marketing seems to be setting a trend for other companies in the teen market to follow.

1985 Award for Excellence

The only shop where Sailors items can be bought

Tsukashin: Community-Oriented Shopping and Leisure Center
Seiyo

Tsukashin is a shopping center whose appeal is enhanced by recreational facilities

Tsukashin is Japan's first genuine multifunctional commercial and leisure facility containing everything from a major department store, restaurants, and 263 specialty shops, to sports facilities, a bank, and a community church. These facilities are in a single area and conform carefully to community-planning principles.

In contrast to other shopping complexes in Japan, the center, located in Amagasaki, between Osaka and Kobe, has no gates and can be entered from any side. In appearance it is much more extravagant than ordinary business facilities, because it has been designed as much for recreation as for commerce.

The Tsukashin branch of the Seibu department store has a coliseum-type stepped roof and a see-through elevator. The garden restaurant section consists of a group of attractive buildings of brick and wood in a fairy-tale-like style. There is an old-fashioned fresh-foods market, a round-roofed gymnasium, and even a community church. A willow-lined river flows between the department store and the fresh-foods market and the garden restaurant area. In corners and windows throughout the complex can be found statues of traditional local deities and symbols of wealth. There is also a wind-powered clock, a computer-operated bell tower, and a musical fountain, as well as some 20,000 trees and shrubs on the center's grounds.

The development of such a facility can best be understood in the context of Japan's recent economic history. The period of explosive growth that continued for the forty years following World War II has come to an end. New consumers are bored with purely commercial boutiques and have begun moving away from simple shopping toward spending their time and money on leisure and cultural activities. This trend has given rise to "lifestyle playgrounds" like Tsukashin that are more like rivals for Tokyo Disneyland than for traditional shopping centers or downtown department stores.

Careful planning principles have integrated Tsukashin into the surrounding community

During the first year after its September 1985 opening, Tsukashin was visited by approximately 11.4 million people. There were an average of 22,000 visitors on weekdays, and 77,000 on Sundays and holidays. A survey showed that 61% stayed "for two to three hours," considerably longer than the 90 minutes spent at most shopping centers. And in that same year, the 59,000-m² complex, constructed at a cost of ¥19.5 billion, took in total revenues of ¥28.5 billion.

It has not been completely smooth sailing for Tsukashin, however. Some of the tenants in the specialty shops complain that there are too few young customers, or that the average amount spent is not very large. Another problem is transportation to the center, since it is a good seven to eight minutes' walk from the nearest railway station. But the chairman of Seiyo is philosophical: "There are many aspects to community planning that are beyond economic accounting, and that can only be evaluated with time. It will probably take about ten years to come to any conclusions on the success of the center. What is important is that we have had the courage to experiment now."

1985 Award for Excellence

Shopping by videodisk

Catteleya Laser Shop: An Automated Store
Matsuzakaya

Searching for a way to increase direct contact with consumers, Matsuzakaya, with the cooperation of Fuji Electric, turned to high technology and videodisks. It set up a round-the-clock, 365-day-a-year retail service in Tokyo. The service utilizes unassuming "video boxes" set up on Tokyo street corners. A customer enters the box, activates a videodisk, and views merchandise displayed on the screen. He then places an order via the built-in, two-way facsimile, and completes the transaction on the spot with a credit card. Goods are delivered a few days later. Matsuzakaya has opened ten of these stores in the Tokyo metropolitan area.

User response was initially strong, with 5,000 orders (totaling ¥100 million) received in the first month. Subsequent sales declined, as the novelty of the service wore off.

1984 Award for Excellence

Seiyu Nōkendai Store
Seiyu

This fully automated Seiyu supermarket uses a total of twenty-eight different high-technology systems to provide more efficient service to customers. Located in Nōkendai, near Yokohama, the store has a sales floor area of 495 m².

Product conveyer systems for moving goods from trucks to the rack-type warehouse and into the store have all been automated. The store is equipped with an overhead monorail to carry sales slips and other documents, and also with an automated parking lot that calculates charges by magnetic card.

On the sales floor, numerous services are automated. A ham-slicing robot, for example, provides the variety, number, and thickness of slices of ham indicated by the customer, then wraps and prices them. A video system suggests meal menus based on the items available in the store.

The company has continued to make improvements and has introduced one more automated store, in the Seibu department store in Tsukuba, since the opening of the first in October 1983.

1983 High Award for Excellence

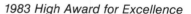

An automatic merchandise transport cart

Home World: A Catalogue-Magazine
Daiei

Home World is both a general mail-order catalogue and a lifestyle magazine. It goes beyond simple product descriptions to present information that keeps readers abreast of changing consumer trends.

Furniture, interior goods, audio equipment, bicycles, outdoor goods, stationery, kitchenware, and a variety of modern items for homemaking are introduced in a 200-page magazine

format. The magazine is compiled by Daiei's home-products merchandising managers. Customers can fill out the order forms conveniently located in *Home World* and order whatever they want by mail.

Home World went on sale in 1983 for

¥280 at 250 stores in the Daiei supermarket chain, as well as at bookstores nationwide. Initially, sales figures reached record levels for a catalogue-magazine, exceeding 300,000 copies annually. Since 1985, the magazine has been published twice annually, in the

spring and fall, at a price of ¥380. Yearly production has been increased to 800,000 copies.

A catalogue-magazine for shopping at home

1983 High Award for Excellence

Shopping and Saving: A Department-Store Savings Plan
Printemps Ginza

Large retailers have been providing financial services for some time in Japan, in order to keep pace with increasing consumer demand for a choice of savings plans. Printemps

Ginza, however, a department store operated by the Daiei supermarket chain, is the first company to link a savings plan with general merchandise sales.

Card holders who wish to participate in this trust savings enroll in a Savings Course. Thereafter, 5% of the value of every purchase over ¥3,000 and made with the company's Printemps Card is deposited in a bond investment trust with the participating Yamaichi Securities Company. Withdrawal is possible at no charge.

The trust is a new type of sales promotion tool that encourages the consumer to shop, since he is secure in the knowledge that he is saving at the same time. The system is also effective in creating a regular clientele.

The plan started in September 1984, and of the approximately 50,000 current card holders, around 10% are subscribers to the plan.

Printemps-card holders can shop and save at the same time

1984 Award for Excellence

INFORMATION AND COMMUNICATIONS EQUIPMENT

VP-50: A Supercomputer
Fujitsu

Fujitsu began marketing its VP-50 supercomputer in April 1985 and took a major step toward popularizing the supercomputer in private industry.

Supercomputers are distinguished from more familiar general-purpose computers by their ultrahigh speed of calculation. The speed of the fastest is now measured in a unit called a gigaflop—that is, 1 billion floating-point operations per second. These speeds are needed chiefly in military, academic, and high-technology research.

Fujitsu's VP-50 operates at 142 million—or mega—flops. As a result, competitors and some experts have questioned whether or not the VP-50 can properly be called a supercomputer. Nonetheless, customers have rushed to the VP-50, attracted by its comparatively low cost. The rental fee for the VP-50 system—computer and software—is ¥46 million per month, 30–40% lower than its other models.

The evolution of the VP-50 began in 1982 when Fujitsu entered the supercomputer market with the first domestically produced machine. While the event caused an international stir in a market dominated by American companies, Fujitsu's orders did not grow. By July 1984, the company had orders for only four supercomputers, all from national universities or government and municipal offices. Private industry was buying from Cray Research, an American company famous for its supercomputers.

So in August 1984, the Fujitsu sales force and development teams from the company's Numazu and Kawasaki plants assembled and decided to create the VP-50, a supercomputer with 75% of the capacity of the existing Fujitsu model and at a significantly lower price.

When the VP-50 reached the market less than a year later, Fujitsu immediately received serious inquiries from over fifty private companies, an enthusiastic response uncommon in the supercomputer world. While the calculation speed of the VP-50 is 14% of that of Fujitsu's fastest supercomputer, its low price compares favorably with the company's major line of general-purpose computers.

The Fujitsu sales force set out to sell a VP-50 to at least one company in each of several different industries. One after another, major companies such as Toyota Motors, Matsushita Electric Industrial, Sony, and Fuji Electric signed up for the VP-50. By the end of August 1986, a total of eighteeen orders had been placed. Other Japanese computer manufacturers quickly introduced their own models competing with the VP-50.

The use of Fujitsu's supercomputers has increased elevenfold since the company began development of the VP-50. With the success of its product, Fujitsu now holds 70% of the domestic supercomputer market, and continues to push its advantage. In the summer of 1986, Fujitsu introduced the VP-30, an even cheaper supercomputer.

1985 High Award for Excellence

Function: Maximum 142 megaflops
Main memory capacity: Maximum 128 Mbytes
Vector resistor: 32 Kbytes
Mask resistor: 512 bytes
Buffer storage: 64 Kbytes

The VP-50 has great speed and power for the efficient handling of scientific calculations

IBM Multistation 5550: A New IBM Computer
IBM Japan

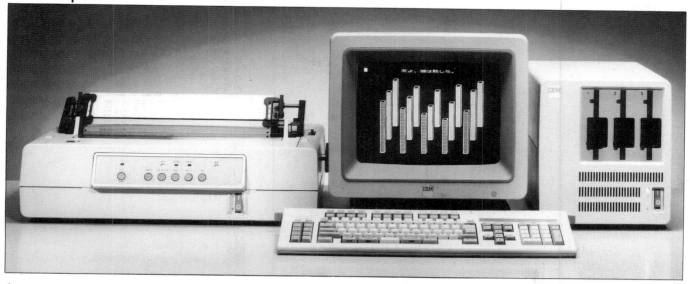

A system made up of (from left) printer, display, keyboard, and disk-system unit

When the personal computer boom reached Japan in the late 1970s, NEC was ready and IBM Japan was not.

NEC, backed by enthusiastic hobbyists accustomed to its products, created a system giving it dominance in the personal computer market.

In contrast, IBM Japan could boast about the general-purpose, mainframe computer market, but was a late starter in the personal computer area.

So IBM Japan got busy. Early in 1981, it established a project team. The target was a top-class computer with performance exceeding that of the domestic competition.

Released in March 1983, the Multistation 5550 series of machines is particularly adapted for business use and has become a best-seller in Japan.

The Multistation's operating system is the Japanese version of MS-DOS, a popular program in the United States. It can be used as a Japanese-language word processor and also for data communications.

1983 High Award for Excellence

PC-1500: A Pocket Computer
Sharp

A sophisticated pocket computer with a four-color graphic printer, the PC-1500 can handle numbers, letters, characters, and graphic images. It contains an 8-bit microcomputer that consumes little energy, and a 16K ROM that allows programming in BASIC. Truly portable at a weight of 375 g, the PC-1500 enables the user to issue receipts, vouchers, and the like away from the office, and to store the data at the same time.

Sharp began development efforts in April 1977. Aware that calculators that process only numerical information would soon be obsolete, the company set out to make a calculator that could also process verbal information. After two years of work, Sharp came up with

The compact PC-1500—195 (W) × 86 (D) × 25.5 (H) mm; wt: 375 g

a commercially viable product.

In recent years, new models have undergone many more improvements, such as upgrading of the character-

processing function to handle even simple Chinese characters.

1982 High Award for Excellence

L/CU: A Personal-Computer Communications Adapter
Logic Systems International

The L/CU, developed by Logic Systems International, permits two personal computers to talk to each other and exchange information quickly and accurately over a public telephone line.

A sophisticated and expensive product, the L/CU is a step beyond cheaper modems and acoustic couplers, simple devices also used to link two computers via a telephone line.

Priced at the time of release at ¥198,000, the L/CU offers 4,800-baud high-speed transmissions and an error-checking feature that assures superior quality transmissions. The latter is important when computer programs are exchanged, since programs will not operate if they contain errors. In 1987 it retails for only ¥98,000.

By contrast, modems and acoustic couplers cost from ¥20,000 to ¥30,000 each. Couplers and, in the last

L/CU's built-in features include a modem and an NCU (network control unit)

M685: A 32-Bit Micro Mainframe Computer
Sord Computer

The Sord M685, the first 32-bit personal-computer system produced in Japan, was developed in a mere three months. It joins 32-bit technology with an operating system from Charles River Data Systems of the U.S. Providing the power and functions of a 32-bit architecture with up to 16 Mbit of direct addressing capability, the M685 permits the use of large programs and data structures without the need for segmentation. It also offers a memory capacity ideally suited to multiprocessing time-sharing environments.

The Charles River operating system,

named UNOS, is an improved version of the UNIX system (with which it is compatible) that was originally developed in the U.S. by Bell Labs. UNOS, written in C, provides event-count synchronization, priority scheduling, and localized disk file allocation in order to support real-time, transaction-oriented applications.

Significantly, this computer offers 32-bit processing equivalent to that of a minicomputer at only one-fifth the price—¥5–8 million.

1983 Award for Excellence

MULTI-16
Mitsubishi Electric

Over the past few years, personal computers have undergone a transformation as their major application shifted from games to business and as they began to operate faster and faster. The chief reason for the change is a faster central processing unit (CPU), the part of the computer that interprets and executes instructions.

Mitsubishi's MULTI-16 series is the first group of 16-bit personal computers produced in Japan, appearing as the industry moved from 8-bit CPUs to swifter 16-bit models.

One of the major selling points of the MULTI-16 is its ease of use. Also, when the MULTI-16 went on the market in April 1982, there were 140 programs already available for it. Its graphic-display functions allow up to 4,000 Chinese characters on its screen.

Many small- and medium-sized companies that have no prior experience with personal computers have begun using the MULTI-16, making it

The M685 is Japan's first 32-bit micro mainframe

three to five years, modems have come into wide use by both computer hobbyists and businesses. The L/CU is designed specifically for business alone. As a result, the L/CU, introduced in August 1985, is still in the process of finding its place in the market.

Logic Systems International became interested in communication between computers in the early 1980s, although its primary business was personal computers.

At the same time, computer information exchange networks such as CAPTAIN, INS, and NAPLPS were growing. They offer services including electronic mail, electronic bulletin boards, and information banks.

Development of the L/CU began in the summer of 1984 and proceeded quickly, since Logic Systems had already designed a similar adapter for exchanging packets of information for DDX (digital data exchange).

At the same time, Japan's Ministry of Posts and Telecommunications was working on new standards for communications between computers. Logic Systems designed the L/CU in conjunction with the ministry to conform to the proposed standards.

However, most of the amateur users of computer information networks are loyal to the cheaper modems or acoustic couplers, not only because of low cost but also because the networks do not require the kind of high-speed transmission and error checking the L/CU offers.

At present, however, professional users include Seibu Saison, the Mitsui Group, Sanwa Bank, and the Kyodo News Service.

In September 1985, Logic Systems, through joint investment with Nippon Telegraph and Telephone, formed NTTPC Communications, and later that year began a test period with 1,500 participants. NTTPC Communications offers electronic mail, electronic bulletin boards, and data-base services. During the test, users were encouraged to exchange programs and try out the L/CU's error-checking function.

NTTPC estimates that it needs 10,000 users initially and that as subscribers increase, so will the amount of information available. The company also predicts that the L/CU's retail price will drop as the number of users goes up.

1985 Award for Excellence

---

profitable for Mitsubishi after its first year on the market.

1982 Award for Excellence

A display that can handle 4,000 Chinese characters

HC-20: A Hand-Held Computer
Seiko Epson

The HC-20 fits neatly into an attaché case

The Epson HC-20 is a portable, laptop personal computer that weighs about 1.7 kg and features a four-line, 20-column display screen, a small built-in printer, clock, music generator, and keyboard that works like the one on your favorite typewriter.

On the crucial subject of memory, the HC-20—marketed as the HX-20 outside Japan—offers a standard 16K RAM that can be increased to 32K with an expansion unit.

Rechargeable nickel-cadmium batteries keep the HC-20 running for up to forty hours at a stretch. The batteries can be recharged in less than eight hours.

A microcassette unit is also standard equipment for storing data externally. The HC-20 can talk on the telephone via an acoustic coupler.

Seiko Epson has been making desktop computers in Japan since 1978. Its goal with the HC-20 was power—light and portable power. Little wonder *Newsweek* magazine hailed the HC-20 as representative of what it called the Fourth Computer Revolution.

1982 Award for Excellence

Panavoice JH-600: A Voice-Recognition Calculator
Matsushita Communication Industrial

The JH-600, a speech-recognition calculator, is the first step toward realizing the dream of operating a computer by voice control. It combines the arithmetic functions of a normal calculator with the ability to interpret up to sixty-

A voice-activated, programmable personal computer

two previously registered spoken commands. It also has an electronic memo unit for storing telephone numbers and accessing them by speech, as well as an external output terminal for connection to a personal computer, which allows the entry of programming data by voice.

The main problem in developing this product was setting the voice-recognition range and the storage range, since they had to take into account the great variations in tone and rhythm in the human voice. Matsushita Communication Industrial's central laboratory was able to integrate the analysis section of the voice-recognition LSI—the "ears"—and the evaluation section—the "brain"—on a single chip, allowing for a compact device and low production costs. The machine retails for ¥135,000.

1983 Award for Excellence

RL-W450: A Handwritten-Character Processor
Matsushita Electric Industrial

The complexity of the Chinese writing system has limited the numbers and kinds of available typewriters and created a class of businessmen with a phobia of difficult keyboards.

Matsushita Electric Industrial set out to address the phobia by developing a machine that allows the user to write by hand directly on the surface of the equipment. The result was a "handwriting word processor"—the Panasonic-brand RL-W450.

Instead of typing text into the unit, the user simply writes on the machine's plastic "tablet" using a special stylus with a pressure sensor in the tip. The machine then identifies the handwritten character and displays it as a printed character on an LCD panel on the front of the machine.

Characters take 0.4 sec to identify, and the RL-W450 has proved 99.5% accurate. The machine also features an editing function that includes copying,

moving, inserting, and deleting. The RL-W450 sells for ¥298,000.

1984 High Award for Excellence

The RL-W450 can read characters drawn with a pen

PW-10: A Japanese-Language Word Processor
Canon

A keyboard arranged in *hiragana* order

The PW-10 laptop computer is distinguished by an entirely new keyboard layout that any Japanese can easily learn how to use. Up until this time, conventional keyboard layouts have required a great deal of time to master. This new keyboard format is based upon the *hiragana* syllabary order that all Japanese learn as children.

The PW-10 features an LCD that shows one easy-to-read row of up to sixteen Japanese characters or English letters. It also allows over 100 different types of phrases, once typed, to be input at a single touch. The built-in memory will hold up to three full standard-sized pages of material.

This word processor is compact, light—a mere 3.0 kg—and reasonably priced at ¥148,000. A battery-driven printer and CMOS VLSI chips were used to make it a truly portable machine. It also takes advantage of Chinese-character data-compression technology and electronic-circuitry design to fit more than 42,000 Chinese characters and their compounds into its dictionary.

1984 Award for Excellence

PCWORD-M: A Japanese-Language Word Processor
NEC

Using a conventional Japanese typewriter or word processor is a laborious and time-consuming process. A new word processor from NEC, the PCWORD-M, uses a new method of entering words that can reduce typing time by as much as half.

On a conventional word processor, one types using a Japanese syllabary or English characters. Then a conversion key is pressed to change the typing into *kana* (Japanese phonetic characters) or *kanji* (Chinese characters).

PCWORD-M features a special vowel-set keyboard

The new method simplifies the process by creating vowel sets such as "An" and placing them on single keys. An adjective such as *kantan* ("simple"), requiring six strokes to type in Roman characters, needs only four strokes under the new system—K, An, T, An.

The PCWORD-M, priced at ¥62,000, also features an arc-shaped keyboard with keys laid out in a pattern familiar to Japanese from a layout used to teach Japanese syllabaries.

1983 High Award for Excellence

My OASYS: Japanese-Language Word Processors
Fujitsu

Fujitsu led the way in popularizing word processors with the general public in Japan. Before My OASYS, word processors were thought of as exclusively for office use. After two years of research, Fujitsu created a line of personal word processors tailored to the needs of the average consumer. The My OASYS machines were placed on the market at a price of ¥750,000, about 25% lower in cost than similar machines.

The distinctive feature of the Fujitsu series is its use of a keyboard thumb-shift method of converting typed information to the proper kinds of characters. On Japanese word processors, information is typed first in English letters or in a Japanese syllabary. Then a conversion key is pressed to change what was typed into *kana* (Japanese phonetic characters) and *kanji* (Chinese characters). On the My OASYS machines, the thumb-shift conversion keys are located in easy reach of the space bar. The 9-in display screen on the original model can hold up to 560 characters.

1982 High Award for Excellence

My OASYS has a keyboard with a thumb-shift bar

Copy-Jack: A Pocket-Sized Copier
Plus

Several years after abandoning a concept for a portable copier to be used with a blackboard (sliding across the board and picking up images), a small group of Plus researchers once again, in the summer of 1984, considered the development of a minicopier. They agreed that a pocket-sized copier would be a boon for many people, particularly businessmen and students, and that this gap in the market provided a great opportunity for Plus.

Within a year, they had developed Copy-Jack, the world's first truly portable copy machine. Shaped like an electric razor and weighing 440 g, the copier can be held in one hand and carried anywhere. A scanner in the head of the machine picks up words and images as it is moved across a surface, and prints them out on a 10-m roll of heat-sensitive paper. The copy is 40 mm wide, the width of a newspaper column.

About the same time that Plus researchers began discussing a portable copier again, Matsushita Electric Industrial approached them about creating a portable copy machine. With Plus's encouragement, Matsushita developed a prototype. But

Plus was not satisfied with the Matsushita model. As designed, the machine would be too expensive. So Plus redesigned the machine using some Matsushita parts. The designers created a machine with a sleek, tapered case, reasoning that its appearance would be an important factor in its sales appeal, and that it should look more like "electronic stationery" than a household appliance.

The basic features of the device were all decided in the test stage. They include a thermal copy function, upright positioning, and rechargeable batteries. The designers considered adding other functions and capabilities, such as variable copy width or an adapter for plugging the machine into a wall socket; but ultimately the additions were rejected in favor of maintaining the company's initial goal of a lightweight, portable copier priced as cheaply as possible in order to make an exciting debut in the market.

In June 1985, retailers were shown the new Copy-Jack—"Jack," meaning "take," as in "hijack"—at an annual new-products show. Store owners were divided in their reactions to the

product, but doubts vanished on the first day of sales—August 21. The 10,000 machines ordered in advance sold out quickly, and new orders flooded in. Many purchasers had to wait for more than two months to acquire their copiers. It was three months before stores had stocks of Copy-Jacks lined up on their shelves. Clearly the public was impressed with the copier, even at a cost of ¥58,000, and the response vindicated the designers' strategy.

Once it was clear that the portable copier would sell well, other companies hastened to catch up. Matsushita Electric Industrial came out with its own brand, and Kaken announced a product using bipolar optical-receptor elements (similar to those used in facsimile machines) in the sensor head. Plus itself put the Copy-Jack into mass production in July 1986 and brought the price down to ¥39,800. Thus the Copy-Jack touched off a new wave in the business machine industry.

1985 High Award for Excellence

Copy-Jack makes
40-mm-wide copies

Panamemo 107: A Telephone and Facsimile Machine
Matsushita Graphic Communication Systems

The Panamemo 107 combines in one machine the functions of a telephone and a facsimile machine. In Japan, facsimile machines have become widespread because of the complexity of the written language. Since each character in the language requires several strokes, words cannot be typed easily on a machine or sent by telex. A facsimile machine overcomes this problem by allowing handwritten text to be transmitted quickly. By 1986, some 1.2 million facsimile machines were operating in Japan, as compared with approximately 150,000 in the United Kingdom.

In the early 1960s, Matsushita developed the prototype of a "fax-phone." It was put on the market, but did not sell well because it was too big and clumsy to have broad consumer appeal. It was not until the 1980s, after the appearance of large-scale integrated circuits and the size reductions they permit, that Matsushita revived the idea.

In March 1985, Matsushita's research division completed the design for a fax-phone capable of performing many functions, but the design was rejected by company officials. They felt that the machine was still too large to have mass appeal and sent the research team back to the drawing board with instructions to come up with a smaller machine and to do so in a hurry. The reason for the haste was the liberalization of Japan's telecommunications industry in 1985. Many companies were rushing to get new products on the market.

In order to produce a smaller machine, a sacrifice had to be made. The research team decided, after much heated discussion, to forfeit high transmission speed for compact size. Instead of transmitting in the high-speed GIII mode, the fax-phone would transmit in medium-speed GII. A Matsushita executive urged his colleagues to think of the machine as an especially endowed telephone rather than as an inferior facsimile machine.

The Panamemo 107 was introduced to the public on October 3, 1985. The following day, another company announced a similar product, but Matsushita's one-day lead garnered it the lion's share of attention.

Orders for more than 10,000 Panamemos—at ¥107,000 for the fax-phone and ¥95,000 for the facsimile machine that attaches to a phone—were placed within its first three months on the market. But after initial enthusiasm fell off, Matsushita faced an uphill climb. The major problem was that unless both calling parties possess a Panamemo, half of the reason for owning one—its facsimile function—cannot be realized.

Consequently, Matsushita has adopted a strategy of encouraging companies to convert their existing telephone systems to ones that use the Panamemo. But the ultimate market is the home market. As one Matsushita executive says, "We want to use it to open up a whole new culture."

1985 High Award for Excellence

Telephone and facsimile functions are combined in Panamemo 107

Performance Auto Control System
Sound Craft

This computer-based control system allows theater and concert directors to manipulate lights, stage sets, and video projections from a single location, with the touch of a single button.

In the past, each system had its own control device, so performances demanded substantial manpower backstage. The Performance Auto Control System (PACS) from Sound Craft allows fully automated stage direction. A director can program everything from sound and lighting to scenery changes in advance. Thus, in addition to eliminating the need for large numbers of stagehands, the program also guarantees that no human errors in timing or coordination of the stage functions will mar a smooth performance.

Sound Craft was founded in 1966 to design and produce all aspects of theatrical acoustics. The company has had a range of experience in Japan, from making soundtracks for television commercials and films to planning acoustics for plays and concerts. Its record includes acoustic production for Miles Davis concerts, Issey Miyake fashion shows, and Yasuko Nagamine dance performances.

Automated systems that controlled theater lighting and sound effects independently of each other began to appear in 1975, and Sound Craft soon made use of them. In time, however, the company found these separate programs unsatisfactory. Around 1980, Yasuhiko Yahata, the president and a founder of the company, formed an internal study group to find better ways to coordinate stage systems.

The project took off when Sound Craft received orders to design, install, and operate comprehensive theatrical equipment in eleven pavilions at the 1985 science and technology exposition at Tsukuba. Even at the level of automation then available, Sound Craft would have needed to station forty to fifty people at Tsukuba during the six months of the fair—far beyond the manpower capacity of the company.

The NEC pavilion utilized PACS (above) and automatic lighting (below)

Yahata and managing director Terukazu Suzuki turned to computer technology to help solve the dilemma, in hopes of developing a comprehensive control system for the fair.

At the time, Sound Craft did not even have a computer technician on its staff, so it had to hire computer programmers to teach the rudiments to the artistic and technical directors on the project team.

The system was completed in December 1984, just months before the opening of the fair. The events held at the NEC and other pavilions using the new system won high praise, and the PACSs functioned without error throughout the fair.

Sound Craft had estimated that it could sell a total of thirty to fifty PACSs during the lifetime of the system, but in two years, it has already sold twenty at ¥10–12 million each for the hardware alone. PACS is being used in such diverse applications as the showrooms of major electronic equipment manufacturers, and entertainment productions in hotels and concert halls. Sound Craft now virtually stands alone in the field of total control systems for theatrical productions.

1985 Award for Excellence

Panafile 1000: An Optical-Disk Filing System
Matsushita Graphic Communication Systems/ Matsushita Electric Industrial

The Panafile 1000 document filing system eliminates stacks of paper and files in an office. It can store 15,000 standard-sized sheets of paper on a 20-cm optical disk smaller than an LP record—1/200th the amount of space needed for the originals.

To store a file, a sheet of paper is put face down on a glass plate. A flat-bed scanner then reads the image and records it sequentially on a disk.

A document can be retrieved after reviewing it on a display screen or by punching in its "address" on a keyboard. Printing can be done in five seconds. If a facsimile machine is added to the Panafile, stored documents can be printed out at remote locations.

When the two Matsushita companies began working on the system, they knew that disks allowing both recording and playback would require a new recording material. Between 400 and 500 materials were considered, and eventually tellurium suboxide was used to make a thin film for the disks.

1982 Award for Excellence

An electronic document file for office automation

Rifax 1300 Series: Plain-Paper Fax Machines
Ricoh

The Rifax 1300 series represents the first facsimile machines that record onto plain paper rather than the thermal paper used in standard machines. Plain paper is considerably less expensive than thermal paper, making it less expensive to operate—¥4 per copy (plain paper/toner) compared with ¥6 (thermal paper/toner). The advantage of plain paper is that, unlike thermal paper, it does not deteriorate over time and is easy to write on.

When Ricoh began development of the Rifax 1300 in 1980, it faced considerable difficulties. With a standard facsimile, print is recorded by the transmission of heat onto thermal paper. Ricoh assigned four separate engineering teams four different methods, encouraging competition among them—an unusual move in Japan, where product development is usually done by consensus. That inspired results, and within six months one team created a method whereby an electric charge imparted to the paper causes the toner to adhere and print.

1983 High Award for Excellence

A facsimile machine that uses ordinary paper

Wink Checker-II: An Electronic Proofreader
Kyodo Printing

The work of a printing company demands meticulous attention to detail. Proofreading and checking printed materials can be an especially time-consuming, tedious job. To relieve this burden, Kyodo Printing developed an electronic film-checking unit called the Wink Checker-II.

After a first printing, or proof, proofreaders check a text for typographic and other errors, and write in corrections that must be inserted into the final copy. Checking to see that all the corrections have been incorporated onto the plate film sheets used in the printing process is easy and efficient with this new machine. The corrected and uncorrected versions of the sheets are placed on a light table and photographed by a camera, which then feeds digitized character and graphic data to a personal computer.

The data from the two sheets is then displayed on a screen, and any areas that do not match flash, or "wink," calling attention to any differences in the texts. The Wink Checker-II sells for ¥8.81 million.

1984 Award for Excellence

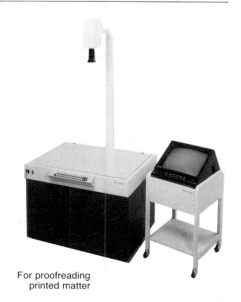
For proofreading printed matter

Electronic Copyboards
Oki Electric Industry/Plus

"If only there were some way to get a copy of the words on the blackboard at a meeting, there would be no need to take notes." This dream of many a business executive has been fulfilled with the invention of two different electronic copyboards by Oki Electric Industry and Plus.

The copyboards work on the same principle as a facsimile machine: images on their surfaces are passed through a lens and absorbed into the visual memory of an integrated circuit, which then issues a photocopy.

The obvious advantage of such a device is that it allows participants at a meeting to concentrate on the matter at hand without being distracted by having to take notes. This situation is particularly useful during scientific lectures or foreign-language lessons, so participants may pay full attention to what is actually being said, yet also obtain notes for future reference. It may be possible in the future to hold "electronic meetings" with the boards.

1984 Award for Excellence

The original is reduced for copying: Plus's Boardfax 1300 (left) and the Oki Copyboard (right)

City Face 21C675P: A Color TV with a Printer
Mitsubishi Electric

A picture on the screen of a color television can be turned into a black-and-white, hard-copy printout using Mitsubishi Electric's 21C675P TV, one of its City Face series of products.

Digital circuitry, combined with a 64K RAM, forms the product's core technology. Prints measuring 100×84 mm appear in 15 sec on a printer separate from the TV.

The 21-in 21C675P television costs ¥258,000 (the printer is built in); an optional printer to attach to other televisions costs ¥69,800. The built-in printer has adjustable contrast and uses a 27-m roll of thermal paper from which about 220 prints can be made. A videocassette recorder, videodisk player, personal computer, and teletext and videotex machines can also be at-tached to the television and printer so that hard-copy stills can be made from their pictures.

1983 Award for Excellence

A color TV that prints

SOFTWARE FOR
COMMERCIAL USE

The Universe: Three-Dimensional Computer-Graphics System
Fujitsu

View the image from inside the image; experience the world of other dimensions

The Universe is the world's first three-dimensional computer-graphics system for projection on a domed screen. It is designed for viewing by large audiences in a cinesphere. Spectators sitting in reclining seats wear glasses with one red and one blue lens to obtain a three-dimensional image of a film that is projected on the dome above them.

Appropriately, Fujitsu chose to introduce The Universe at the Tsukuba Expo '85, a science and technology exhibition held near Tokyo. Visitors to The Universe saw highly detailed, three-dimensional models of DNA chains, and simulations of nuclear fusion and of the transformation of water to ice at the molecular level.

The accuracy of such three-dimensional presentations depends on the compilation of huge amounts of scientific data and requires a great deal of time for programming the computer. The scene that showed the freezing of water lasted less than ten minutes, yet took seventy hours to perfect.

Fujitsu developed The Universe at a cost of ¥2 billion, a substantial investment for any company considering that the system is intended for display only and is not commercially available. The Universe was created as a public

relations tool to promote the company's image among consumers and to advertise its expertise in computer graphics to potential corporate clients. Toward this purpose, since the end of Tsukuba's Expo '85, The Universe has been displayed throughout Japan and at various locations in the United States, including the Smithsonian Institution.

Three-dimensional computer-graphics technology is not yet widely available because of its high cost, but the gap between technology and price is expected to narrow in five to ten years. Fujitsu is using its experience with The Universe to position itself for anticipated growth in the market.

At present, Fujitsu is marketing a computer-graphics programming tool called CGMS. The new software

A semispherical screen 20 m in diameter

package is designed to be used in the development of computer-graphics software for both general-purpose and super computers. To design graphics software requires an enormous amount of programming time, and Fujitsu hopes that the CGMS program will be able to shorten this time. It is also able to turn a flat image into a three-dimensional one with the simple input of the numerical data that defines the depth of the object.

Computer graphics has a wide range of applications, including the highly publicized film and cartoon animation. Fujitsu has decided to limit its endeav-

ZMap: Residential-Map Information System
Zenrin/Hitachi

It is simple to create a map data base

Zenrin, a publisher specializing in maps of residential areas, developed this computer program to systematize the map-making process.

Map information on Tokyo is entered into the computer, compiled, and cross-checked in 130 categories. As a result, highly detailed information about the city, such as its administrative divisions, topographical formations, roads, and major structures, can be retrieved rapidly.

Zenrin was able to offer the advantages of high-speed search and functions that allow the user to add his

own data to a map through the help of Hitachi's CAD. Such functions make the system an extremely useful tool for companies such as banks and direct mail businesses in planning their sales strategies. The names of buildings, address lists, and demographic data such as age and income distribution can be visually correlated with a map.

Zenrin has received inquiries from a variety of companies, and is now planning to provide easy-to-use systems tailored to meet specific needs.

1984 Award for Excellence

C&C-NET: Optical Local-Area-Network System
NEC

C&C-NET is a telecommunications system that establishes a synthetic LAN (local-area network) by connecting office computers, personal computers, facsimiles, telephones, and other office-automation facilities together with optical cables. This allows all the machines in a single network, often within one building, to communicate directly with each other, permitting high-speed, high-quality transmission of written, aural, and visual information.

The great advantage of this network is that it is multifunctional. It can be adapted for use in extraoffice communications as well as for internal communications, and thus has the potential for greatly expanded use. At present, it is being used in the new subway systems of Sapporo, Sendai, and Kyoto, and, in addition, in what are known as intelligent buildings. Since it can coordinate several LANs into one system, it can also allow buildings to transmit information to one another. C&C-NET holds great promise for systematization of corporate operations.

1982 Award for Excellence

ors to technical and scientific areas such as aircraft design and molecular analysis. Three-dimensional computer graphics can be used, for example, in simulating the conditions of a wind tunnel for development of new aircraft. The CGMS program, if successful, may be of considerable value in such a commercially attractive field as simplifying the computer testing of new aircraft prototypes. Thus, Fujitsu's investment in The Universe, while of no immediate financial benefit, may reap substantial rewards in the future.

1985 Award for Excellence

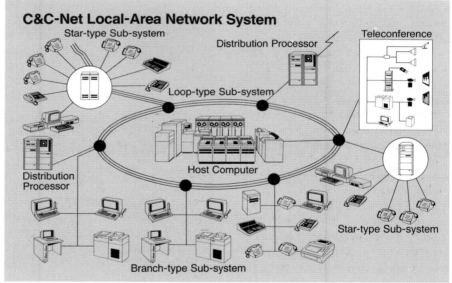

C&C-Net Local-Area Network System

ZUKEN ES-II: Automatic Clean-Copy System for Circuit Diagrams
ZUKEN

The ZUKEN ES-II system automates the making of clean copies of hand-drawn circuit diagrams as well as the CAD (computer-aided design) input of circuit diagrams. It significantly cuts the time required for the production of a clean copy of a circuit diagram (sometimes as much as 90%) when compared with previous copying methods. Furthermore, since the system does not use graph paper, the arrangement of a rough circuit diagram is quite simple. Correction and modification of the diagram are also easily accomplished. In addition, the system permits the input of Japanese characters.

CAD systems are used widely in the automatic design of PCBs (printed circuit boards); however, entering the circuit diagram into the computer is a painstaking and time-consuming task. ZUKEN ES-II simplifies this operation since it analyzes the actual structure of a diagram.

The entire ZUKEN ES-II system, including both hardware and software, retails for ¥45 million (as of March 1987).

1983 Award for Excellence

A handwritten circuit diagram and the final output

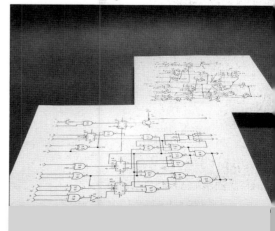

Ichitarō Version 1: Word-Processing Software
Just Systems

Ichitarō stands at the top in the market for Japanese personal-computer business software. Since its release in August 1985, the company has shipped a total of 31,000 packages at ¥58,000 each, a new record for business software.

It comes with the Japanese character conversion utility ATOK-5, which allows one-touch conversion to *kana* (phonetic characters) and *kanji* (Chinese characters) of long sentences containing as many as eight clauses. Ichitarō allows conversion into the proper sentence with the lowest possible number of keystrokes and with no need to re-enter the sentence.

Seven sizes of characters are available: 4×, vertically expanded, horizontally expanded, double size, normal size, ¼ up, and ¼ down. Ichitarō also provides a wide range of functions available for decoration, including underlining, light and dark shading, deletion lines, and boldface, as well as six different types of ruler lines for easy creation of complex tables.

In general, there is not much difference between the functions offered by the various Japanese-language word-processing software packages available. However, the user often finds it hard or time-consuming to do the things he wants, leading to dissatisfaction. Ichitarō surveyed personal computer users before designing this software package and attempted to satisfy as many different needs as possible.

Ichitarō offers 300 functions, including a wide range of editing options. These include, for example, a function for adding comments and memos that appear on the screen but are not printed. One of the exclusive features of Ichitarō is a multifile, multiwindow function that permits two documents to be displayed and edited at the same time. The screen is divided into four parts, and document processing is available in each of these windows.

Ichitarō's dictionary contains 46,000 words for high conversion efficiency. Those who use many special words or technical terms can create their own dictionary containing up to 8,000 words, each consisting of a maximum of twenty-five characters. In addition, 100 short phrases containing up to 128 characters as well as eighty-three special characters can also be registered.

EGWord: Word-Processing Software
Ergosoft

Most Japanese-language word-processing systems require the user to type in from twenty to forty *kana* (Japanese phonetic characters) and then to press the "convert" key. The typed characters are then changed into the mix of *kana* and *kanji* (Chinese characters) natural to written Japanese. On the Macintosh, Apple's popular personal computer, the limits of screen size and of the memory allow up to about 500 *kana* characters, but EGWord eliminates the need for the troublesome "convert" operation. Moreover, when the user types in a punctuation mark, EGWord automatically converts the text entered up to that point into written Japanese. This means the user can enter a natural stream of text uninterruptedly, as if writing with a pen on paper.

Until now, Japanese-language word processors have tended to be tools for printing out text in a clean, legible form. Word processors were not conceived of as tools for actually composing text, since operators usually typed from a handwritten draft. With EGWord, however, the user can freely enter and convert text without regard to grammatical division, and can thus create text without interrupting the flow of his thought.

EGWord's new conversion method scans two clauses at a time, converting whatever phrases are grammatically consistent with its lexicon into the true Japanese-character equivalents. Most Japanese-language word processors use the "single clause" method.

To give an example of this complicated process, let us assume that someone has typed in the sentence *Watashi wa Suzuki desu* (I am Mr. Suzuki). The computer would then shave it down to *wa-ta-shi-wa-su-zu-ki-de*, and then to the shorter *wa-ta-shi-wa-su-zu-ki*, and so forth, until it became *wa-ta-shi-wa*, which the built-in dictionary would recognize as *watashi wa* and then convert that phrase into the *kanji* for *watashi* (first-person pronoun) and the *kana* for *wa* (topic-marking particle). In other words, the computer attempts to convert the longest possible string of characters at a time. EGWord's lexicon—the heart of any word-processing system—contains about 38,000 words.

Ergosoft spent a year developing this new conversion method. The result

EGWord—for easy word processing

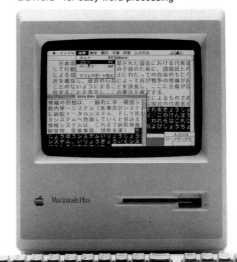

One of the main areas that makes Ichitarō special is its compatibility with data and software running under the popular MS-DOS operating system for personal computers. There is a command key that automatically converts the file format into one with general compatibility. This feature allows the user to transfer data between programs with no tricky preprocessing. Ichitarō can also be used in an integrated environment with the Multiplan spreadsheet program and the dBase II data-base management program. It was developed especially for NEC's popular PC-9800 series of personal computers. Just Systems released Version 2 in May 1986.

1985 Award for Excellence

Just Systems developed Ichitarō for NEC's PC-9800 series

can be seen in EGWord's ease of use, high degree of refinement, speed of conversion (three to ten times greater than that of other popular word processors) and rate of accuracy (twice as high). It costs ¥59,800.

Ergosoft, which developed EGWord (which is meant to be pronounced as "E"-"G"-Word—and sounding like the Japanese pronunciation of "easy"; the "E" and the "G" come from "Ergosoft," itself derived from "ergonomics"), is a relatively new software house. It was opened in January 1984 to take advantage of the opportunity created by the introduction of the Apple Macintosh into the Japanese market.

EGWord stands out in the ratings it was given by the strict judges of the Nikkei Personal Computer Software Evaluation Committee: "For individual use, of a level that more than satisfies."

1985 Award for Excellence

Matsu: Word-Processing Software
Kanrikogaku

Matsu, developed for general use by the average person at the Institute of Administrative Engineering, has realized far better performance than other conventional Japanese-language word-processing software. It was especially designed for use on NEC's popular PC-9800 series of personal computers.

In addition to the usual function of converting words typed in *kana* (the phonetic Japanese syllabary) into the mix of *kana* and *kanji* (Chinese characters) used in written Japanese, Matsu is also capable of converting Arabic numbers into their Japanese equivalents (which are reckoned in units differing from those used in the West). It also has ruler and logo (compounding of letters) capabilities. Such functions make Matsu almost equivalent in capacity to dedicated word processors.

The dictionary in the 5-in disk software program was expanded from 60,000 words to 75,000 in the 8-in disk, which has an actual capacity for 110,000 words. This is certainly more than sufficient for day-to-day use.

1984 High Award for Excellence

The best-seller software Matsu being used on a PC-9801

PLANNER18: A Multipurpose Distribution System
Obic Business Consultants

Making its own contribution to the information revolution, a group of certified public accountants at Obic Business Consultants developed a simple language for distribution management on a personal computer. Drawing on their considerable know-how in the day-to-day operation of businesses, the accountants were able to produce both a language and a type of software that are extremely easy to use but also very versatile. Their product, PLANNER 18, is well suited to the rationalization of distribution systems, including

Makes ledgers concerning goods and accounts

the taking of inventory.

Users need not memorize commands to operate the program. The screen displays easy-to-understand, step-by-step instructions that users can follow to produce a program suited to their own needs. The system's filing function allows a virtually limitless

number of programs to be devised.

Obic is now developing a completely new line of software, employing artificial-intelligence technology.

1982 Award for Excellence

PIPS-III: A Multipurpose Data-Processing System
Sord Computer

The first nonprogrammed language in Japan

PIPS-III is an improved version of the previously developed PIPS (Pan-Information Processing Systems) computer-language data-processing systems that do not require programming. Its advantage over the previous PIPS systems is that the user can set page size by himself, within the limits of 150 letters, 72 items, and 60 lines. Another improvement is that a single bit of data is not limited to one program line, as it was in previous PIPS versions.

Increasingly, businesses are beginning to understand that the personal computers that they employ in their

work should be integrated within their buildings into what is known as a LAN (local-area network). This need is met easily by the PIPS-III system, since it incorporates telecommunications functions. PIPS-III embodies the idea of "Nonprogrammed Language for Business" by freeing the firms who opt to use the PIPS systems from the sometimes extremely difficult and always time-consuming task of actually programming personal computers.

1982 Award for Excellence

Shunkan: Customer-Information Management Software
MMIC

Shunkan is a software program designed to maintain a data bank on clients for small- and medium-sized companies. Between 2,000 and 3,000 pieces of data can be stored on disk with the Shunkan system. It was developed to fully utilize the power of 16-bit personal computers, which were still new at the time. It is designed for easy operation and eliminates the need for lengthy and expensive training of company employees who must use it.

One of its most convenient functions is its address-storage system. When the user types in the postal code

of a city, the computer automatically records the name of the city in *kanji* (Chinese characters). This feature eliminates the need for *kana-kanji* conversion in dealing with addresses, thus saving operators a great deal of time. An additional feature is that Shunkan was designed for those unfamiliar with computers. For example, a correction command appears on the screen when a disk has been replaced before a transaction was completed, reminding the user to complete the task.

1984 Award for Excellence

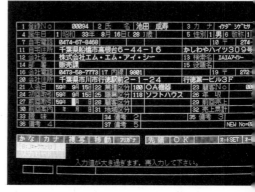

Shunkan explains use via on-screen prompting

GRS-810: A Restaurant-Control System
Fujitsu General

Fujitsu General has developed a computerized restaurant-control system that helps eliminate long waits for food and incorrect delivery of orders, all too common in larger restaurants.

With the new system, customers purchase food tickets at the entrance, seat themselves, and hand the tickets to a server. In the meantime, the order is transmitted by computer from the ticket register to the kitchen, after which cooks begin to prepare the food. When the food is ready, the computer relays the information to the delivery counter and the food is delivered to the indicated table.

The system has been installed in many large restaurants throughout Tokyo. They report increased customer turnover due to more efficient production and a decrease in customer waiting time. Moreover, restaurants can spend less time and money training register operators and servers, cutting back on their costs.

1982 Award for Excellence

Food preparation starts with sale of food tickets

Ōbantō: Financial Management Software
Milky Way

This software, an easy-to-operate financial management system, is compatible with NEC's popular PC-9800 series of personal computers. It is designed for the easy processing of statements of accounts, detailed estimate statements, and records such as deposits, withdrawals, and other financial transactions.

Ōbantō, meaning "general manager," sells for ¥200,000 and was created to provide a way to help small- and medium-sized businesses systematize their own accounting operations. The software was developed in consulta-

Closing of accounts is completed in real time

tion with two CPAs and is both practical and user friendly.

More than 10,000 companies have adopted Ōbantō. Milky Way was at first surprised to find that the demand was greater outside of Tokyo, but then realized that this was due to the preponderance of small- and medium-sized businesses outside of the city.

Although new financial management software programs have sprung up to compete with Ōbantō, Milky Way's system remains popular.

1983 Award for Excellence

Mercury-J: A Multipurpose Controller
Niigata Engineering

This versatile, multipurpose controller is designed to make factory automation more efficient. Until now, robots, personal computers, and numerical-control machines, all made by different manufacturers, could not communicate with one another without a special interface. Mercury-J, however, is an interface that establishes a LAN (local-area network) within a factory, allowing both factory- and office-automation facilities to be coordinated into a single network.

The heart of this controller is a software protocol ROM (read-only mem-

ory) converter with numerical-control and input/output functions. It is powerful enough to connect up to 256 factory- and office-automation facilities into a single network.

A very flexible unit, the Mercury-J can easily incorporate telecommunications software because it employs a two-way dialogue system. This feature is supplemented by a control function in the module, allowing the user to establish a system suited to his own specific needs.

1983 Award for Excellence

A factory- and office-automation network

Atlas: Japanese⇌English Dual Translation System
Fujitsu

Atlas is a pair of software programs for computer translation. Atlas I translates from English to Japanese, and Atlas II from Japanese to English. Although neither system is capable of conveying the complete sense and flow of a passage, each can deconstruct a sentence, analyze the relationship of the words within it, and produce an intelligible translation into the target language.

The two systems operate on Fujitsu's standard M Series computers and on its S-3000 Series minicomputers.

Both of the systems can translate the equivalent of 60,000 English words per hour. It takes a human translator approximately forty minutes to translate a single page of 300 English words and another fifteen minutes to enter it into a word processor; the Atlas system does the same work in two minutes. The key to the development of this product was extensive consultation with translation specialists to guarantee quality. Some 190 companies had adopted the systems as of February 1987.

1984 High Award for Excellence

Powerful support of translation in the field of scientific technology

---

MICRO-PAK J/E / MEDIUM-PAK J/E:
Japanese-English Computer Translation Systems
Bravice International

Bravice International was one of the first companies in Japan to produce software for machine translation. The Bravice systems, costing from ¥15.8 million to ¥19.5 million, can translate from Japanese to English on both a personal computer (MICRO-PAK J/E) and a minicomputer (MEDIUM-PAK J/E) at a rate of approximately 3,000 words an hour. Companies that switch to the Bravice systems can reduce average translation costs by about 50–60%.

Computer translation begins with the breaking up of the Japanese sentence into single words. While searching the built-in dictionary for the meaning of each word, the system identifies its position in the sentence and determines its grammatical identity. On that basis, it selects the most appropriate translation of each word from the range of possibilities in the system's dictionary. It then proceeds to analyze the original sentence, translate it into English, check the grammar, and finally produce an intelligible English sentence.

1984 Award for Excellence

Suitable hardware for Bravice's systems includes NEC's PC-9800 and IBM's 5550 series

ELECTRONIC
AND MEDICAL
ELECTRONIC
DEVICES

1-Mbit CMOS DRAM
Toshiba

Toshiba began DRAM (dynamic RAM) development by establishing two separate teams, and work proceeded simultaneously on both 1-Mbit and 256-Kbit DRAMs, since the company did not feel that it was expedient to wait for the perfection of a 256-Kbit chip before starting on the 1-Mbit chip.

Previously, DRAM devices used an N-channel MOS-type construction, but it was discovered that the IC overheats so much that it melts when the memory capacity is increased. Toshiba thus decided to change the peripheral circuitry to the CMOS-type, which has a significantly lower power consumption. This shift was a major technical innovation in the development of more powerful DRAM devices.

Development work centered around this major change while the company decided to use existing 256-Kbit DRAM technology in as many other areas as possible. For example, for the capacitors that form the constituent elements of the memory cells storing actual digital information, Toshiba chose not to use groove capacitors, which

had been hailed by many as the next generation of technology. Instead, it decided to use planar capacitors, the same as those that are used in conventional chips.

The first prototype of the 1-Mbit chip was completed in the fall of 1984. The device contained over 2.2 million transistors and other components on a 5.0 × 12.5-mm silicon substrate, with a minimum wire spacing on the electronic circuit of 1.2 μm. A single chip can hold some 65,000 Chinese characters, or the amount of information contained on four full pages of a newspaper.

Toshiba announced its 1-Mbit DRAM in 1985 at the International Solid-State Circuit Conference. NEC, Hitachi, Fujitsu, and Mitsubishi all announced similar devices at the same time. Toshiba, however, was confident that its product was the closest to completion.

Almost as soon as the product was introduced, Siemens of West Germany approached Toshiba with a request to license the 1-Mbit DRAM technology. Normally in the high-tech field companies are

reluctant to supply their latest technology to other companies. Toshiba, however, responded positively to this request, judging it beneficial to increase the number of manufacturers supplying 1-Mbit DRAM chips in order to encourage market formation.

At present, Toshiba has set up a production system that is capable of producing 1 million chips each month. On the government level, the U.S. Department of Commerce has set a fair price for DRAM chips as a result of the U.S.-Japan semiconductor talks, and has forbidden exports to the U.S. at any price lower than that. That price is somewhat high, leading some to predict that it will check the spread of these chips, but Toshiba remains highly confident that its product will do well.

1985 Award for Excellence

Structure: 1,048,576 words × 1 bit
Access time (maximum, ns):
 + rac 100/120, + cac 35/45
Cycle time (minimum, ns): 190/220
Power: + 5 V
Active current (mW): 330/275

1.2-μm ultramicro-processing technology has been utilized to pack 2.2 million components on this advanced ultra-LSI

Thin-Film Magnetic Heads
TDK

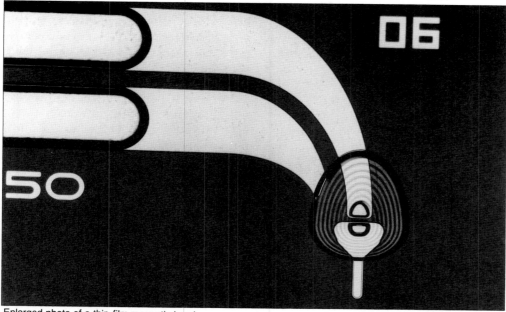

Enlarged photo of a thin-film magnetic head

Thin-film magnetic heads were developed for supercomputers; they can also be used in fixed-head DATs (digital audio tape recorders) no bigger than a standard cassette tape and in industrial equipment such as computer peripherals. TDK was the first Japanese manufacturer of thin-film magnetic heads for high-capacity hard-disk drives.

Magnetic heads demand greater compactness and better performance each year, as recording equipment becomes smaller and achieves higher recording density. However, conventional heads require the winding of each coil around a processed core made of ferrite or some similar material and are approaching the limits of processing methods and performance as they become smaller. For this reason, there is a great demand for thin-film magnetic heads; their high performance and precisely controlled composition ensure both the electrical and flying performance stability essential for future disk-storage systems.

Thin-film heads use the same sputtering technology (attaching metallic molecules) that is used in VLSI production. A thin magnetic film for recording is formed over an insulating substrate. The coil winding stage, the most troublesome during the production of magnetic heads, is eliminated. In theory, mass production of these heads should be possible in the same manner as it is for semiconductors, and thus these compact and lightweight magnetic heads for high-density recording and playback hold a great deal of promise.

Originally, TDK was one of the two top manufacturers of conventional magnetic heads using ferrite. However, the production of thin-film magnetic heads required a technology that is quite different from that employed previously in the making of heads. Thus, the company had to master an entirely unfamiliar technology in order to establish a lead in this field.

For the production of thin-film magnetic heads, it was obvious that membrane-formation technology equivalent to that used in VLSI technology was necessary; ultra-precise processing technology such as that required in grinding was also needed to form the gap that determines the quality of the head. While conventional heads demand micron precision, thin-film magnetic heads require precision in angstrom units (10^{-10} m). Japan is a world leader in these two technologies, due to its accumulated basic research in such areas as discrete semiconductors, thin-membrane thermal heads, and ferrite heads.

Realizing that there are great opportunities available in this field, TDK has recently embarked on an impressive plan of capital investment. Part of this involves an outlay of ¥4.5 billion for a new plant that will be capable of producing 100,000 thin-film magnetic heads a month. This capital initiative comes just in time to prepare for the competition that is beginning both domestically and internationally.

1985 Award for Excellence

Track width: 10~25 μm
Gap length: 0.3~0.8 μm
Flying height: 0.2~0.3 μm
Resonance frequency: above 50 MHz
Overwrite: above −25 dB

VLSI 64-Kbit CMOS Static RAM
Toshiba

Toshiba has integrated approximately 400,000 transistors and other components into the 25-mm² silicon substrate of this microchip, each with a minimum wire spacing of 2 μm. This static RAM (SRAM) rivals the 256-Kbit CMOS dynamic RAM (DRAM), which requires memory-refresh operations, and which is the most common VLSI device. SRAM devices differ from DRAM devices in that data can be recorded without refreshing the memory. The power consumption of the memory is thus reduced,

A 400,000-component ultra-LSI

making this type of memory ideal for portable, hand-held computers. Toshiba introduced the 64-Kbit SRAM chip to the computer industry. At present, these chips have grown to dominate the SRAM field. Manufacturers such as Toshiba, Hitachi, NEC, Fujitsu, and Seiko Epson have already started mass production of 256-Kbit CMOS SRAM chips, which have a capacity equivalent to that of four 64-Kbit SRAM chips.

1982 High Award for Excellence

VLSI 256-Kbit CMOS Static RAM
Toshiba

As a VLSI (very large-scale integrated-circuit) computer chip, this product rivals the performance of Toshiba's 1-Mbit DRAM (dynamic random access memory). The company's SRAM (static RAM) integrates 1.6 million transistors and other elements on a 6.68 × 8.86-mm silicon substrate, has a minimum wire spacing of 1.2 μm, and an access time of 46 nsec (1 nsec= 10^{-9} sec). Its CMOS (complementary metal-oxide semiconductor) structure gives it a standby power consumption of only 30 μW.

Toshiba is one of Japan's top semiconductor makers. The company has made substantial capital investments over the last three years. Traditionally strong in CMOS technology, it is competing with Hitachi for the position of largest maker of SRAMs, which, unlike DRAMs, do not require any memory-refresh operations. The company was the first to commercialize the 256-Kbit SRAM.

1984 Award for Excellence

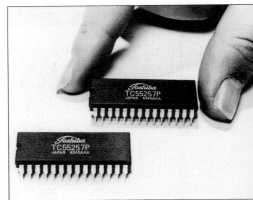

A 1,600,000-component ultra-LSI

VLSI 1-Mbit Mask ROM
NEC

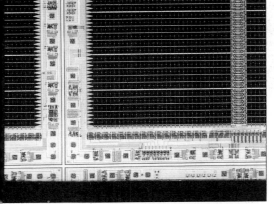

Around 1.1 million components on a single 49-mm² chip

This is the first 1-Mbit CMOS-ROM LSI (large-scale integrated circuit) produced in Japan. It integrates approximately 1.1 million electronic elements such as transistors into a 49-mm² silicon substrate.

The minimum wiring width of the electronic circuitry is 1.8 μm, and the device is manufactured by substituting a stepper (reduced-projection-type exposure unit) for the conventional mask aligner (exposure unit for semiconductor production).

Chinese characters (*kanji*) can be stored in the chip for use in elec-

tronic translators, electronic dictionaries, and word processors.

Two of these VLSI devices can store up to 8,000 *kanji*, with a resolution of 16 dots by 16 dots. This is sufficient to supply the 6,349 *kanji* specified as first and second level by Japan Industrial Standard.

A CMOS structure is used for low power consumption. In 1984, NEC doubled the capacity of this chip in a 2-Mbit mask ROM.

1982 Award for Excellence

YM5214: An LSI for 8-Bit Computers
Nippon Gakki

A special MSX LSI that utilizes SIT; its thinnest wire is 2.5 μm; memory and I/O-related control is carried out in accordance with MSX specifications

This product is an LSI (large-scale integrated circuit) using the third-generation transistor, SIT (static-electricity induction transistor), developed at Japan's Tōhoku University. It controls the memory and input/output devices of 8-bit MSX personal computers. MSX is the standard Microsoft/ASCII format for Japanese 8-bit software. This single device is able to perform the functions of twenty general-purpose TTL (transistor-transistor logic) devices. The minimum wiring width of the electronic circuitry is 2.5 μm.

The number of electronic parts required for an MSX personal computer can be reduced by one-third with the use of this LSI. The usual MSX computer has a slot in the upper right portion of the machine for the insertion of ROM cartridges containing software. However, if an MSX personal computer is manufactured with this LSI, the extra space gained by using it makes it possible to add a side slot for an additional ROM cartridge.

1983 Award for Excellence

V30: A 16-Bit Microprocessor
NEC

This is the first 16-bit microprocessor developed exclusively in Japan for popular use. Up to now, microprocessors made by U.S. manufacturers (or copies of them produced in Japan) were used, but as Japan developed expertise in the semiconductor field, lawsuits involving patent disputes with U.S. manufacturers increased.

In response to this, NEC developed this microprocessor independently. It employed the technology of a CMOS structure to facilitate low power consumption; as a result, some 63,000 components are integrated onto a silicon substrate that is only a few millimeters square.

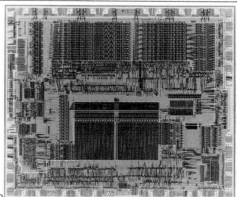

An IC with 63,000 components on one chip

NEC has called these chips the V Series, and has six models available. In order to widen the availability of these chips, it has granted manufacturing and sales rights to Zilog in the U.S., and Sony and Sharp in Japan.

1984 High Award for Excellence

DN-304: Ultrahigh-Power Infrared LEDs
Stanley Electric

In 1976, Stanley Electric completed an LED that used gallium-aluminum-arsenide (GaAlAs). This LED was shown for the first time at a trade fair in Los Angeles, and boasted a brightness of 60 mcd on a current of 20 mA. This brightness was three times stronger than the previous record and six times brighter than the average product. It opened up the way for Stanley Electric in the area of high-brightness LEDs.

Drawing upon this technology, the company went on to develop 2,000-mcd and 5,000-mcd high-brightness LEDs. These upgraded LEDs, which can be clearly seen even in direct sunlight, have led to the development of new applications for outdoor illumination. Various other applications for them are expected, and already attempts have been made to combine hundreds of high-brightness LEDs for use in signal lamps on roads and railroads, as well as in automobile lights.

Based on such experience, the company has developed ultrahigh-power infrared GaAlAs LEDs providing an extremely high output of 15 mW. They are housed in a molded package with a diameter of 5 mm and feature a parabolic lens ideal for light output ensuring high-efficiency radiation.

High-output infrared LEDs involve the application of the same technol-

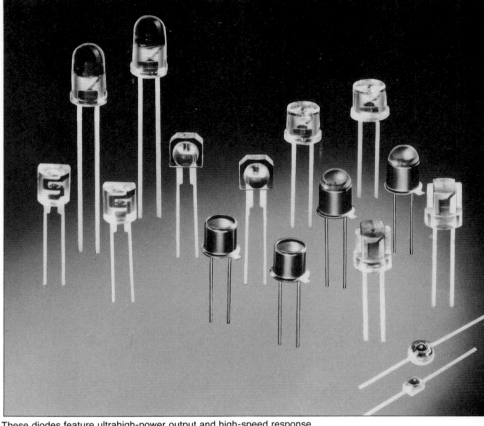

These diodes feature ultrahigh-power output and high-speed response

ogy as that used for high-brightness visible-light LEDs. Both types of diodes have a sandwich-type heterojunction structure, unlike the single heterojunction structure used by other manufacturers. LEDs with a GaAlAs double-heterojunction structure call for the formation of a thin layer of less than 1 μm be-

tween two cover layers having a thickness of 100 μm. Using this technology to form a thin layer of crystals over a gallium-arsenide semiconductor substrate having a diameter of 5 mm is comparable to spreading a 20-mm film smoothly and evenly over an entire baseball field.

Amorphous Silicon Solar Cell/Amorton Power Solar Modules
Sanyo Electric

Solar cells are now used in everything from space satellites to pocket calculators. Sanyo has developed a large-scale solar-panel cell that employs a current generated by sunlight striking an amorphous silicon semiconductor. It succeeded in dividing amorphous silicon into a series of clusters of cells that were then joined together to form a

series of solar modules. They are available in twelve sizes ranging from 142 × 149 mm to 398 × 1,202 mm. It can be used as a power supply for outdoor clock towers, illumination towers, small pumps, and other equipment that operates on regular electrical power. It is even possible to use a panel as a portable power supply for camp-

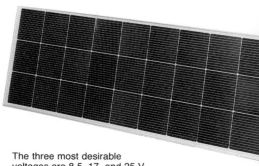

The three most desirable voltages are 8.5, 17, and 25 V

Both high-brightness and high-output LEDs boast an efficient energy conversion rate of 20%, considerably better than the industry norm of 10%. As LEDs have previously been incapable of transmitting large amounts of information in the infrared range for quartz-type optical fibers, their primary use has been as light sources for short-distance plastic optical fibers. Yet Stanley Electric's high-output infrared LEDs distinguish themselves by their improved performance in the infrared range and are suitable for use as a low-cost light source for quartz optical fibers.

In addition, their ability to transmit information through the air over distances of 100 m holds the promise of creating new markets in such areas as light sources for the remote control of robots, factory communications, and long-distance automatic focusing of cameras.

1985 Award for Excellence

Forward voltage: Maximum 2 V
Reverse current: Maximum 100 μA
Junction capacitance: 65 pF
Radiant intensity: 30 mW/sr
Total output: 15 mW
Peak wavelength: 850 nm
Spectrum half bandwidth: 40 nm
Half-intensity directional angle: 35°

ing or fishing. The voltages are 8.5, 17, and 25 V, with an output ranging from 0.7 to 15 W, and the appropriate panel can be selected according to need. Further development in this area is being undertaken on solar energy systems for home and office.

1984 Award for Excellence

Noncontact Displacement Sensor
Kangyo Denki Kiki

This sensor can detect the displacement of an object without direct contact. Consisting of two In-Sb (indium-antimony) magnetic reluctance elements—with an extremely high electron mobility of 30,000 cm^2/VIC—vapor-deposited end-to-end onto an alumina substrate, it possesses very strong magnetic inductance. The sensor is able to translate magnetic variations into highly accurate measurements of displacement.

This development was made possible by the mass production of hole elements. Advances in the technology of In-Sb vacuum vapor deposition made mass production of hole elements possible, and led to the development of the magnetic inductance element. Although noise was a major problem, the company's comprehensive survey of

vapor deposition technology enabled it to solve the dilemma through the use of heat processing.

1982 Award for Excellence

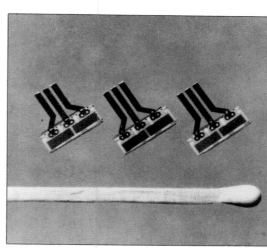
Displacement sensors shown with a matchstick

Hi-Super Bright LEDs
Stanley Electric

Originally, the major application for LEDs was as indicator lights for televisions and audio-video equipment, since they exhibit the characteristics of long life and low power consumption. However, their brightness has up until now always been insufficient for outdoor use, in such items as signal or automobile lights.

Stanley Electric took the initiative in paving the way for the outdoor use of these devices with the production of a 2,000-mcd LED that is four times brighter than conventional LEDs. The technology employed was based on the "continuous-liquid-phase epitaxial growth technology" invented by Professor Jun'ichi Nishizawa, and has already surpassed that of U.S. manufacturers.

Another company began competing with Stanley by placing a 3,000-mcd LED on the market, but Stanley is now returning to the forefront with the development of its own 5,000-mcd LED.

A diode 4 times brighter than earlier ones

1983 Award for Excellence

CR-101: An X-Ray Diagnostic Device
Fuji Photo Film

A diagnostic machine that uses highly sensitive X-ray detection plates

In 1975, the X-ray film and equipment section of Fuji Photo Film badly needed new ideas. Discussions among seven young technicians at the Basic Emulsion Section of the company's Ashigara Laboratory led to the birth, seven years later, of the CR-101, an X-ray diagnostic machine that uses highly sensitive X-ray detection plates instead of a pickup tube and X-ray film.

This machine enables laboratory technicians to store X-ray information on the detection plate, to process it as image data using a computer, and then to create a precise X-ray photo on film. Compared with conventional X-ray scans, examinations using this image plate reduce the amount of X-ray exposure by 50–90%. In addition, the clarity of the image is improved and the information is converted to digital signals, allowing for electronic filing.

Fuji Photo Film has signed an agreement to supply this machine's technology to the Dutch company Philips, and is taking other steps to establish a worldwide sales network.

1983 High Award for Excellence

MRT-15A: A Magnetic-Resonance Imaging System
Toshiba

When a proton-rich material is placed in a static magnetic field, it absorbs and discharges electromagnetic waves at a frequency specific to that material. This is known as the nuclear-magnetic-resonance phenomenon. Toshiba's Magnetic-Resonance Imaging System is a CT (computerized tomography) device that induces this phenomenon in order to trace the tomographic distribution of protons within the human body. The data collected is then transformed into an image by a computer.

Toshiba is the first company in Japan to have developed such a device, using a powerful electromagnet to create an image of hydrogen distribution within the body. In an attempt to catch up with American and European manu-facturers, the company began research in this field in 1981. After placing the MRT-15A on the market, Toshiba went on to market the MRT-22 and MRT-50. These are expected to become major products in the medical electronics field.

1983 High Award for Excellence

This magnetic-resonance imaging system allows doctors to view CT scans on special consoles

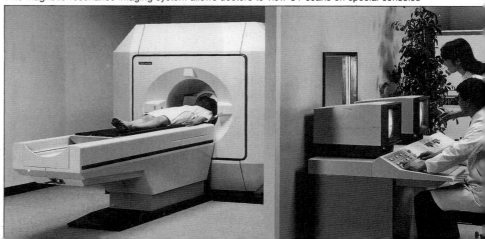

HER-100: Lactate Analyzer
Omron Tateisi Electronics/Toyobo

It is important to know the metabolic state of a patient during and after surgery, and one way of determining this is by measuring the lactic acid concentration in the blood. For years, hospitals used large, automatic analyzers that were immobile and very slow in processing data. Omron Tateisi and Toyobo have made a significant advance in this technology with a device that does the job in approximately 2 minutes. Instead of using chemical reagents, it employs an enzyme electrode method, using an immobilized lactate-

A portable lactate measuring device

oxidase membrane. This permits the lactic acid concentration to be measured from as little as 100 µL of blood.

Crucial to success was the development of biosensors. The technology needed to immobilize delicate enzymes on the membrane was very complex, but Omron Tateisi and Toyobo successfully developed sensors that could be used as many as 1,000 times.

1984 Award for Excellence

PO-200: A Transcutaneous P_{CO_2} Monitor
Sumitomo Electric Industries

PO-200 and calibrator measure P_{O_2} and P_{CO_2}

Normally, the body keeps the pressure of CO_2 in arterial blood at around 0.05 atmospheres. In premature infants, however, poorly functioning respiratory and circulatory systems are sometimes unable to keep CO_2 pressure, P_{CO_2}, within the normal range, with the result that such infants risk brain damage. The conventional method of P_{CO_2} control requires that blood be drawn for analysis, yet this allows only intermittent measurement.

The PO-200 P_{CO_2} monitor allows continuous monitoring of CO_2 in the arterial blood by means of a small sensor that measures the release of CO_2 gas from the skin.

The PO-200 monitor was developed and commercialized in a period of three years, a surprisingly short span for medical equipment. The speed of its development derived largely from intensive efforts by the engineering team and close consultations with physicians from the outset of the project. Sumitomo Electric has gone on to develop a new P_{CO_2} monitor as well as a combined P_{O_2}/P_{CO_2} monitor.

1982 Award for Excellence

Ken'on-kun MC-8: A Digital Thermometer
Omron Tateisi Electronics

Electronic thermometers differ from conventional ones in using a thermistor instead of mercury to measure temperature. Thermistors register temperature variations as changes in electrical resistance and display them digitally. The digital display enables temperatures to be read at a glance. Furthermore, there is no fear of injury from this thermometer, since it contains neither glass nor mercury.

At first, electronic thermometers were prohibitively expensive, but the price of Ken'on-kun was brought down to a reasonable level by collecting all

The Ken'on-kun MC-8, which has brought to reality a low-priced product fitted with an LSI

the circuitry into a single LSI.

Omron began marketing this thermometer in March 1983, and has sold more than 20 million thermometers at less than ¥3,000 each as of February 1987. Recent advances in circuit technology and a drop in the price of LSIs have further lowered the price. Future

innovations may include connecting the thermometer to a printer for recording temperature readings over several weeks.

1983 Award for Excellence

Company Index

Product Index

Directory of Advertisers

Credit 109, Inc.

31-2, Sakuragaoka-cho, Shibuya-ku, Tokyo 150

Credit 109 was incorporated by 14 companies of the Tokyu Group to promote sales and to build a larger customer data base through credit card operations centering on the Tokyu TOP card. With member companies prominent in the transportation, real-estate development, retail, and health and leisure industries, the Tokyu Group provides a wide spectrum of consumer goods and services. In addition to making the TOP card available to customers of all Group companies, Credit 109 is developing a wide variety of financial services, such as insurance, factoring, and mortgage-backed securities.

(See page 236.)

President:	Mamoru Miura
Incorporated:	November 1983
Capital:	¥450 million
(as of the end of March 1987)	
Number of employees:	100

Sales (¥ million)

'86	3,020
'85	673
'84	446

Composition of sales by business segment:
Card operations	24%
Loans and cash advances	3%
Other financial services	73%

Research and development: Research and development of new products and services is determined and conducted by the Corporate Planning Section.

Contact: Terutaka Ihara, Director of the Planning Division
Tel: (03) 476-0503

One card for just about everything. The TOP card.

Your Passport to the Whole Wide World of Enjoyment. The TOP Card.
Like any card, the TOP card can be used to shop, but that's where the similarity ends.
Just consider how many places accept the TOP card: over 5 million stores in over 170 countries around the world. And it doesn't stop there.
You can use the TOP card for cash advances at over 27,000 banks and 2,000 cash dispensers around the world.

Truly, this gold card is your international passport to the good life.
When you carry it, you're recognized as a prestigious V.I.P. wherever you go because TOP cardholders are registered with the MasterCard system in the U.S. as well.
With advantages like these, you might think the TOP card comes at a top premium.
But that's the best news of all, because at ¥3,000 per year, the TOP card is a deal that is too good to miss. The TOP card; it's the one card you can't do without.

Here are just some of the advantages you'll get with the TOP card:
- Cash rebates of up to 5% of your total yearly purchases at participating shops of the TOP card system.
- Discounts of up to 10% at all Tokyu hotels, participating travel agents, movie theatres and stores.
- Premium gifts when you save stamps received from participating merchants.
- Various financial services including loans and investment opportunities.
- A free subscription to Hā Wā Yū, one of Japan's most fashionable living magazines.

Make yourself at home around the world. With the TOP card.

TOKYU CARD TOP

Please contact with
CREDIT 109 INC.
☎03-476-6026

Kajima Corporation

2-7, Moto-Akasaka 1-chome, Minato-ku, Tokyo 107

Since its founding in **1840**, Kajima has developed expertise in many fields, including the construction of high-rise buildings, nuclear power plants, and in-ground liquid natural gas tanks. The corporation applies its comprehensive skills in projects around the globe, coordinating each step from planning and design to management, execution, and maintenance. Kajima is currently expanding its activities as a developer participating in large-scale urban and regional development projects, thus evolving from a coordinator of isolated projects to a fully integrated enterprise that provides a wide range of construction and land development services. (See pages 205-206.)

CFRC
A New Material from Kajima

President:	Shoichi Kajima
Incorporated:	February 1930
Capital:	¥43,460 million
(as of the end of March 1987)	
Number of employees:	15,200

Sales (¥ million)

'86	1,022,248
'85	913,628
'84	932,062

Net income (¥ million)

'86	13,267
'85	13,107
'84	13,536

Composition of sales by business segment:
    Construction works   91%
    (Architectural projects, 60%)
    (Civil engineering projects, 31%)
    Development works   9%

Research and development: Kajima's commitment to R&D has always been strong. In 1949, the corporation established the Kajima Institute of Construction Technology, one of the first such facilities in the industry, to conduct basic research and seek solutions for technical problems arising in design and construction. Other R&D units include the Muto Institute of Structural Mechanics and the Kobori Research Complex, both conducting theoretical research that leads to new applied technologies, and the Information Processing Center, which is engaged in software research. These and other sections of the company are cooperating in a flexible R&D arrangement that contributes to Kajima's constant technological advances.

Kajima has nine branch offices in Japan. In addition, the company has 1,300 domestic sales offices and project sites, and its extensive activities abroad are currently conducted at 70 locations, including sales offices and project sites.

Stock exchange listings: Listed on the First Sections of the Tokyo, Osaka, and Nagoya stock exchanges.

Contact: Publicity Department
Tel: (03) 404-3311

Kajima Corporation knows concrete. We know its strengths. And its weaknesses. We've been studying concrete's limitations for some time now, trying to develop a new material that does away with its problems of heavy weight, fragility, and cracking. Kajima's new carbon fiber reinforced concrete, CFRC, does just that, and more. CFRC is produced by blending pitch carbon fiber in cement mortar. This new material is as lightweight as wood, just as flexible, and its cured dimensions vary less than conventional concrete. CFRC stands up to the elements, resisting both freezing temperatures and the baking heat of the sun in top form.

KAJIMA CORPORATION

Headquarters Office
2-7, Motoakasaka 1-chome, Minato-ku, Tokyo 107

Konishiroku Photo Industry Co., Ltd.

26-2, Nishi-Shinjuku 1-chome, Shinjuku-ku, Tokyo 163

Konishiroku Photo Industry manufactures a wide range of photographic equipment and supplies. The company was founded in 1873 and has played a leading role in the Japanese photographic industry ever since. Main products include photographic film and paper, cameras, photofinishing systems, plain paper copiers, laser printers, videotapes, and floppy disks. By combining its fine chemicals, optoelectronics, and precision machinery technologies, Konishiroku will continue to develop innovative products that satisfy society's need for visual information media.   (See pages 128-129, 230.)

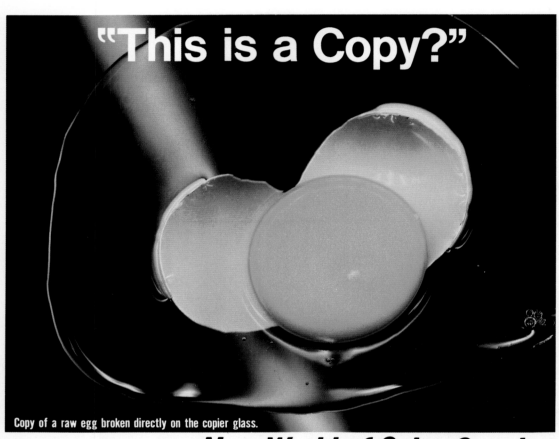

"This is a Copy?"

Copy of a raw egg broken directly on the copier glass.

Konica Color 7: a New World of Color Copying

Able to Copy on OHP Film In addition to copying on paper as thin as normal copy paper, the Konica Color 7 can also make color copies on overhead projection film and has unique applications in the production of display boards and illuminated decorative panels.

Realistic 3-D Copies The Konica Color 7 also copies small three-dimensional objects, with depths of one to two cm, delivering an image amazingly close to the real thing.

One-Touch Color Balance Control One-touch control keys independently set yellow, magenta, and cyan tones at nine 10% point intervals, allowing color adjustments to suit individual tastes.

Capable of Reductions or Enlargements from 50% to 150% The Konica Color 7's zoom reduction and enlargement function enables size adjustments in 1% increments on A4, B4, and A3 size copy paper.

An Asset to Any Business

Created in response to today's need for copies that display colors realistically, the Konica Color 7 has attained an image quality that dramatically alters the concept of color copying. With color and tone reproduction that usher in a new era in color copying, the Konica Color 7 has received an overwhelming reception as the copier the industry has been waiting for.

KONISHIROKU PHOTO IND. CO., LTD.
COLOR COPIER DIVISION
No. 26-2, Nishishinjuku 1-Chome
Shinjuku-ku, Tokyo 163, Japan

Konica COLOR 7

President: Megumi Ide
Incorporated: December 1936
Capital: ¥25,542 million
 (as of February 1987)
Number of employees: 4,720

Sales	(¥ million)
'86	313,612
'85	272,906
'84	258,077

Net income	(¥ million)
'86	15,909
'85	18,688
'84	16,593

Composition of sales by business segment:
Photographic materials and photo-related industrial equipment	66.8%
Business machines	25.3%
Cameras and accessories	7.9%

Research and development: Konishiroku maintains extensive R&D facilities, including the Research and Development Center, the Optics Research Laboratory, the Photo Products Division's Development Center, and the Development Department of the Copier Business Division.

Konishiroku's Japanese branch offices are located in Osaka, Nagoya, Fukuoka, Sapporo, Sendai, Hiroshima, and Takamatsu. The company also has 18 overseas offices—in the United States, Canada, Mexico, Great Britain, France, West Germany, Switzerland, Italy, Greece, Australia, Hong Kong, Singapore, and the People's Republic of China.

Stock exchange listings: Listed on the Tokyo, Osaka, Nagoya, and Niigata exchanges in Japan, as well as the Luxembourg, Frankfurt, Düsseldorf, and Paris stock exchanges.

Contact: Color Copier Department, Business Machines Marketing Division

The Kyoto Shinkin Bank

Shijo-Yanaginobanba, Shimogyo-ku, Kyoto 600

The Kyoto Shinkin Bank is one of the leading financial institutions in the Kyoto area, with total assets exceeding ¥1 trillion. The bank has a network of 77 branches throughout the southern part of Kyoto Prefecture and adjacent parts of Osaka and Shiga prefectures, a region with approximately 3.7 million people. Using its extensive network to provide a range of financial services, the bank is contributing to the economic and social prosperity of the community. The Kyoto Shinkin Bank adheres to an innovative and progressive management approach that stresses the importance of regularly introducing new financial products and services.

(See page 233.)

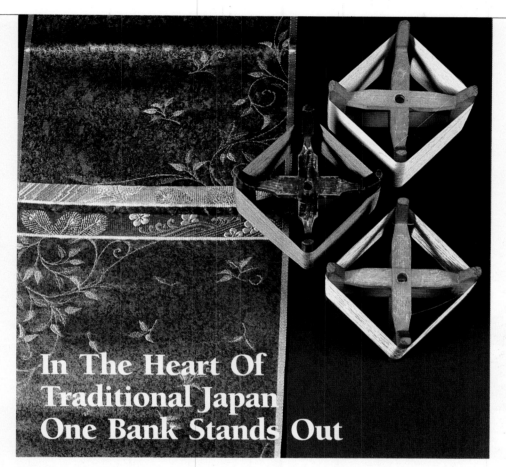

In The Heart Of Traditional Japan One Bank Stands Out

President: Takashi Anan
Incorporated: September 1923
Capital: ¥10,229 million
 (as of January 1987)
Number of employees: 2,290

Deposits
(¥ million, as of March 31)

'86	1,093,264
'85	943,688
'84	840,280

Net income
(¥ million, for the years ended March 31)

'86	4,003
'85	3,726
'84	3,866

Main types of accounts and
 services:
 Deposits
 Loans and bills discounted
 Foreign exchange
 Promotion of high-technology
  industries
 Electronic banking services

The Kyoto Shinkin Bank has 63 branches in Kyoto Prefecture, 49 of which are in Kyoto City. In addition, the bank maintains 10 branches in Shiga Prefecture and four branches in Osaka Prefecture.

Contact: Yoko Suita, International Department
Tel: (075) 211-2111

The Kyoto Shinkin Bank is one of the leading financial institutions in the Kyoto region, where businesses are known for their strong entrepreneurial spirit. Having served many of the area's small and medium-sized companies for over 60 years, the Kyoto Shinkin Bank has developed strong ties with local enterprises and has acquired a deep knowledge of the regional economy. Today, many of our clients are looking to the world for markets and materials. When they do, they turn to us for our proven leadership and innovation. We offer complete correspondent banking services and are thoroughly experienced in foreign exchange. When doing business in Kyoto, deal with Kyoto's bank—the Kyoto Shinkin Bank.

THE KYOTO SHINKIN BANK
INTERNATIONAL DEPARTMENT
Shijo & Yanaginobanba, Shimogyo-ku
Kyoto 600, Japan

Nippon Suisan
Kaisha, Ltd.

6-2, Otemachi 2-chome, Chiyoda-ku, Tokyo 100

Founded with the goal of providing Japan with a stable supply of food from the sea, Nippon Suisan has grown into a leader of Japan's fishery and marine products industry, with activities centering on fishing, seafood sales and trade, and food processing. In recent years, Nippon Suisan has also begun constructing its own energy-efficient ships for use in short-range fishing fleets. Seeking to become a more comprehensive food products enterprise, Nippon Suisan is aggressively expanding its product lineup and moving into the restaurant business. In addition, the company is developing expertise in the fields of fine chemicals and biotechnology. (See page 202.)

Delicious alternative to tuna.

President:			Fumio Imanaga
Incorporated:			May 1911
Capital (as of March 1986):			¥15,921 million
Number of employees:			4,034

Sales		(¥ million)
'86	473,921	
'85	484,351	
'84	470,001	

Net income		(¥ million)
'86	3,030	
'85	2,908	
'84	2,532	

Composition of sales by business segment:

Fresh and frozen fish	65.6%
Frozen foods	16.0%
Processed foods and others	7.0%
Canned goods	5.7%
Fats and oils, fish meal	4.0%
Ship, refrigerator, and other equipment leasing	1.7%

Research and development:
Nippon Suisan conducts its R&D through two separate units. The Central Research Center is engaged in research on marine products and the Product Development Division is responsible for development of new processed food products.

Nippon Suisan has eight offices in Japan and maintains three branch offices and three representative offices overseas.

Stock exchange listings: Listed on the First Sections of the Tokyo, Osaka, and Nagoya stock exchanges and on other exchanges throughout Japan.

Contact: Public Relations Division
Tel: (03) 244-7106

New product information:
Nippon Suisan's innovative mix of real and imitation crabmeat has won wide acclaim in Japan and enjoys steady sales under the brand name Sea Dish.

Secom Co., Ltd.

10 Fl. Shinjuku Nomura Bldg.,
26-2, Nishi-Shinjuku 1-chome, Shinjuku-ku, Tokyo 163

Secom, Japan's first private security company, employs state-of-the-art technology to provide highly reliable security services to corporations and other institutions, to private homes, and to industrial and building complexes. The company researches and develops, designs, manufactures, installs, and maintains a variety of security systems, in addition to offering integrated security services and a line of security-related merchandise. Capitalizing on a nationwide electronic data processing network built to support its security activities, Secom is advancing into such new business areas as value-added network (VAN), videotex, and cable television services. (See page 246.)

Beverly Hills speaks out on home security:

The good life gets better

Jon Douglas, President of Jon Douglas Company.

For further information, please contact: SECOM CO., LTD. ADVERTISING AND PLANNING DEPT. 10TH FL. SHINJUKU NOMURA BLDG., 26-2, NISHI-SHINJUKU 1-CHOME, SHINJUKU-KU, TOKYO, JAPAN PHONE: (03)348-7511

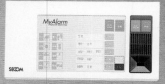
Chairman:	Makoto Iida
Incorporated:	July 1962
Capital:	¥12,175 million
Number of employees:	6,803
(as of the end of November 1986)	

Sales (¥ million)

'86	77,987
'85	70,089
'84	65,689

Net income (¥ million)

'86	7,051
'85	6,541
'84	6,061

Composition of sales by business segment:

Centralized electronic security systems	75%
Static guard services	14%
Armored car services	2%
Others, including local electronic security systems	9%

Research and development:
R&D at Secom is divided into three units. The Secom TE Center is responsible for R&D on advanced security technologies; the Secom SD Center develops new information processing techniques and software for Secom's administrative departments; and the Secom HD Center is the site of personnel training and development activities.

Secom has 697 domestic offices and numerous consolidated subsidiaries in Japan as well as two subsidiaries in the United States and affiliates in Korea and Taiwan.

Stock exchange listings: Listed on the First Sections of the Tokyo and Osaka stock exchanges.

Contact: Advertising and Planning Department
Tel: (03) 348-7511

Showa Aluminum Corporation

6-5, Iidabashi 3-chome, Chiyoda-ku, Tokyo 102

Showa Aluminum is engaged in every step of the production of aluminum, from rolling to fabrication. Products range from materials—such as extrusions, foils, sheets and coils—to fabricated products, including heat exchangers, beverage cans, housing materials, prefabricated freezers and refrigerators, refrigerated display cases for supermarkets, and clean rooms for high-technology industries. The company has numerous subsidiaries and affiliates in Japan and abroad, including Ohio-based Showa Aluminum Corporation of America, which will begin producing heat exchangers in the summer of 1987.

(See page 219.)

Showa Aluminum Helps Your Car Beat the Heat

Since 1965, Showa Aluminum has applied its unsurpassed skills in aluminum manufacture to the production of heat exchangers for automobiles. Our expertise in alloy engineering yields the thin, strong, corrosion-resistant tubes essential to high-performance heat exchangers. Proprietary extruding technologies enable us to produce these tubes with great precision in a range of intricate shapes, and have led to the development of lighter, more compact heat exchangers.

Now, Showa Aluminum introduces a supercompact evaporator that, along with Showa's superior condensers, increases the efficiency of automobile air conditioning. Like all Showa products, the condensers and supercompact evaporator are produced completely in-house to assure prompt delivery and adherence to the strictest quality standards—a fact that 20 automobile makers in 10 countries can attest.

SHOWA ALUMINUM CORPORATION

President: Chikashi Ishii
Incorporated: December 1935
Capital: ¥10,737 million
 (as of November 1986)
Number of employees: 3,007

Sales	(¥ million)
'86	114,236
'85	125,445
'84	124,664

Net income	(¥ million)
'86	984
'85	699
'84	1,153

Composition of sales by business segment:
Extrusions	27.4%
Foils	18.3%
Sheets and coils	9.1%
Fabricated products	45.2%

Research and development: Showa Aluminum is using its extensive technical expertise and a unique R&D system to develop new types of aluminum, aluminum alloys, and fabricated products. Past R&D breakthroughs include superhigh-vacuum alloys, an ultra-pure aluminum metal (trade name Corjunal), and a food-packaging system.

Showa Aluminum maintains an executive head office in Tokyo; branch offices in Osaka, Nagoya, and Fukuoka; five sales offices; and a liaison office in New York.

Stock exchange listings: Listed on the First Sections of the Tokyo, Osaka, and Nagoya stock exchanges.

Contact: J. Yamasaki, Corporate Planning Department
Tel: (03) 239-5325

Showa Aluminum Corporation of America

Head Office
79 Chestnut Street,
Mount Sterling, OH 43143, U.S.A.
Contact: M. Yoneyama,
Vice President
Tel: (614) 869-3333

Liaison Office
18402 Haas Avenue,
Torrance, CA 90504, U.S.A.
Contact: T. Urayama
Tel: (213) 532-0833

Toppan Printing Co., Ltd.

1, Kanda Izumi-cho, Chiyoda-ku, Tokyo 101

Toppan Printing is energetically employing its accumulated know-how to meet the needs of today's society, providing services and materials vital to the dissemination of information. Toppan's activities center on printing—from advertising materials to securities and business forms—and extend to such related fields as publishing, packaging, and the manufacture of interior decor materials and precision electronic components. The company is also developing expertise in new information media, such as multimedia image-processing, data bases, and electronic publishing. In addition, Toppan has established several creative centers that engage in a wide range of activities, from planning promotional materials and events to designing spaces for public exhibits.

(See page 212.)

President:	Kazuo Suzuki
Incorporated:	January 1900
Capital:	¥35,554 million
(as of the end of February 1987)	
Number of employees:	11,000

Sales (¥ million)

'86	595,610
'85	571,705
'84	531,073

Net income (¥ million)

'86	17,812
'85	17,480
'84	16,060

Composition of sales by business segment:

General printing (commercial printing, precision electronic components, interior decor materials) 47.5%
Packaging 28.8%
Publications 20.1%
Securities printing 3.6%

Research and development:
All R&D has been concentrated in the Toppan Technical Research Institute, which includes specialized laboratories for research in advanced technology, precision electronic components, interior decor materials, plastics engineering, packaging, engineering technology, and machinery development.

Stock exchange listings: Listed on the Tokyo, Osaka, and Luxembourg stock exchanges.

Contact: Head Office, Public Relations Department
Tel: (03) 835-5811

Communication creates links between people, between enterprises and between people and enterprises, links which lead to mutual understanding. Communication begins with connection, and it is this connection, represented by the symbol "&", which is the basis of all Toppan's operations. Toppan plays a leading role in today's communications industry —— from commercial printing, publications, securities and packaging to the printing of precision electronic parts. It isn't easy to keep up in an increasingly complex world. Toppan knows this and smooths the way by strengthening its connections in all related fields, bridging the boundaries between them and providing technological know-how. Toppan —— connection is our watchword, communication is our business.

COMMUNICATIONS INDUSTRY

TOPPAN

TOPPAN PRINTING CO., LTD.
1, Kanda Izumi-Cho, Chiyoda-Ku, Tokyo, Japan